Game Theory and
Related Approaches
to Social Behavior

SELECTIONS

Game Theory and Related Approaches to Social Behavior

SELECTIONS

EDITOR: *Martin Shubik*

THOMAS J. WATSON RESEARCH CENTER
INTERNATIONAL BUSINESS MACHINES CORPORATION
YORKTOWN HEIGHTS, NEW YORK

John Wiley & Sons, Inc., New York · *London* · *Sydney*

Contributors

ARROW, K. J.

AUMANN, R.

BIXENSTINE, E.

BLACK, D.

DEUTSCH, M.

ELLSBERG, D.

GOLDHAMER, H.

GUETZKOW, H.

HARSANYI, J.

HAUSNER, M.

IKLÈ, F.

KAPLAN, A.

KRAUSS, R.

LEITES, W.

LUCE, D.

MANN, I.

MARSCHAK, J.

MCDONALD, J.

MILNOR, J.

MORGENSTERN, O.

NASH, J. F.

ORWANT, C.

RAPOPORT, A.

RAIFFA, H.

ROGOW, A.

SCHELLING, T.

SHAPLEY, L. S.

SHUBIK, M.

SPEIER, H.

TUKEY, J. W.

VON NEUMANN, J.

WILSON, K. V.

WOHLSTETTER, A.

TO SIDNEY SIEGEL AND STEFAN STYKOLT

Contents

ix

part **1**

INTRODUCTION

1

Game theory and the study of social behavior: an introductory exposition

1. Mathematics and Models in the Behavioral Sciences

One of the greatest areas of misunderstanding between those of us interested in the behavioral sciences on the one hand and mathematicians, physical scientists, and, to some extent, engineers on the other, has been the interpretation of the role and the value of mathematical and other formal models in the study of behavior. Partisans of the "more conversational disciplines" claim that the mathematical models constructed by some of their colleagues are too sterile and restricted; that in the oversimplification of the representation of the phenomena, the subtleties and vital content of their subject matter are often destroyed. The more enthusiastic proponents of mathematical model building may claim that almost the reverse is true. An extreme form of this position would be reflected in the claim that if the problem is *really* understood, it can be mathematised.

Actually both extreme views illustrate important and partially correct positions that should always be kept in mind by those who attempt to construct and manipulate models of behavioral processes. The apparent precision and greater analytical power of the mathematical model is often bought at the cost of narrowing the field of vision. Nuances are destroyed in many formulations of models. The language of mathematics is, in general, poor in adjectives, and complex qualifying statements cannot usually be made with the ease and elegance displayed by a historian or a literary sociologist. In spite of these drawbacks a good mathematical model is amenable to analysis of a type that enables us to follow through chains of reasoning which would be tedious in the extreme, if not impossible, without the assistance of powerful methodological tools. From this reasoning results can be discovered which may even meet the ultimate of tests: that all will claim them to be obvious once they have been obtained.

The languages of sociology, political science, psychology, and the other behavioral sciences are rich in adjectives and replete with many specialized words. They are designed to describe the distinctions perceived by the specialist but overlooked by the layman. By use of such languages the field of vision can be maintained, the nuances kept, qualifications added, and insights displayed. A cost is incurred, however, in terms of the depth of analysis that is feasible with verbal descriptions of behavioral phenomena.

We need insight and breadth of view. It is necessary to couple these with logical clarity and analytical ability. The type of mathematical thinking exemplified by the theory of games provides a useful methodology such that with care at least some aspects of the essential features of important problems can be examined.

Mathematical models in an applied science serve as a vehicle for studying the properties of a system. For example, a model designed to predict the number of customers at an amusement park over a summer weekend distinguishes factors deemed important and worth measuring and relating. In this instance, the factors may be age and distribution of population, weather conditions, the general financial level of the population, estimations of tastes and reactions to prices, and evaluation of the attractiveness of alternatives, such as bowling, baseball, or Bridgette Bardot.

If we were able to characterize with sufficient accuracy the relationships between the various factors, it would be feasible to construct a model which would be of use for prediction and planning. Changes in taste or population could be postulated and estimates made of their effect on attendance. If our knowledge of tastes were sufficient, it would be feasible to predict the effect of changing some of the attractions. In operations research work, models of systems such as this have been built with a reasonable amount of success. Often the mere process of getting them down on paper in a consistent and complete form has provided a clarification of understanding worth as much if not more than any subsequent numerical manipulation.

Most situations of interest to the behavioral scientist may be more subtle and complex than those facing the operations research worker. Measurement may be unfeasible, the number of important variables greater, and the relationships between them extremely difficult to describe, even using no more than educated guesses. With these, even more than in an operations research problem, the construction of a logically consistent and complete model provides an invaluable check against unclear thought and poorly formulated concepts. Often controversies arise and achieve mammoth proportions in both journals and debate, where the differences hinge on implicit assumptions well hidden in the wording. The better one understands the concept of a model and is able to use it as an aid to thought, the more quickly differences in fundamental points of view can be located. If for no other reason, the application of mathematical methods to the study of human behavior has great value in that bad simple mathematical models can be spotted in far less time than bad verbal models. The same poor assumptions and conclusions clothed in four hundred pages of words require much more time to locate the basic structure and with it the errors, fallacies, and omissions.

Mathematics has been useful in the behavioral sciences for a long time. If it is so useful and powerful, where are the early results? In some subjects, they exist. Cournot and Jevons were forerunners of a successful and great branch of economics, Malthus in population, Fechner in psychology, Galton in statistical applications to botany, biology, and many other areas. The giant work of Pareto contributes to both mathematical economics and sociology. Yet, even with many great forerunners, the mathematical tools which yielded deep and significant results in the physical sciences for several centuries have by no means proved as successful in the behavioral sciences. One important reason for this is that until as recently as 1930, and for the most part until around World War II, most applied mathematics was developed for the use of the physical sciences, where individuals with training and interest were available. Only the last twenty years have seen any concerted effort to develop the mathematical techniques and methods needed for the study of human behavior.

Some idea of the state of ferment can be seen when we observe that L. F. Richardson's works on war appeared first in 1919, then in 1935, and then in the 1940's; the somewhat fruitless attempt in the quantification of sociology, *Dimensions of Society* by Stuart C. Dodd, appeared in 1942; von Neumann's and Morgenstern's *Theory of Games and Economic Behavior* in 1944; N. Rashevesky's *Mathematical Theory of Human Relations* in 1947; Norbert Wiener's *Cybernetics* in 1948; G. K. Zipf's *Human Behavior and the Principle of Least Effort* in 1949; Kurt Lewin's *Field Theory in Social Science* in 1951; Kenneth Arrow's *Social Choice and Individual Values* in 1951. The mathematical sophistication in the works noted ranges from next to nonexistent in the case of Dodd, to the outer bounds of modern mathematics with von Neumann and Morgenstern, and Weiner. The range of sophistication with respect to behavioral science content also covers the complete spectrum. Yet in the last five years, textbooks of high calibre dealing with applied mathematical methods in the behavioral sciences have already begun to appear. *Games and Decisions* by Luce and Raiffa appeared in 1957 and is an excellent expository work which can be read even by those with relatively little formal mathematical background. *Introduction to Finite Mathematics* by Kemeny, Snell, and Thompson is designed specifically to provide an understanding of the new areas of mathematics which have application to the behavioral sciences. It appeared in 1957 and has been used extensively at both graduate and undergraduate levels.

In 1954 when my small book of *Readings in Game Theory and Political Behavior* appeared, it would have been easy to give a complete bibliography on the theory of games and allied topics. It was difficult to find more than ten or fifteen good articles on the subject relevant to the behavioral sciences. Today there are well over a thousand books and articles involving game theory; several hundred addressed to the behavioral sciences and a growing literature in allied topics, such as gaming and simulation.

During the last fifteen to twenty years great strides in methodology have been made. During the last five years, considerable advances in technology have begun to influence our techniques of investigation and to broaden possibilities for research and experimentation. Relatively few behavioral scientists have been trained to use or to adjust to the use of electronic computers. Yet the startling growth of large-scale computer establishments not only in government and large industries but also in every major university and college in the United States is a harbinger of a revolution in data analysis and theory testing.

New tools for the behavioral scientist, designed increasingly by younger behavioral scientists now being trained, are in existence. It would be foolish to present the recent advances as a cure-all. They cannot displace the well-read scholar, scientist, and humanist with a broad understanding of his subject. They are there to complement his capacities in a vital manner.

Although this book of selections is designed to sketch in a non-technical manner a part of the new developments in game theory and allied topics, it is important for the behavioral scientist to see these advances as part of an integrated extension of the subject areas under consideration. For those who have passed their last formal examination and are no longer in a position to acquire completely new sets of skills, these selections may give a knowledge of the types of problems to which these new methods apply and indicate where they may fruitfully sponsor or otherwise support projects they do not perform themselves.

For graduate students and others in the behavioral sciences, the intent is to provide enough examples and sufficient detail to

serve as an introduction and guide to further work.   Therefore a
relatively large bibliography with annotation is supplied.
Furthermore, several articles which are relatively technical are
included so that at least the names and the nature of the work of
those developing the new mathematics and its applications are
known to those who may eventually wish to use them.   For the
mathematicians, these selections may serve to indicate the type
of problems to be faced in mathematising the ideas of the behavioral sciences.

2. What Is Game Theory?

Game theory is a method for the study of decision making in
situations of conflict.   It deals with human processes in which the
individual decision-unit is not in complete control of other decision units entering into the environment.   It is addressed to
problems involving conflict, cooperation, or both, at many levels.
The decision-unit may be an individual, a group, a formal or an
informal organization, or a society.   The stage may be set to
reflect primarily political, psychological, sociological, economic,
or other aspects of human affairs.

Diplomats involved in international negotiations, generals
engaged in fighting an enemy, labor unions striking against the
firms in an industry, members of a family arguing over who should
have the car, the missionary trying to talk his way out of the
stewing pot, a player in a poker game, politicians striving for a
nomination, children trying to condition the experimental
psychologist, duelists, bandits, and bridge players are all engaged
in activities which may be usefully viewed in the context of game
situations.

The essence of a "game" in this context is that it involves
decision makers with different goals or objectives whose fates are
intertwined.   The individuals are in a situation in which there
may be many possible outcomes with different values to them.
Although they may have some control which will influence the
outcome, they do not have complete control over others.   There
are many examples of decision making where this is not so.   An
engineer or production manager who has been allotted a specific

budget and given control to redesign an industrial process to cut costs or to produce a machine to perform a specific task contends with a minimization or maximization problem over which he exerts all the relevant human control. There may be elements such as the variability of the weather, the possible failure of machinery or the malfunction of his digestion which influence his actions, but in most cases he can make allowances for these and to a good first order of approximation we may regard him as being in control of the situation. Hence if he is not in a psychotic state which causes him to believe that "his machines are against him," he faces a situation which can, in general, be characterized by a minimization or maximization problem.

Although the experience and beliefs of some of us may lead us to feel that the weather intends to rain every time we go on a picnic, it is usually not reasonable to assume that it is a super-human agency engaged in thwarting our desires. On a battle-field, during a nomination, or in a poker game, it is reasonable to assume that there is a conscious active force opposing at least some of our interests.

The problems faced in game theory are more complex than those of simple maximization. The individual must consider how to achieve as much as is possible, taking into account that there are others whose goals differ from his own and whose actions have an effect on all. The decision maker in a game faces a cross-purposes optimization problem. He must adjust his plans not only to his own desires and abilities but also to the desires and abilities of others.

It is my opinion that the term "Theory of Games" is unfor-tunate. Although, as will be shown, for many purposes the analogy is good, the word "game" carries with it too many unde-sirable connotations, especially to sociologists and other behav-ioral scientists. In general, diplomatic relations are not a game in the usual sense. The players are not there for their enjoyment. The slaughter on battlefields and the destruction caused by nuclear warfare are not subjects of amusement. Their many ramifications make such conflicts difficult to study dispassion-ately in any formal and isolated context. Certain abstractions, however, of part of a social or diplomatic process may be made.

There is great danger in displaying an irrational penchant for "rationality." Even though deep analysis may be carried out on a formal model with apparent objectivity, the investigator's biases and misperceptions may be hidden by omissions or protected by the armor of irrelevant mathematics.

Several *caveats* have been made; with these in mind we are in a position to investigate this new methodology together with its language and to use it to broaden our understanding of some of the aspects of human interaction.

3. The Characterization of a Game

In this section several heroic assumptions and simplifications are made in order to expound the basic elements of game theory. Many of them can be and have been modified. Some modifications will be discussed later, and many are indicated in the papers following. Even so, as Rapoport has pointed out so ably and entertainingly in his discussion of fights, games, and debates,[1] many examples of political, social, or other human behavior do not fit easily into the current framework of game theory and call for more modifications or other approaches.

The elements which describe a poker game are the players, the stakes, the deck of cards, a set of rules describing how the game is to be played, together with the definitions of what constitutes a winning hand under all circumstances. Different types of poker vary from each other in the moves and in the information conditions. These are described in the rules. There are, of course, several other aspects of the situation which describe a poker game as it is usually played. Are the players friends? Do they observe any set of informal conventions based on their social relationships? Are they professional poker players? Do they expect to play more than once as a group? These vague, more informal, social, and socio-psychological aspects of a competitive situation are difficult to formalize, and for many purposes are evidently of great importance. When this is the case, great care must be taken in the construction of any model. Yet even

[1] Rapoport, A.: *Fights, Games and Debates,* University of Michigan Press, 1960.

with the difficulties in model construction, much of the anatomy of strategic decision making can be explored.

The battle situation of two opposing field commanders can be described in terms of the number of men at their disposal, their skills, the state of their morale, the amounts, types, and locations of their equipment, their information and intelligence services, the terrain over which they are engaged, the weather conditions, the state of their reserves, and the commanders' evaluations of the importance of various objectives. It may also be important to know if such rules of war as the Geneva Convention will be observed and possibly if other informal rules, such as an understanding not to use bacteriological weapons, will be honored.

In diplomatic negotiations the description must include the independent parties to the negotiation (the personalities of the actual delegates may or may not be important, depending to a large extent on their powers to act), an evaluation of the goals and the importance of the goals to the states involved, an assessment of the methods available and resources of each participant, and a description of the intelligence services and the information available to each participant. It is also necessary to make explicit assumptions concerning the enforcement mechanisms for the carrying out of threats and the penalties for revoking agreements.

As a final example, we turn to economics to describe the situation of two firms interlocked in an advertising campaign. The elements are the two sets of executives in control of the decision making, the types of products, amounts of money available, their information, the forecasts of the effectiveness of different types of advertising, and the laws and physical conditions delineating which actions are legally or physically possible.

All the examples noted obviously have a common core. A game is described in terms of the *players* or individual decision makers, the *payoffs* or the values assigned to the outcomes of the game; and the *rules* which specify the variables that each player controls, the information conditions, and all other relevant aspects of the environment.

These elements are the building blocks of game theory and, hence a detailed discussion of them is given.

A *player* in a game is an autonomous decision-making unit. A player is not necessarily a single person. He may be a country, a political party, a politician, a firm, or a group of individuals. The distinguishing feature of a player is that he or it has an objective in the game and operates under its own orders in the selection of its actions.

Each player is in control of some set of resources. In poker, these resources are cards and money; in battle, military materials, men, and the resources of a supporting economy. In politics, the resources may be money, the press, and the control over organizations and institutions. The *rules of the game* specify how the resources may be utilized.

In chess, the game commences with the pieces (the resources of each player) arranged on the board in a certain manner. The rules specify the nature of the board, the initial positions of the pieces, and the manner in which any piece can be moved. Given the rules, we can work out the possible first moves in a chess game. As we can see the enemy's men, we can also calculate every alternative that he can choose for his first move. In fact, it is theoretically possible to work out the entire game of chess without ever playing it because we could calculate every way to play in advance. Practically, even with the fastest of computers, this is impossible; nevertheless we can imagine the game of chess being played in which both players go up to the referee and each hands him a book containing his complete *strategy* for the game, after which the players leave and the referee works out the actual *play* of the game according to the instructions.

A strategy for chess or any other game is a set of instructions which states in advance how a player intends to select each *move* until the end of the game, taking into account the knowledge that he will have available at the time at which he is called upon to select his move. It takes into account all contingencies and provides instructions as to how to act under every circumstance. Although all contingencies are accounted for, they may be treated in a very aggregated manner. Thus, for example, "Fire when you see the whites of their eyes" covers all contingencies. "Attack across the Marne, regardless of weather conditions, enemy strength, artillery cover or supplies" provides a broad rule for action; as does "When in danger, when in doubt, port your helm and go about," or "Never back a two-time loser for the nomination *regardless* of all information or special features in his favor." These maxims, in the proper context, can be interpreted as strategies. They treat all contingencies, but they have in common the aspect that they use little of the available detailed information. In the game of chess, no simple strategy that wins is known. It is likely that a winning strategy is very complex and uses a great amount of information. In social, political, military, and economic affairs, "rules of thumb," maxims, and general instructions combined with a plan for recognizing and treating special cases and "exceptions to the rule" can be quite effective.

A *strategy* in politics or business or war or chess can be defined generally as a general plan of action containing instructions as to what to do in every contingency.

The outcome of a game will depend on the strategies employed by every player (and possibly on events beyond the control of any player, such as a natural disaster). For ease of exposition and primarily as a shorthand notation, a few symbols will be introduced. We will denote the set of all possible strategies that can be used by a specific player, whose name is i, by the symbol S_i. This is the set of every possible plan of action that the ith player can have, taking into account his resources, the resources of his competitors, and the rules of the game. Suppose that this player selects a specific strategy, which we will call s_i, out of the set of all his available strategies. Suppose that there are n players. The outcome of the game will depend on the strategy that each of them selects. For every outcome of the game, each player will have a valuation. We call the table which gives the valuation of a player for all outcomes of the game his *payoff function*. We denote the payoff function of the ith player by $P_i(s_1, s_2, s_3, \ldots, s_n)$.

The possible outcomes in chess, as it is usually played, are win, lose, or draw; in poker, the outcome is usually in money and occasionally in clothes (the valuation of the outcome, i.e., the payoff, in strip-poker is not easy); in business, it may be profits and/or growth. The outcomes in politics can be in money, post, or prestige, or many other things. In each case we must attempt to describe the player's method of valuation, preferences, or utility which enables him to decide whether one outcome is preferred to another. In many business and game situations, the outcome may be in money, and this may serve as a good approximate measure of the payoffs to the players. In general, they will individually prefer more to less. In many other areas of endeavor, the valuation is not as simple. For example, the outcome from one line of action in battle may be 1000 enemy casualties at a cost of 200 casualties to your own side; whereas another possible action would have resulted in 5000 enemy dead at a cost of 2000 men of your own. In some cases, in an attempt to evaluate the payoff, we are forced to place a value on human life; in this example, the general in command might have to attempt to do so.

Although our wants and aspirations may change over the years, for many purposes it is desirable to assume that over some range of time an individual has a valuation scheme whereby he can evaluate the worth of any prospect with which he is confronted. The outcome of a game presents a prospect which must be evaluated. It results in an allocation of resources or a distribution of posts and honors or, in war, in a distribution of casualties and destruction. The *payoffs* are the values attached by the players to these prospects. For example, Hitler, when faced with the alternative prospects of a totally destroyed Germany or one which surrendered more or less intact, might have evaluated his payoff as being greater for the first outcome than the second.

Using our shorthand notation, we can describe a game as a situation in which there are n players; each player i is required to select a strategy s_i from a set of strategies S_i which is available to him. Given the choices of all of the players, there is a resulting outcome whose value is determined by player i and called his payoff; it is denoted by $P_i(s_1, s_2, s_3, \ldots, s_n)$.

4. The Normalized and Extensive Form of a Game

There are two ways in which games can be represented: in a compact manner, called the *normalized form;* and in more detail,

TABLE 1 PAYOFF TO THE POLICE

	1	2	Strategy of guerillas
1	−5	−7	
2	+8	+1	

Strategy of police

called the *extensive form*. Although, as far as the mathematics
of game theory is concerned, the two are equivalent, they illustrate two different approaches to the modeling of human affairs.
The first is primarily static and the second includes dynamic
features.

For simplicity we use the normalized form to illustrate one
of the most elementary forms of a game situation. This is the
two-person zero-sum game. The important property of this game
is that it is one of pure opposition. The amount that one
player loses is equal to the amount that the other one wins.
Many board and card games are of this variety. For example,
chess and two-handed poker can be described as two-person
zero-sum games. Duels, search and pursuit games, and battle
strategy also may be viewed as this type of game. Few political,
social, or psychological situations are of this type, although this
sort of game is a good approximation for many military tactical
problems.

Call the players 1 and 2. Suppose that in the very simple game
we will consider they have only two strategies each. The payoff
to the first player can be presented in a *payoff matrix*, as is shown
in Table 1 and denoted by $P_1(s_1, s_2)$, where s_1 is the strategy of
the first player and s_2 is the strategy of the second. We observe
that it has four values, one for each pair of strategies. $P_1(s_1, s_2)$
has a value of -5 if both players use their first strategy; i.e., when
$s_1 = 1$ and $s_2 = 1$, and 1 if each uses his second strategy,
$P_1(2, 1) = 8$ and so forth. We have represented the strategies
and payoffs by numbers. An oversimplified example serves as
an illustration. Suppose that Player 1 is a police force; it has

TABLE 2 PAYOFF TO POLICE

	Battle	Skirmish	Row minima
Enter jungle	−5	−7	−7
Protect supplies	+8	+1	+1 Maximin
Column maxima	+8	+1 Minimax	

two major strategies or approaches to its task; it can try to render Player 2, which is a guerilla group, ineffective either by punitive action in the jungle or by using its resources to guard sources of food and supplies. In each case the guerillas have the choice of open battle or irregular skirmishes. The payoffs reflect the conditions that a jungle campaign would be costly to the police with attrition under skirmishes worse than in open battle. The payoffs resulting from guarding sources of supply indicate that a direct attack by guerillas would be disaster to them, whereas skirmishes would cause them a mild loss.

We have emphasized that this is only a highly simplified example presented for expository purposes. In an actual situation of the variety described, the tactical short-run aspects of police action may be reasonably well modeled as is done here; the longer-run socio-political aspects require a far more sophisticated treatment.

In this very simple situation there is an optimal choice (at least in the short run) for each of the players. Tables 2 and 3 illustrate the payoffs to both players and contain in their margins the type of analysis both can perform. The police observe that if they enter the jungle, the worst that could happen to them is that they would have to fight skirmishes under unfavorable conditions, and they evaluate this at −7. This is indicated in the column of row minima attached to Table 2. If, on the other hand, they guarded the sources of supply, the worst that could happen is that they would be subject to irregular attack under circumstances favorable to them and would gain an outcome of value of at least 1 to them.

The guerillas can calculate that under all circumstances a policy of open battle is not as desirable as a policy of skirmishing. This is illustrated in the column minima on Table 3 or, equivalently, in the column maxima shown on Table 2. They are equivalent because the entries in Table 3 are the negative of the entries in Table 2. What is good for the police is bad for the guerillas. Thus when the guerillas analyze the possibility of using an open attack, they may examine what is the worst that can happen to them. This is given by the column minima in Table 3. They could rephrase their analysis in terms of what is the best that can happen to the police if they adopt a given policy. This is given by the column maxima in Table 2.

It is easy to see that both sides will adopt their second strategy. The police will guard supplies and the guerillas will avoid open battle. When we look at the maximum entry in the column of row minima in Table 2, we observe that it has a value of 1. Furthermore, when we look at the minimum entry in the row of column maxima, we observe that it has the same value. When this holds true, a game is said to possess a *saddlepoint*. It has been suggested by von Neumann and Morgenstern that *the rational* way to play in this type of game is for each player to adopt a strategy which guarantees that each will obtain the

TABLE 3   PAYOFF TO GUERILLAS

	Battle	Skirmish	Row maxima	
	5	7	7	
	−8	−1	−1	Minimax
Column minima		−1		
	−8	Maximin		

maxmin payoffs or the best of the worst possible outcomes. This suggests that the rational player who knows that the desires of his competitor are diametrically opposed to his own should examine the worst outcomes on the assumption that every one of his actions is countered by the actions of a hostile environment and should then select the one which minimizes the damage that the other can inflict upon him.

Von Neumann and Morgenstern call the payoffs associated with the maxmin the *value* of the two-person zero-sum game. It must be stressed that the recommendation that individuals should actually behave under the assumption that the environment or their competitors are always trying to cause them the most damage has been suggested as sensible or rational behavior only in situations equivalent to two-person zero-sum games.[2]

One of the most pernicious and misleading common fallacies concerning the theory of games is the belief that in some magic manner all game theory reasoning, model building, and advice depends on recommendations for maxmin behavior. There are basically two reasons for this error. (1) Popular discussions and simple examples have tended to give a false impression of the importance of the role of two-person zero-sum games. (2) Less obvious and more important, the formal mechanism of the theory of games is addressed to two related but different problems. The first is the development of a language and a method for describing the fine structure of interlinked decision processes. The second is the investigation of the implications of assumptions concerning the goals and behavior of players, given a description of the game. These assumptions may be based on *normative* or *descriptive* considerations. The suggested solution theory for the two-person zero-sum game is a normative theory based on the concept of a rational individual. Most of the competing thirty or forty different theories of solutions for more complex games are a blend of assumptions based on normative and descriptive considerations. One of the reasons for the growth of experimental gaming in the past decade has been the need to provide

---

[2] von Neumann, J. and O. Morgenstern: *Theory of Games and Economic Behavior*, Princeton University Press, 3rd ed. 1953.

empirical evidence in support of some of the basic assumptions of the different theories of solution. We return to a discussion of different theories in Section 5 below.

Von Neumann and Morgenstern suggest that the rational player in a two-person zero-sum situation *should* avail himself of a maxmin strategy. This is pessimistic in the extreme inasmuch as it implies that not only is the opponent out to render him as much damage as possible but also that he is intelligent and fully understands how to take advantage of any situation. If it were known in advance that the opponent had a bias, made errors, or was generally somewhat stupid, then this normative theory would not necessarily be the best one to follow.

We have presented a simple matrix game. Let us enumerate and consider several of the important features of model building and theory construction that are implicit in even this simple example.

First we note that we managed to gloss over the central problem of valuation or utility. A basic problem which confronts behavioral scientists in almost any field is the construction of a preference system and the investigation of the possibilities for the measurement of preference. The numbers in the payoff matrix have to be obtained in some manner or the other. It is difficult enough to be able to state with certainty that an individual prefers to see Jones as a senator rather than Smith; it is more difficult (and some may say impossible) to state by how much he prefers Jones to Smith. There is an extensive literature on the subject of the measurability of preferences, including one of the articles in this collection of readings; no further discussion is given here.

Second, as we have already observed, the payoff matrices contain a summary description of a game but do not contain any comments or information on how to play the game. The *normalized* form in a very compact manner summarizes all details concerning strategies and payoffs and presents them in a simple array. In order to fully appreciate this condensation, it is necessary to examine the *extensive form* and to contrast the two.

The normalized form presents a game as though it consisted of a single move made by each player simultaneously. This is, of

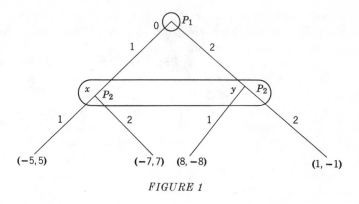

FIGURE 1

course, a fiction, for each of the moves in that context is actually a strategy and hence could be a vast book of instructions covering all contingencies in different ways.   Harking back to our familiar and, to some extent, implausible example of chess, it could be presented in a normalized or matrix form.   In order to do this, we would require a rather large amount of paper, for each player would have trillions of choices, each being a possible strategy in chess.

The extensive form of a game can be best illustrated by means of a diagram known as a *game tree*.   It is called a tree because, at least to mathematicians, it looks like one.   (They, in common with babies, do not particularly worry about the orientation of the tree; hence they ignore the possibility that it might appear to be upside down to the more literally minded behavioral scientist.) A simple example of a game tree is given in Figure 1.   It is the extensive form representation of the matrix game we have already examined.

The vertices in the game tree represent choice points.   The branches indicate alternatives.   All the vertices are labeled with the name of the player to whom they belong.   Thus at the vertex 0 (where the game starts), which is also labelled with P_1, the first player is called on to make a choice between two alternatives. After each player has made his move, the game reaches a terminal point on the game tree and each player obtains his payoff.   For

example, if both players select their second alternative, the game terminates with the payoff of $(1, -1)$. This is the saddlepoint indicated in Table 2.

The two vertices labeled with P_2 are enclosed by a single curve. This indicates that these choice points belong to the same *information set*. We have noted that the matrix game is a simultaneous move game. The players select their strategies without knowledge of each other's actions. Thus in the game tree, although the first player selects between his two alternatives first, in effect the second player is not aware of the choice and hence cannot tell if he is making a choice at the vertex x or y. The game tree representation of the game of Tables 1, 2, and 3 given in Figure 1 is now repeated in Figure 2. We note, however, that the order in which the players move has been reversed. Here, however, this makes no difference inasmuch as they are both moving in the dark. In this situation, if 1 moves first or 2 moves first, provided neither finds out˙ before he has selected his move, the outcome is not affected. The important feature is not the temporal sequence but when they find out about what has happened.

If it were possible for the second player to manage to get a "peek" at the move of the first, we would be describing a different game. In political and social situations we are often interested in problems involving the sequencing of moves, in the possibility of information leaks, in the opportunities to plant false information, to bluff, threaten, precommit, recontract, and

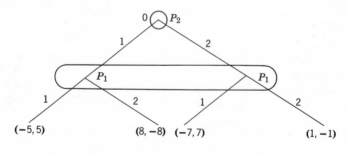

FIGURE 2

TABLE 4

	1	2	Strategies for 2
Strategies 1 for 1	$(-2, +4)$	$(0, 0)$	
2	$(-100, -100)$	$(0, 0)$	

so forth. It is for these reasons that descriptions of games in extensive form or descriptions of "dynamic" or ongoing games are of importance. In order to fully illustrate this we can do so more naturally in the context of a *nonconstant sum game*. After a brief digression on the meaning of a nonconstant sum game, we return to the extensive form.

An examination of the entries in Tables 2 and 3 shows that the values in each cell of the two matrices when added together sum to zero, or, symbolically:

$$P_1(s_1, s_2) + P_2(s_1, s_2) = 0.$$

This indicates the complete opposition in the desires of the players. It is of interest to note that in this context, without added sociological or psychological considerations, it is meaningless to talk about cooperation, competition, or collusion. They are not distinguishable in this situation. There is no way in which the players could improve matters to their satisfaction by joint action.

Even though the competitors may have interests which are heavily opposed, there may still be some important common interests shared. Thus in the realm of international politics each side may want to achieve extremely different goals, but neither may wish to pay the price of a war which could be a disaster to both. In Table 4 a simple type of threat situation is presented. Both for ease of comparison and to save space, the payoffs to both players are entered in each cell. Thus the payoffs resulting from both selecting their first strategy is $(-2, 4)$

or -2 for the first player and 4 for the second. These sum to -2; the other entries sum to 0 and -200. This indicates that there is great value to joint action. Instead of using numbers for the strategies, we can state what they stand for. Suppose that this game represents the guarantees for the *status quo* for an island or a free city. The first nation may have decided on one of two strategies: (1) maintain the status quo but give up the city if attacked or (2) maintain the status quo but declare all-out nuclear war if attacked. The second nation may choose, if negotiations fail, to attack or, as its second strategy, not to attack. In Figure 3a, the extensive form representation of Table 4 reflects the conditions that each country moves independently without information about the move of the other.

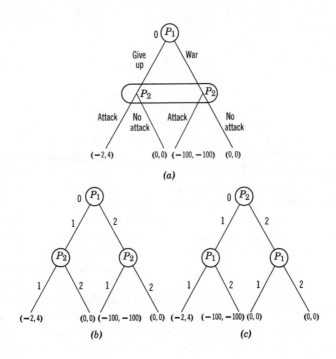

FIGURE 3

In the two-person zero-sum game example, although we noted that the players moved simultaneously or at least without knowledge of each other's moves until both had been committed, reexamination will show that in this special case an information leak would not have changed the outcome. In this *nonconstant* sum game model of an international situation, the structure of information is vital. Depending on our assumptions concerning the availability of information, we obtain three very different strategic situations. The three game trees given in Figures 3*a*, *b*, and *c* should be contrasted with Figures 1 and 2. The first game tree reflects the conditions that, as part of the *rules of the game*, the players are committed to their strategies simultaneously and with no possible knowledge of their opponent's action. The rules explicitly make peeking, bluffing, reneging, and so forth impossible. It is easy to observe that in most cases of international politics this is not so. When it is not so, and that is the situation you wish to study, you have constructed the wrong model and must modify it. This is done in Figures 3*b* and *c*.

In Figure 3*b* the vertex 0 is labeled with P_1, indicating that Player 1 must move. After he has selected one of his alternatives, the vertices at the next level bear the label of P_2, hence call on Player 2 to move. Here we observe that there is a small circle around each individual vertex. This circle indicates the information conditions. All vertices which lie within the same circle cannot be distinguished by the player being called on to move. In this situation, as there is only one vertex in each circle, this fact indicates that the second player is completely informed about what is going on. He knows that the first player has committed himself to a specific line of action. Again we must emphasize that in this model we have exhibited the conditions under which the first player *must* (as required by the rules of the game) declare his move first. In some situations this may be a great advantage. In the model presented here, the first player's commitment is firm. If the second player decides to attack, then there will undoubtedly be war. Even if the first may wish to change his mind, he does not have the choice.

Figure 3*c* illustrates a third situation. Here Player 2 has the

Strategies for Player 2

		(1, 1; 2, 1)	(1, 1; 2, 2)	(1, 2; 2, 1)	(1, 2; 2, 2)
Strate-	1	(−2, 4)	(−2, 4)	(−0, 0)	(0, 0)
gies for					
Player					
1	2	(−100, −100)	(0, 0)	(−100, −100)	(0, 0)

opportunity to make the first move and commit himself to carrying it out before Player 1 selects his move. The *normalized* or *matrix form* of these three games are all different, as is shown in Tables 4, 5a, and b. In Table 4 each player has two strategies; hence there are four outcomes (some of which may have the same value to the players). The players move simultaneously, as is shown by the information conditions. Without yet having

Table 5b

Strate-	Strategies for Player 2	
gies for	1	2
Player 2		
(1, 1; 2, 1)	(−2, 4)	(0, 0)
(1, 1; 2, 2)	(−2, 4)	(0, 0)
(1, 2; 2, 1)	(−100, −100)	(0, 0)
(1, 2; 2, 2)	(−100, −100)	(0, 0)

discussed concepts of solution for a nonconstant sum game, it is still nevertheless evident that this situation is loaded with danger. There is the possibility of a joint blunder. Each may underestimate the intentions of the other and select actions which might lead to war.

Table 5a shows that when Player 1 has the chance of precommitment, he still has two strategies, while his opponent now has more (four) strategies and is thereby placed at a disadvantage. The four strategies of Player 2 can be read and described as follows:

(1, 1; 2, 1) If he chooses 1, I choose 1; if he chooses 2, I choose 1.
(1, 1; 2, 2) If he chooses 1, I choose 1; if he chooses 2, I choose 2.
(1, 2; 2, 1) If he chooses 1, I choose 2; if he chooses 2, I choose 1.
(1, 2; 2, 2) If he chooses 1, I choose 2; if he chooses 2, I choose 2.

If Player 1 precommits himself to his second strategy, which is "declare all-out nuclear war if the city is attacked; maintain the status quo otherwise," then an examination of the columns will show that the best strategy for Player 2, which in all circumstances will be (1, 1; 2, 2), will lead to the maintenance of the status quo. Under all possibilities, this strategy will yield a payoff to the second player which is as good as or better than any other strategy he has available.

Table 5b shows that when Player 2 has the chance of precommitment, he has two strategies, while his opponent who now has four strategies is placed at a disadvantage. The second player precommits to attacking the city if negotiations fail. An examination of the rows shows that the first player is advised to select either his first or second strategies. Both of these involve giving up the city.

Even at this extremely simple level both the powers and weaknesses of the language of game theory can be illustrated. The normalized form of the three games is sufficient to demonstrate the important different effects of precommitment. The game tree presenting the extensive form shows the details of information and the sequencing of moves. When we contemplate the actual situation—negotiations over the status of a city—we can list many important features which may not be adequately accounted for by the game model:

1. Is it possible for a country to precommit itself to a line of action?
2. Are there actually only two major alternatives?
3. Do values stay fixed over the period of negotiations?
4. Does not timing affect the negotiations?
5. Do individuals think in terms of strategies? Can they be taught to think in terms of strategies? Should they think in terms of strategies?
6. Surely negotiations between two countries are part of a larger on-going process and cannot be studied in isolation but must be investigated in a complete dynamic context?

In general, complete precommitment is difficult to achieve and even if it is achieved, it may not be believed by an adversary. Unless the Deity is enforcing the rules, the mere statement that you intend to stick to your announced policy is not sufficient. Tables 5a and 5b showed cases of absolute commitment. In order to reflect the possibility of imperfect precommitment, further moves can be introduced which with certain probabilities allow the precommitted player to change his policy.

In human affairs, when the individual is confronted with a choice between A or B, his selection is often C, which was not present, offered, or discovered until the last minute. No matter how we study the processes of conflict resolution, there is always the danger that we will fail to consider elements vital to the problem at hand. This is primarily a failure in observation or perception. A good methodology may make it easier to avoid such errors; it does not eliminate them.

As pointed out by Rapoport[3] and many others, in negotiations there is an effort to make the opposition "see things your way." The values held by the participants at the start of the negotiations may not be the same as those held at the end of the negotiations. The adaptive models of Simon and others, the role of aspiration

[3] Rapoport, A.: *op. cit.*

level,[4] the possibilities for the rationalization of one's actions through the mechanisms described by Festinger as cognitive dissonance[5] lead to the framing of negotiations in terms of an intermix of a competitive process together with an adjustment of values. Such a process is sketched by Iklé and Lietes in their article reprinted here.

Even in such games as chess, the time allotted to each player for his moves is specified in the tournament rules. In diplomatic negotiation the time bounds may also be stringent. If, as a rule of the game, certain moves must be made before a specified deadline, we must make explicit the alternatives and penalties that will occur if the deadline is not met. Thus the Czechoslovakians, when confronted by Hitler's threat prior to the occupation of the Sudetenland, could choose between replying to the ultimatum before the time limit or failing to reply. The time element introduced a third alternative: yes, no, or no reply.

A fundamental and not satisfactorily resolved difficulty concerns the concept of strategy. Do decision makers commit themselves to complicated plans, taking into account myriads of contingencies? An examination of a simple game such as checkers shows that it is hardly practical even to try to write down a detailed strategy that will be worth utilizing. Aggregation must take place. General rules must be developed to handle large categories of situations. "Artificial intelligence" programs[6] have been developed which do this. It is generally recognized that even the most rational of human beings, armed with the largest of computers, can hope only to explore a very limited selection of alternative strategies in any detail. Computation and conscious enumeration of alternatives, combined with the use of maxims, principles of behavior, or rules-of-thumb, appears to describe how many decision makers behave. The overwhelming number of alternatives (many of them scarcely different) con-

---

[4] Siegel, S.: "Level of Aspiration and Decision-Making," *Psychological Review,* **64,** 253–262, 1957.

[5] Festinger, L.: *A Theory of Cognative Dissonance,* Row Peterson, 1957.

[6] Minsky, M.: "Steps Toward Artificial Intelligence," *Proceedings of the IRE,* January 1961, pp. 8–30.

fronting the individual suggests that exhaustive examination of all of them is out of the question.

We have already noted that a rule-of-thumb may provide a means for generating a broad aggregated strategy. Those interested in the construction of computer programs to simulate decision processes have been forced to search for *heuristics*, the word used to describe the formalized rules-of-thumb which in some situations appear to produce good strategies. Possibly there are still many important tasks to be performed in political science in collecting and analyzing political maxims and rules-of-thumb. The folklore is rich concerning voting, campaigning, negotiations, city government, and military action. There are some of us who would not even be surprised if a set of heuristics, put together and used instead of some of the ward bosses or city mayors, did a better job than the incumbents. Admittedly, an IBM 7090 might not kiss babies as handily as a campaigner, but, beyond that, it might be more sensitive to the needs and wants of the constituents.

Most people do not appear to use the concept of strategy consciously, as understood in game theory, in their planning and decision making. Many tend to "play by ear" rather than plan in detail. It is the belief of students and advocates of game theory and decision theory that individuals *should* consciously attempt at least to consider their problems in terms of alternative strategies. Although it is recognized that exhaustive search of alternative strategies is more or less impossible, political, diplomatic, and military decision making may be assisted and possibly improved by the formal structuring of alternative paths of action.

Much of game theory has been presented in a basically static framework. A game is portrayed as having a finite duration. The payoffs for playing in the game are awarded at the end. If an analogy is to be drawn between a game and human affairs, we may imagine a poker game which has no known end; players join and leave the game; payoffs are made at the end of each hand in chips which may either be consumed or be used to bet in the succeeding hand. Political and social behavior are best studied in the context of on-going processes. For this reason, extreme care must be exercised when going from the study of the normalized form of a game to the dynamics of the process it is purported to portray.

5. Solutions, Intent, and Behavior

DECISION MAKING UNDER UNCERTAINTY: NORMATIVE AND DESCRIPTIVE APPROACHES

How should individuals behave in the political arena? How should the diplomat or general act? How do they act? Can we describe the rules of social interaction for Indians from New Mexico or socialities from New England? The economists have a simple model of a rational economic man which might be said to provide a broad approximation of observed behavior under some circumstances. Beyond that, economic man serves as a guide to how individuals should act if they wish to maximize their welfare when confronted with choices between known alternatives. Economic, political, military, or other types of social man are usually confronted with far more than choices between known alternatives. The environment may be misperceived, the goals only partially known, the outcome subject to the actions of others or subject to chance. In dealing with these broader aspects of decision making, the body of knowledge loosely referred to as the theory of games offers a special methodology and many theories to describe the behavior of individuals. The theories may be interpreted normatively or behavioristically. For two-person zero-sum games discussed in Section 4, the maximin solution, which entails maximizing on the assumption that your opponent will do you as much harm as possible, is a normative solution. It is suggested that this is the way a rational man *should* play.

The many different cooperative and noncooperative solutions to nonconstant sum games have been prompted by a desire to understand phenomena, such as bargaining, power, bluffing, threats, and fair division. They have been based on an intermix of normative considerations invoking features such as symmetry, as well as a formalization of the insights, special knowledge, and understanding of those concerned with decision-making in different contexts.

In a world filled with paranoids and other madmen, it may not be possible to explain to them that your interests and welfare and theirs may be closely related. Their distorted view of the environment may cause them to inflict harm on you regardless of the harm they inflict on themselves by doing so. It is unreasonable to assume that in all walks of life our fellowmen are "out to get us." The life of the Hobbesian man in such a state would indeed be nasty, brutish, and short.

In a two-handed game of poker, it is most reasonable to assume that your fellow player is your opponent. Regardless of his general feelings toward you, in the narrow world of the poker game his interests and yours are opposed. By assuming the worst you are not ascribing any violently hostile intent to your opponent; you are merely observing that in the context of the situation, one man's poison is the other man's meat.

In the narrow context of the game, most two-person card and board games are zero-sum. The amount that one man loses is the amount that the other wins. In a broader context, both sides may derive pleasure from playing; they may only be playing to improve their skills or to pass the time. Leaving these considerations aside, if both players are trying to win, their interests are strictly opposed, and a rational man *should* expect that if his opponent is also rational, he will act in a manner utterly against the goals of the first.

Returning to a nonconstant sum game, for example, suppose that two men are trapped in a cellar. The water is rising. Above them is a trap door which needs the efforts of both to open. The game and the payoffs can be described by a simple two-by-two matrix, as is shown in Table 6. In this example no attempt has been made to assign values to the lives or deaths of the two men, although in situations involving calculations of the cost of national defense it may be necessary to attach at least approximate values to such states. If we were merely to assume that each individual prefers his own life to his death, then regardless of their feelings or attitudes toward each other, they will select their first strategies and cooperate in opening the trapdoor.

In summary, when a game, a tactical struggle, or some aspect of a conflict situation can be represented by a two-person zero-sum game, it is recommended that a rational individual employ his maximin strategy unless he has specific and trustworthy information concerning the irrationalities of his opponent.

When a situation does not lend itself to portrayal by a two-person zero-sum game, unless *very pessimistic* assumptions are

TABLE 6

	Push	Do nothing
Push	Life for both	Death for both
Do nothing	Death for both	Death for both

being made, the various solution concepts for nonconstant sum games *do not* advocate the employment of a maximin approach. If not, what do they suggest instead? Some of the alternatives are dealt with in the succeeding sections.

NONCOOPERATIVE EQUILIBRIUM SOLUTION

A concept of solution to a nonconstant sum game which underlies much of economic thought and applies elsewhere calls for the type of individualistic behavior characterized already in the examples of international guarantees to an open city and the men trapped in the cellar. You do not assume that the others are hostile to you or your desires. They are merely interested in their welfare and are not directly concerned with your desires. Their indirect involvement with your welfare will depend on the strategic interlinkage of your fate and theirs. The following examples illustrate this. In Table 7a we show the payoffs to two individuals trapped in the cellar. We have called the value of death $-b$, where b is a very large number, and the value of life d, which is a large positive number. The interests of the two players happen to coincide completely. "What is good for Player 1 is good for both." The only possible problem that faces the players is how to coordinate their actions, not why to do so. In this situation it is easy for the players to coordinate; hence there is no problem. Marshak, Radnor, Schelling, and others have discussed team problems and games of coordination. The goals and desires of individuals may coincide, but there may

TABLE 7a

	1	2
1	(d, d)	$(-b, -b)$
2	$(-b, -b)$	$(-b, -b)$

be blunders in attempts to coordinate action. For example, two individuals are running in opposite directions along a platform, trying to catch trains about to leave. If the first one veers to the left and the other keeps on course, or if the second one veers right and the first stays on course, they will not collide and will catch their trains. If neither moves off course, or if both move off course, they will collide. The payoff is as in Table 7b. Their interests are parallel, but they can wreck each other by failure to coordinate.

Many rules of the road, customs, standard procedures, and some maxims exist to handle precisely such situations. It does not really matter if cars drive on the left- or right-hand side of the road provided that everyone knows which side to drive on. Custom, based on a private whim of King Henry VIII, or a decision by the French Academy, may be equally adequate, provided that everybody knows which applies.

Cues are needed to take care of details of coordination. The

	No change	Veer
No change	−5, −5	10, 10
Veer	10, 10	−5, −5

knowledge and experience of a Bohemian coming into a new town tells him to head for the coffee shop to make his connections, at least in parts of the United States. A more difficult game problem is brought about when individuals have the same interests and need to coordinate their actions but must do so in the face of hostile forces. Signaling in bridge is an example of this type of problem. The design of passwords and classification systems for secret documents is possibly the most important problem in this category. The precautionary actions may cost a group more in loss of internal communication and coordination than is gained in security.

Ploys such as dropping bogus complicated equipment or allowing false plans to be captured in order to use up the intelligence time of the opposition are well recognized methods. Perhaps more universal and more deadly is the utilization of the Good Soldier Schweik, or Gunner Asch, or other simple souls of their ilk whose happy combination of a sense of self-preservation combined with shrewdness and the appropriate lack of intelligence may spell disaster to schemes too dependent on trying to outguess the system with chains of "He knows that I know, that he knows . . . ."

The examples in Tables 7a and 7b illustrate situations in which no matter what the players did, their interests were parallel. Provided that they were even moderately rational, it paid them to coordinate their actions if they could find out how to do so. In a situation such as the two individuals running for their trains, formal game theory offers no further solution than that they should get out of each other's way. Social and psychological experimentation and observation are needed to determine and record how this is to be achieved. When the problem is more complicated, such as in the design of codes and security checks or command and control systems, a combination of work is needed which involves both the more formal aspects of the methodology of game theory and statistics, combined with an understanding of the nature of the organizations and the level of the intelligence of the individuals for whom the system is designed.

The example in Table 7c represents the end-all or epitome of a *laissez-faire* situation. Let the two players under consideration be the writer of this page and the reader. We are faced with a problem: shall we independently decide to go or not to go to see a film tonight? Let us assume that somewhere in our respective neighborhoods there are films we would like to see. As is shown in Table 7c, we have no interaction. My decision to go to the film or to stay home makes no difference to you and vice versa. An examination of the matrix shows that neither of us appears to be eager to go to the films tonight and that by merely following our own individual tastes we will both elect not to go. It might be argued that our decisions may eventually bring ruin to the film industry and then to the whole economy. From which we might deduce that it is our duty to go to the films, drink beer, and do a few other patriotic things of this ilk in support of the economy. Nevertheless, as a good first approximation, it is going to make no difference to me if you go to the films tonight, even if you see a double feature.

TABLE 7c

	Go	Stay home
Go	1, 2	1, 5
Stay home	3, 2	3, 5

TABLE 7d

	Abide	Struggle
Thumbs down	0, Death	0, Death
Thumbs up	0, Life	0, Life

In this example, not only may the individuals have no direct involvement with each other's welfare, they also have no indirect influence on this welfare—or at least their indirect influence is so slight (reacting through, say, the whole economy) that each may follow his own bent, allowing for "the Invisible Hand" to take care of the over-all economy.

One obvious difficulty with all the examples presented has been that we have assumed that the individuals are not concerned with the welfare of others, regardless of the state of their own welfare. It is easy to dismiss any group's interest in others as a manifestation of unadulterated self-interest. Thus, for example, the Peace Corps, aid to Africa, famine assistance, and so forth can be regarded as strictly selfishly motivated in order to preserve some form of long-term gain. The problem posed by interrelated utilities can be seen clearly in the example in Table 7d. The choice is thumbs up or thumbs down in the Roman arena. The vanquished gladiator can abide by the sentence or struggle against fate. Whatever he does makes no difference to the outcome. As the situation is presented, the emperor is indifferent to the outcome, although he controls it. We assign a payoff of zero to the emperor under all outcomes. This presents him as totally dispassionate and uninvolved in the situation. In this circumstance, our theory of behavior offers no guide for the emperor. Perhaps we could advise him to flip a coin, evince some humane feelings towards the gladiator, or take into account the spirit of the mob and their image of him as emperor.

There is room for two on the life raft. The left side has protection against the sea and wind; the right side does not. If two individuals try to sit on the same side of the raft, it will upset. The payoffs are as in Table 7e. There are two stable possibilities, both of which, as will be seen below, fulfill the definition of an equilibrium point. It is in the interests of both survivors not to upset the raft. Their interests are not completely parallel, for each one would prefer the favored position. This is represented by the values (5, 10) and (10, 5), respectively. How are we to resolve the impasse? If one survivor reaches the raft first, it may be resolved in the same manner that a firm precommitment may resolve a situation. "First come, first served" might apply. If one were stronger, faster, and brighter than the other, he might outmaneuver him. They might cooperate and take turns. If they did this, then the simple two-by-two matrix representation of the game would not be sufficient. We would have to consider more of the dynamic process of survival.

The next example is the renowned "Prisoner's Dilemma" and is attributed to A. W. Tucker. Two prisoners have been taken into custody by the police. The district attorney interviews each one separately. They both know that if neither turns State's evidence, the worst that can happen is that each gets a light sentence for vagrancy. If one confesses and the other does not do so, one will be let off with a very minor punishment while the other will receive a stiff sentence. If both confess, then both will receive a relatively heavy sentence. Numbers have been attached to the payoffs in Table 7f merely for ease of discussion. If each selects the individually rational action with no consideration for the other, then both will make a selection that is jointly disasterous.

TABLE 7e

	Left	Right
Left	0, 0	10, 5
Right	5, 10	0, 0

TABLE 7*f*

	No confession	Confess
No confession	$-1, -1$	$-10, 0$
Confess	$0, -10$	$-8, -8$

We carry out our analysis from the point of view of the first prisoner. He observes that if he does not confess, then, depending on the actions of his fellow prisoner, he will obtain a payoff of -1 or -10. If, on the other hand, he confesses, he will obtain a payoff of 0 or -8, depending on the action of his fellow prisoner. He prefers 0 to -1 and -8 to -10. Hence by merely applying the criterion of individual rationality, he will be motivated to select his second alternative, which is to confess. A similar argument holds for the second prisoner. The result may be that both confess and are both far worse off than had they both maintained silence.

The examples of two-person nonconstant sum games have been presented to show some of the different interrelationships which can exist between the strategies and objectives of several decision makers. The definition of a noncooperative equilibrium point and its meaning as a possible solution to a nonconstant sum game can now be given. Although we define it for two players, it can easily be generalized for any number.

Let the sets of strategies available to Players 1 and 2 be denoted by S_1 and S_2, respectively. The payoffs to each player can be described by the functions $P_1(s_1, s_2)$ and $P_2(s_1, s_2)$, where s_1 and s_2 are strategies belonging to the sets S_1 and S_2, respectively. A pair of strategies $(\bar{s}_1, \bar{s}_2)$ forms an equilibrium point if

$$P_1(\bar{s}_1, \bar{s}_2) \geq P_1(s_1, \bar{s}_2) \text{ for each } s_1 \in S_1$$

$$P_2(\bar{s}_1, \bar{s}_2) \geq P_2(\bar{s}_1, s_2) \text{ for each } s_2 \in S_2$$

In words, if Player 1 attempts to maximize his payoff on the assumption that Player 2 will use his strategy $\bar{s}_2$, then Player 1 may select as his strategy $\bar{s}_1$ and vice versa. There is a stability to the equilibrium in the sense that if one competitor knows that the other is at the equilibrium point, he will not be motivated to change. As presented mathematically, there are no aspects of dynamics included in the definition of an equilibrium point. However, it is evident from the most elementary considerations of political, social, and other human processes that we are concerned with action and reaction, interplay and motion.

The discussion of all the examples has been carried out in a dynamic context, at least implicitly. In certain economic processes, such as the business cycle, in psychological and sociological experiments with small groups, the dynamics have been made explicit. Our interests then center on the two basic questions that we must ask of any human organization. Do the dynamics tend to lead the participants toward an equilibrium? If equilibria exist, are they stable? There are great differences between uneasy truces and genuine settlements. In the former, an accidental shot, a minor error, or a false statement may precipitate a crisis. In the later, the mechanisms are strong enough and have sufficient flexibility that the accidents, minor provocations, and disturbances are dealt with.

Returning to the example involving precommitment in the defense of the city, we may examine the equilibrium points in Tables 4, 5a, and 5b and interpret them in a dynamic as well as in a static context. In Table 4, both the strategy pairs (1, 1) and (2, 2) are equilibrium points. In the static sense, they satisfy the property that in the first case, if the first player knew that the second would fight if opposed in the takeover, his best choice is to let the city go; similarly, if the second knew that the first would let the city go, his best choice is to take it over with a threat of war. The equilibrium point (2, 2) has the same type of circular stability, only in this case the first player is favored. If the second player knew that the first were committed to fight, his best strategy is not to fight. In this model of the situation, however, we have specified that *neither side* knows what the intentions of the other are, and, furthermore, they are not given the opportunity to communicate or negotiate before making their choice. Although from a formal mathematical point of view there are two possible equilibria, the situation is dangerous in the extreme.

In Table 5a, the situation has been alleviated in the sense that Player 1 has been allowed to state his intentions in advance. If his precommitment is firm, then his strategy to threaten war if the status of the city is violated, combined with the second strategy of his opponent, forms an equilibrium point. The opponent's second strategy is to attack only if a statement has been made that the city will not be defended, otherwise leave it if war would result.

A similar analysis can be carried out with Table 5b. The three games together represent a situation in which the information and bargaining processes are symmetric and two situations with a nonsymmetric setup in favor of the first player to move.

EQUILIBRIUM, IDIOTS, MADMEN, BUREAUCRACY, AND ERRORS

The two situations with communication and precommitment were apparently more stable than that without. If we were to interpret them strictly with the full formalism of game theory, they would be completely stable as, in each case, the player moving second would know that his opponent is *irrevocably precommitted*. We have already noted that without the Deity holding the stakes, it is difficult to precommit. Our rationalistic game presentation in its pristine form leaves out important influences, which nevertheless can be added.

What is the role of madmen? The record of political assassinations suggests that in the same way the drunk or dangerous driver presents an occupational hazard to other drivers, so must the political system be prepared for the random unreasoning event. What about the cynics and skeptics and their influence on action? If we do not believe the threats of the opponent as representing a firm precommitment, what do we believe? A measure of credibility is required. The problem of the avoidance of an atomic war hinges not so much on the design of firm commitment mechanisms as on the design of mechanisms and methods of communication which make even the most hardened cynics understand that it is very plausible for the threat to be carried out.

What is the role of idiots, oafs, and bureaucracies? In the *Brave New World* of Aldous Huxley, an island was populated only by Alphas. The results were almost disaster. The oversupply of clever men acting *in vacuo* allowed for instabilities that are modified when one must contend with junior tax inspectors, lawyers, and review committees. The mere presence of Forms 4 to 40, all to be filled out in triplicate, places lags and insensitivities in the system which may be of vital necessity as soon as the speed of reaction starts to far outstrip the accuracy of perception. The placement of a direct telephone from the White House to the Kremlin could easily destroy more stability than it creates.

EQUILIBRIUM: TWO EXAMPLES

Two examples of equilibrium are presented here in a game theoretic and a gaming context. They pose more problems than they solve and in this manner may be most useful in providing insights.

The Self-Policing System. The problem is to design a prison from which no one will escape even though the prison has no guards and it is technologically possible for the prisoners to open the main gate. Figure 4 provides a design. There are n prisoners consigned to the prison. We assume that they are all cooperative in the sense that any individual would prefer to see as many of his comrades as possible escape with him. However, each is individually motivated to the extent that if it were a choice between his freedom, with the others all left in prison, or the freedom of all others with him left in prison, he prefers the former. The outer walls of the prison contain a gate marked G.

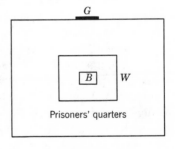

FIGURE 4

The only way out is through the gate. In the middle of the prison, say half a mile from the gate, is a blockhouse marked B. There is no mechanized transportation in the prison. Surrounding the blockhouse is a barrier W. In the barrier are n buttons, each button activated by the thumb print of a specific prisoner. If all the prisoners stood around W together and simultaneously pressed their buttons, the barrier would sink into the ground and they would all be able to reach the blockhouse. Inside the blockhouse, which has room for only one prisoner, are two buttons. The first opens the main gate for ten seconds. The second activates a set of gyros which lift the blockhouse and fly it over the prison wall, leaving the gate closed.

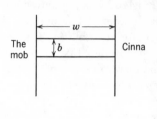

FIGURE 5

The Mob and Cinna the Poet. When the mob found Cinna the poet on the streets of Rome, they lynched him first and asked questions after. We take the poetic license of the mathematical model builder and gaming experimentalist to consider the mob of n individuals charging across a plain, intent on lynching any Cinnas they find. In order to give poor Cinna a better chance, we give him a revolver, say a six-shooter. In Figure 5, we indicate the experimental setup. There is a chasm separating Cinna from the mob, of a width which cannot be jumped. There is a bridge of width b across the chasm. Cinna knows the intent of the mob; furthermore, they can see his gun. He has the problem of convincing them that he is Cinna the poet and that they do not want to lynch him. Let us further suppose that he has a healthy voice; hence he can be heard at least across the bridge. What is the outcome of this "Identification, Friend or Foe?" problem as the length, width, and stability of the bridge vary? If the bridge were very stable and wide, this would be the equivalent of no chasm and we would place higher odds on the lynching taking place than if the bridge were rickety and permitted only one to pass at a time.

NONCOOPERATIVE EQUILIBRIUM:
DO THE FITTEST SURVIVE?

As a final and somewhat different example in our discussion of the noncooperative equilibrium solution to a nonconstant sum game, a "truel" or three-way duel provides an illustration of some of the problems of cross-purposes maximization. It is well known that in a duel the man who is the best shot has the best chance of surviving. Accidents happen and chance plays its role. Sometimes the weaker man survives. Nevertheless, it has been observed that "Although the race is not always to the swiftest, nor the battle to the strong, that is the way to lay your dough." Suppose three individuals stand each on the corner of an equilateral triangle. They decide the order in which they fire and keep firing until there is only one survivor. Suppose, for instance, that their rating as marksmen is respectively 0.8, 0.7, and 0.6. What are their chances for survival? A marksman rating of 0.8 means that at the distance they are firing, 8 out of 10 bullets will find the target. As has been discussed in greater detail elsewhere,[7] in this case the chances of survival are not directly related to the skill of the participants. Intuitively, we can see this by observing that as long as the two better marksmen A and B are alive, they will draw each other's fire. As soon as one has killed the other, C will fire on the survivor. Depending on the relative strength of the participants, sometimes C's optimal strategy is to fire into the air until one of the other two is dead; on other occasions it will pay him to fire at the strongest.

There are many political analogies to the situation portrayed by this three-cornered struggle. In elections competition between two strong nominees may give the third and initially weaker candidate a chance to win. "Strength through weakness" is a dangerous, yet nevertheless feasible, role for a weak country to play, provided that it can be sure the two strong countries it deals with will behave noncooperatively. There is

---

[7] Shubik, M.: "Does the Fittest Necessarily Survive?," in M. Shubik (Ed.), *Readings in Game Theory and Political Behavior*, Doubleday, 1954, pp. 43–36.

always the danger that the strong may decide to cooperate in dispatching with the weak prior to returning to the settlement of their own differences.

6. Cooperative Solutions: Power, Bargaining, and Fair Division

JOINT OPTIMALITY, THE COOPERATIVE SOCIETY

An approach to the solutions of nonconstant sum games radically different from those dealt with in Section 5 is offered by the various so-called cooperative solution theories.   The fundamental idea behind cooperative solutions is that, in general, there are gains to be had from cooperation, and rational individuals will realize these gains.   They will argue only about their share of the joint product.   With communication and cooperation, no two nations should engage in destructive wars.   It is in the interests of both to work out a peaceful settlement.   The cooperative solutions are normative.   They recommend that even though some of the goals of individuals may be opposed, any parallelism of interests *should* be exploited to the utmost.

There are many different theories for the cooperative solution of games.   Among the better known are those of von Neumann and Morgenstern,[8] Shapley,[9] Nash,[10] Aumann and Maschler,[11] and Harsanyi.[12]   A sketch of some of them, together with a discussion of the problems to which they are relevant, is given below.

---

[8] von Neumann, J. and O. Morgenstern: *op. cit.*

[9] Shapley, L. S.: "A Value for *N*-Person Games," in H. W. Kuhn and A. W. Tucker (Eds.), *Contributions to the Theory of Games*, **II,** Princeton University Press, 1953, 307–317.

[10] Nash, J. F.: "Equilibrium Points in *N*-Person Games," *Proceedings of National Academy of Science, USA,* **36,** 1950, 48–49; "Non-Cooperative Games," *Annals of Mathematics,* **54,** 1951, 286–295.

[11] Aumann, R. and M. Maschler: "The Bargaining Set for Cooperative Games" (forthcoming), No. 52, *Annals of Mathematics Studies,* Princeton University Press, 1963.

[12] Harsanyi, J. C.: "Measurement of Social Power in *N*-Person Reciprocal Power Situations," *Behavioral Science,* **7,** No. 1, January 1962, 81–91.

The theory of von Neumann and Morgenstern is concerned with the stability of a society as the result of the interplay of the countervailing forces of many groups. In order to examine the role of the forces of different groups, some radical abstractions and simplifications of many of the important social, political, and economic processes had to be made. Suppose that people knew what they wanted; furthermore, suppose that they were able to compare their value systems (this mammoth assumption can be modified in several ways). Let us consider a game with n players who we will name (with an inspiring lack of imagination) 1, 2, 3, . . . , n. We let N stand for the set of all of the players and S for some coalition of players. If we wish to talk about the set of players 1 and 3 or 2 and 7, then we refer to $(\overline{1, 3})$ or $(\overline{2, 7})$. We shall also refer to a set which contains no player. This will be called the *empty set* and denoted by the symbol θ.

The *characteristic function* of a game is a function $v(S)$ which assigns a value for every subset of players. For an n person game, the characteristic function will have 2^n values. We use the three-person game as an illustration. Suppose that three countries 1, 2, and 3 were in a position to enter into a joint development program, say on some common waterways. The characteristic function below gives the values of the eight possible levels of cooperation that might take place.

$$v(\theta) = 0$$

$$v(\overline{1}) = 0 \qquad v(\overline{2}) = 0 \qquad v(\overline{3}) = 0$$

$$v(\overline{1, 2}) = 0.5 \qquad v(\overline{2, 3}) = 0.5 \qquad v(\overline{1, 3}) = 0$$

$$v(\overline{1, 2, 3}) = 1.0$$

The first value merely records the not very impressive piece of information that a coalition of nobody obtains nothing. The next three values record the information that no individual nation is in a position to do any of the development by itself. The next two values indicate that joint work by the second nation with either the first or the third can derive half of the value of a totally cooperative project. The value assigned to (1, 3) indicates that the second country is in a position to block all development; 1 and 3 can derive no gain from cooperation without 2. The last value specifies the worth of a cooperative effort among all three.

The two properties of the characteristic function are

$$v(\theta) = 0$$

and $$v(S \cup T) \geq v(S) + v(T)$$

whenever $S \cap T = \theta$. The first condition is merely a mathematical formality which has already been noted in the example just given. The second condition states that, if two sets of players S and T who do not have any member in common decide to act in unison, they will be able to obtain as much or more in unison, as they were able to obtain separately. We see immediately that the example has this property; for instance,

$$v(\overline{1, 2}) = 0.5 > v(\overline{1}) + v(\overline{2}) = 0,$$

or $v(\overline{1, 2, 3}) > v(\overline{1, 2}) + v(\overline{3}) = 0.5$.

An *imputation* in the sense of von Neumann and Morgenstern is a division of the total proceeds gained by cooperation among the players where each obtains at least as much as he would obtain without cooperation. Thus, in this example, the triplet of numbers $\alpha = (0.2, 0.6, 0.2)$ is an imputation in which the first and third players obtain 0.2 each, while the second player receives 0.6. In this example, based on the development of a common waterway, the actual division of the proceeds would probably be achieved by a taxation and international payment scheme.

A set of players, which we will call S, is *effective* for an imputation β if the members of S can by independent action obtain at least as much for themselves as they are being offered in β. For example, suppose that $\beta = (0.1, 0.4, 0.5)$; the set of players $(\overline{1, 2})$ is effective for β because without the cooperation of the third, they can jointly derive 0.5 from a development program.

An imputation β dominates an imputation γ if there is a set of players S which is effective for β and every member of S obtains more in β than he does in γ. Let $\gamma = (0.05, 0.3, 0.65)$. We have seen that the set of players $(1, 2)$ is effective for the imputation β; we may also observe that both 1 and 2 obtain more in β than they are offered in γ. Hence if in the course of bargaining and negotiation γ is suggested as a reasonable way to divide the proceeds, 1 and 2 are in a position to reject it in favor of β, pointing out that they not only prefer β but that they also are in a position to obtain it unilaterally if negotiations break down.

The von Neumann and Morgenstern concept of solution to a cooperative game consists of a set of imputations which contain a form of inner stability. A set V of imputations is called a *solution* if no imputation α in set V dominates any other imputation γ in set V and, furthermore, if for any imputation β not in the set, there is an imputation α in the set such that α dominates β.

The solution consists of a set of agreements, no one of which is preferred to another, by a group that can make its preferences effective by unilateral action. If anyone suggests an agreement other than one in the set, there will always be another group in a position to reject it by threatening to resort to one of the agreements offered in the set.

The von Neumann and Morgenstern solution represents an extension of some fundamental ideas of political economy. In particular, it is an extension of welfare economics. The rational society is presumed to select a division of proceeds which is Pareto optimal (a division of proceeds is said to be Pareto optimal if no individual can increase his welfare by departing from it without at least one other individual suffering a decrease in his welfare). Not only must this weak welfare or joint optimality condition be satisfied, but the power of potential coalition structures must be accounted for.

Even in the simple example presented here, the von Neumann and Morgenstern solution does not narrow the field of choice as much as we would like. In other words, given the political and economic information and the ability to calculate a von Neumann and Morgenstern solution, we would soon find numerous imputations which satisfy the conditions, but we would have no guide or criterion to enable us to select one over another. The von Neumann and Morgenstern solution is weakly normative in the sense that it requires that all participants *should* jointly maximize. Beyond that, however, no suggestions are made as to which coalitions should or will form.

Another solution concept of extreme importance to welfare economics and bargaining is *the core*.[13] This is closely related to the von Neumann and Morgenstern solution. Limitations of space prevent further discussion of the core here.

Two other different game theoretic approaches to fundamental problems of political science help to illustrate the normative approach. The first deals with the assignment of a value to each participant which reflects his *a priori* power. The second is concerned with concepts of arbitration, fair division, and equitable settlements.

THE SHAPLEY VALUE

Returning to our example of the three countries engaged in negotiations over waterways development, an examination of the characteristic function indicates that the second country plays a more vital role than the others. Without special information concerning the nature or intentions of the negotiators, we would suspect that the share in the joint gain obtained by the second country will be larger than the shares of the other two.

Shapley has suggested as an appropriate measure the average of the amount added to every coalition formed in every possible way by the entry of each country into an agreement. We carry out the evaluation for the second country. There are six cases to consider:

2 joins a coalition consisting of 1. $\qquad v(\overline{1, 2}) - v(\overline{1}) = .5$

2 joins a coalition consisting of 3. $\qquad v(\overline{1, 2}) - v(\overline{3}) = .5$

2 joins a coalition formed by 1 joining 3.

$$v(\overline{1, 2, 3}) - v(\overline{1, 3}) = 1.0$$

---

[13] Luce, R. D. and H. Raiffa: *Games and Decisions*, John Wiley and Sons, 1957, pp. 192–194.

2 joins a coalition formed by 3 joining 1.
$$v(\overline{1,\,2,\,3}) - v(\overline{1,\,3}) = 1.0$$
2 remains by himself, opposed by 1 and 3.
$$v(\overline{2}) - v(\theta) = 0$$
2 remains by himself, opposed by 3 and 1.
$$v(\overline{2}) - v(\theta) = 0.$$

These six cases cover the dynamics of coalition formation. For this reason we note that a coalition of 1 and 3 could have been formed in two manners. As we have no *a priori* knowledge which leads us to favor one over the other, we consider both equally. Furthermore, when we consider the amount added by 2 when he joins a coalition with no members, there are two ways the others could have formed a coalition excluding him. When we average the contribution of 2, we observe that in 6 situations he brings in 3 *in toto;* hence we assign a value of 0.5 to him. Similar calculations yield 0.25 and 0.25 for 1 and 3.

Unfortunately, when the number of players becomes large, there are $(n)\,(n-1)\,(n-2) \cdot \cdot \cdot (3)\,(2)\,(1)$ possible alignments which must be evaluated (this number is called n factorial and may be written as $n!$). In certain important cases, however, it is possible to make the evaluation. In particular, it is possible for majority games which may be used to represent voting systems. In voting on a bill, there are usually only two and in some cases three possible outcomes: win, lose, and possibly draw. Often there may be special rules such that a draw can never occur. In other cases the bill may be regarded as killed or passed after a certain amount of time. Assuming that there is some manner in which draws are resolved, if we denote the worth of being on the losing side by 0 and the worth of winning by 1, we may describe the characteristic function for a *simple game*[14] as being

$$v(S) = 0 \text{ if } S \text{ is a losing coalition}$$

$$v(S) = 1 \text{ if } S \text{ is a winning coalition.}$$

---

[14] Shapley, L. S.: "Simple Games: An Outline of the Descriptive Theory," *Behavioral Science,* **7**, No. 1, January 1962, 59–66.

Shapley and Shubik have applied the Shapley value to several voting situations including the Security Council of the United Nations. Their paper appears in these readings, together with an evaluation by I. Mann and Shapley of this power index for the Electoral College. Luce and Rogow have suggested modifications which are also given in these readings.

It would be foolish in the extreme to pretend that the authors of these articles are attempting to present *the* power index in a political situation. The work is devoted to illustrating some of the properties we would wish to associate with any attempt to measure power. Among the more glaring oversimplifications needed to construct the index is the assumption that it is always possible or meaningful to define a characteristic function; some of the difficulties in this construction are discussed by Luce and Raiffa.[15] A more important difficulty which not only appears here but is also present in much of the pristine simplicity of utilitarian economic theory is that it is possible to take a static view of a dynamic process, give the actors fixed values, and assume that useful analyses can be made. It has been observed before that "Come the revolution, not only will all the workers have strawberries and cream, but they will like strawberries and cream as well!"

BARGAINING, ARBITRATION, AND "FAIR DIVISION"

The spirit of cooperative solution theories is essentially the spirit behind the economics of welfare, the goals of diplomacy or the aims of the socialized but, nevertheless, possibly self-seeking administrator or politician. The stress of cooperative theories of solution dealing with nonconstant sum games is that almost always individuals stand to gain by joint action. In spite of the gain from joint action, interests are usually opposed when the gain must be divided. Processes of arbitration usually not only recognize the needs and wants of the parties to the procedure but also their power to obtain satisfaction. "For them, the simple rule, the grand old plan; that he will take who has the power; that he will hold who can."

---

[15] Luce, R. D. and H. Raiffa: *op. cit.*, pp. 117–118.

Lurking behind concepts of justice, equity, fair treatment, and good arbitration are the basic and deep assumptions concerning symmetry. Justice carries her scales. Political slogans and legal maxims call for equality along with liberty—equal treatment under the law and equal access to opportunity, regardless of race, color, or creed. Under certain forms of government it is held to be self-evident that all men are created equal. At the core of many of the fundamental problems encountered in human affairs is an implicit concept of symmetry.

The role of symmetry in the theory of games has been much misunderstood, as it has been in human affairs in general. Equal opportunity in some countries may imply equal opportunity to vote but not to go to college; in others, vice versa. As Orwell has noted, "Some animals are more equal than others." Some aspects of symmetry are intuitively appealing and easy to grasp. As soon as an attempt is made to go from the abstract to the concrete, however, many difficulties are encountered. These difficulties are precisely those encountered when one attempts to analyze the contents of political statements concerning equality or legal maxims concerning justice. The sons of the beggar and the millionaire may both have the vote, but in many ways their opportunity is not equal, nor are the opportunities of the sons of the kulak and the commissar.

The mathematicians working in game theory, especially on problems concerning fair division, have made use of an axiomatic approach. A series of apparently innocuous statements are made; the reader is asked to accept them, and, if he does so, to his consternation he may discover that he is forced to accept a series of possibly quite paradoxical or "unreasonable" situations which follow from the axioms. If we reject the conclusions of the mathematicians, we find ourselves faced with the task of finding out what was wrong with the innocent statements we were willing to believe on first reading, or what was left out of consideration.

In order to illustrate the axiomatic approach, its relevance, and some of the difficulties involved, we discuss the model of a two-person bargaining situation proposed by J. F. Nash. He makes four basic assumptions concerning the properties that any "fair" division or arbitration scheme should possess.

Assumption 1. There is no interpersonal comparison of utilities. This implies that we can assign any numbers to the initial valuations of the starting positions of each side. Furthermore, we can multiply the utility scales of either side by an arbitrary number, and the outcome will not be influenced. For example, suppose that the bargainers are J. P. Morgan and a beggar who have been jointly offered a $5 bill which they must divide. If they do not both agree on the division, neither will obtain anything.

If we wished to make an interpersonal comparison of utility, we might state that the five dollars are worth a thousand times more to the beggar than to Morgan. The *characteristic function* for a game can be written only when interpersonal comparisons of utility can be made. Here we have three values $v(\overline{1})$, $v(\overline{2})$, and $v(1, 2)$ standing, respectively, for the initial value attached by Morgan to his current state, the value attached by the beggar to his initial state, and their joint valuation for the state in which they obtain the extra $5. We can equally well write $v(\overline{1}) = 0$ and $v(\overline{2}) = 0$ or $v(\overline{1}) = a$ and $v(\overline{2}) = b$, where a and b are any numbers used to describe the worth attached to the initial positions. The addition or subtraction of an arbitrary constant to the valuation of a player gives rise to a game which is strategically equivalent to the original game. This becomes transparent when we observe that the role of the constant is equivalent to that of a prize awarded to the player regardless of the outcome of the first game.

If there is no interpersonal comparison of utility, we *cannot* write down a single number as the value for $\overline{1, 2}$. We must use a number for the value attached by each individual to every outcome. Thus we need to abandon the simple characteristic function description. Instead we must note that the coalition $\overline{1, 2}$ can obtain $5 together, and they can split it into $5 − x$ and $x, where $0 \leq x \leq 5$. Hence we must have a pair of values for every division of the money. We may represent the initial position valuations for both by (a, b); then there will be another pair of valuations for the split $5 − x$ and $x, say $(a + c, b + d)$. Because no interpersonal comparison of utilities is postulated, not only can we add a constant to the utilities of each player, but even the multiplication of the utilities of a player by an arbitrary constant should not affect the game. This is because without comparison of utilities, statements such as "an additional $5 is worth a thousand times more to the beggar than to Morgan" have no meaning. If we used $(0, 0)$ or $(5a, 3b)$ for the initial position valuations and (c, d), $(20c, 5d)$ or $(5a + 5c, 3b + 3d)$ for the valuation of the split, this should make no difference to the outcome.

In spite of the difficulties encountered working *with* the assumption of interpersonal comparison of utility, there are many difficulties encountered if we try to work *without* it. Intuitively it may sometimes appear to be more reasonable to make a comparison between the worth of a dollar to a millionaire and to a pauper, or even the relative cost of loss of face in diplomatic relations between the chiefs of the United States and the Soviet Union, than not to do so.

Assumption 2. The solution will be Pareto optimal. If the valuation of the arbitrated split is (u_1, v_1), then for any other outcome valued at (u, v) we cannot have both $u > u_1$ and $v > v_1$.

The Pareto optimal condition states that neither party will take as a resolution to their negotiations any outcome for which an alternative outcome is better for both. This assumption implies that no individual will adopt a "dog-in-the-manger" attitude. Whenever actions can result in a gain to both, they will be taken.

Assumption 3. The solution is independent of irrelevant alternatives. Consider two situations, both with the same *status quo*, which differ only in that one contains more bargaining possibilities than the other. If the fair division solution to the situation with more possibilities is a feasible outcome for the situation with fewer possibilities, then it should also be the solution to the situation with fewer possibilities.

At first glance it appears reasonable that if an alternative that neither side wants is added to the possibilities, its existence will make no difference to the outcome. In many negotiations the dynamics are such that new threat possibilities may be provided by these extra outcomes.

Assumption 4. Symmetry is assumed in the following sense:

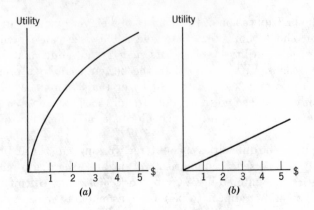

FIGURE 6

suppose there is a bargaining situation in which the players enter in a completely symmetric manner. For instance, if a settlement which yields (u, v) is possible, then so is one which yields (v, u). The arbitrated solution to this bargain will give both players the same payoff.

In the simplest case, Nash's axioms imply that if the two individuals faced with splitting the $5 are in the same position and their utility for money is the same as is shown in Figure 6a, then they will split the money at $2.50 each. It is of interest to note that in the case of J. P. Morgan and the beggar, Morgan's value for an extra dollar will probably be the same for the first as it is for the fifth. This is shown in Figure 6b. The gain to the beggar for each dollar, as is shown in Figure 6a, is probably less than was obtained from the previous dollar. The Nash division scheme in this situation will award most of the money to J. P. Morgan!![16]

The important feature to note is that, if you are willing to believe these four assumptions, a specific method for arbitration can be shown to be the *only one* mathematically satisfying all the conditions. The reader interested in the actual division scheme

---

[16] Shubik, M.: *Strategy and Market Structure*, John Wiley and Sons, 1959.

is referred to the paper by Nash[17] or to the exposition of Luce and Raiffa.[18]

It is important to accept the strengths and understand the weaknesses of the axiomatic approach. It is a powerful tool for isolating basic problems. The attempts to formulate acceptable axioms uncover many ambiguities in the substantive aspects of the social sciences. Words such as fairness, equality, power, cooperation, communication, threat, bluff, and competition have many ill-defined connotations and vague interpretations. There is still much to be gained in the social sciences by mere clarification and classification of the many aspects of these words.

Returning to the Nash axioms as an example, it must be stressed that a valuable test that the social scientist should perform before accepting or rejecting the axioms is to see if he can construct a concrete example to which they apply. There is a great danger from misplaced abstraction. We must ask how general and broad-ranging a set of axioms happens to be. Bargaining methods between two individuals, countries, organizations, or informal groups are all different. Which cases are covered by the Nash axioms? Which are missed? What other assumptions are needed to cover the other cases?

Specifically, the Nash assumptions may be questioned in their treatment of the *status quo* aspects of bargaining. Bargaining is a dynamic process in which threats, counterthreats, and jockeying for position all play a vital role. The ascribing of values to the initial or no-trade points involves many implicit assumptions.

Another limitation to the applicability of the Nash assumptions is encountered when an attempt is made to generalize from two-person to many-person bargaining situations. The maneuvers to set up the basis from which to bargain, when there are many parties to the affair, may involve joint threats by coalitions. This is not taken into account by Nash. The work of Harsanyi has

---

[17] Nash, J. F.: "The Bargaining Problem," *Econometrica*, **18**, 1950, 155–162.

[18] Luce, R. D. and H. Raiffa: *op. cit.*, pp. 117–118.

been specifically addressed to this problem.[19]   In these readings, part of Harsanyi's formulation of the bargaining problem is presented. The methods he suggests have direct application to the study of power.

OTHER SOLUTIONS

Other arbitration schemes have been suggested by Raiffa[20] and Braithewaite.[21]   Different solution concepts attempting to reflect some of the aspects of policing and coalition formation have been put forward by Luce,[22] Vickrey,[23] Aumann and Maschler.[24]   A quasicooperative solution for dynamic games or games of indefinite length has been suggested by Shubik.[25]   Stone[26] and Schelling[27] have stressed the importance of cues in providing solutions in some circumstances.   Simon, Siegel, and other psychologists have suggested more broadly adaptive processes where the preferences of the individual are modified as the situation unfolds.

In summary, it must be re-emphasized that "*the* theory of games" for *n*-person games does not exist.   A broad and useful methodology does exist and is an aid in providing insights. Many solution concepts have been proposed, many of which appear to be of value to various aspects of the behavioral sciences.

---

[19] Harsanyi, J. C.: "Approaches to the Bargaining Problem Before and After the Theory of Games: A Critical Discussion of Zeuthen's, Hicks', and Nash's Theories," *Econometrica*, **24**, 1956, 144–157.

[20] Raiffa, H.: "Arbitration Schemes for Generalized Two-Person Games," *Annals of Mathematics Study*, No. 28, Princeton University Press, 1953.

[21] Braithwaite, R. B.: *Theory of Games as a Tool for the Moral Philosopher*, Cambridge University Press, 1955.

[22] Luce, R. D.: "A Definition of Stability for *N*-Person Games," *Annals of Mathematics*, **59**, 1954, 357–366.

[23] Vickrey, W.: "Self-Policing Properties of Certain Imputation Sets" in A. W. Tucker and D. Luce (Eds.), *Contributions to the Theory of Games*, **IV**, Princeton University Press, 1959, 213–246.

[24] Aumann, R. and M. Maschler: *op. cit.*

[25] Shubik, M.: *op. cit.*

[26] Stone, J. J.: "An Experiment in Bargaining Games," *Econometrica*, **26**, 1958, 286–296.

[27] Schelling, T. C.: *The Strategy of Conflict*, Harvard University Press, 1960.

Good dynamic theories of behavioral processes are needed, and at this stage it would be presumptuous in the extreme to pretend that the various solution concepts have provided more than some hopeful early steps toward the goal.

7. "Pseudogames" and Problems in the Behavioral Sciences

BASIC QUESTIONS AND SUGGESTED MODIFICATIONS

In the previous sections a brief summary is given of the essence of the work extant in the theory of games, and its relevance to the behavioral sciences is discussed. As pointed out, the methodology has enabled us to define well and to formulate many new problems in our attempts to solve old ones. In this section we note some of the basic features of choice and conflict situations which must be taken into account in a successful theory of decision making in the political, diplomatic, military, or other arenas. The relationship of these features to the current theory of games is shown.

ASSUMPTIONS CONCERNING PREFERENCE SYSTEMS

Much of the work in political and economic theory and in the theory of games has been based on the concept of the rational utilitarian individual. He is often implicitly or explicitly assumed to be confronted with known alternatives which he can evaluate, for he possesses a fully known, infinitely sensitive preference system. His roles as social, psychological, poetic, or heroic man are often completely suppressed in the abstraction. Although there are several areas of economics for which these assumptions provide useful models, they are not adequate in political science and in general when we wish to examine decision making. The following questions, by no means complete, are all relevant to selecting assumptions that concern the value system of the decision-making units.

1. Do individuals have a preference system fixed through time?
2. How are preferences for uncertain events obtained?
3. Is an individual's preference system measurable?

4. Are values comparable between different decision-makers?
5. Is "utility" transferable between decision makers?
6. Are individual preferences transitive? That is, if a is preferred to b and b is preferred to c, does this imply that a is preferred to c?
7. Do individuals misperceive the value of certain outcomes?
8. What is the fineness an individual may perceive with respect to slightly different outcomes?
9. Are there gaps in an individual's knowledge of outcomes?
10. Are there gaps in an individual's knowledge of the alternatives available to him?
11. Does an individual's value for an outcome depend on the value of the outcome to others than himself?
12. Can there be social values independent of individual values?
13. Can a consistent social preference system be constructed from an aggregation of individual preferences?

In most game theory models, various assumptions are made concerning questions 2, 3, 4, 5, and 6. Given fixed known individual preferences without comparable measurable transferable "utilities," Arrow[28] and others have investigated the possibilities for the construction of social preference systems. Devising various fair division procedures and constructing indices of power depend on the specific assumptions concerning questions 2, 3, 4, 5, and 6.

The various psychological theories of learning, aspiration, and cognative dissonance all point in different ways to models of man with a changing and changeable value system. The distinction made by Rapaport between fights, games, and debates is relevant to this point. Courses on "How to win friends and influence people" and adages such as "Always be sincere whether you mean it or not" illustrate the vast and important possibilities of changing value systems. Simple game theory models in general do not take these into account. Modifications can be and have been

---

[28] Arrow, K. J.: *Social Choice and Individual Values*, John Wiley and Sons, 1951.

made. The paper by Iklé and Leites in these readings is one which does this.

Through miscalculation, faulty learning, or misperception of the environment, individuals may act as though they are in a situation other than the one they happen to be in. Not only at the broad anthropological and societal levels, but specifically in international and military affairs, the problem of misperception becomes vital.

War through error is a recurrent theme in many writings and justly so. War through misperception is possibly even more important. For example, much of the value of the book *On Thermonuclear War*[29] by Herman Kahn comes from his appreciation of the dangers of misperceiving the payoffs at stake. The popular literature on thermonuclear warfare has been far too ready to present the situation as though peace or Armageddon were the only two possible outcomes. Duncan Luce,[30] Harsanyi,[31] Milnor,[32] and others have investigated some of the aspects of games with misperceptions.

In the economics of small businesses, in acting and other arts, in gambling and in unseasoned guerilla warfare, the game-theoretic aspects of misperception are amply displayed. The constant entry of untrained, undereducated, undercapitalized individuals into small retailing invites high mortality rates not only for the inefficient but for the others as well. The misjudging of the odds of success in acting or gambling helps to provide for cheap labor and expensive casinos.

The overestimation of the chances for success in guerilla warfare may lead, on the one hand, to bloodbaths and, on the other, to success. The prudent man knows that if he charges the guard

---

[29] Kahn, H.: *On Thermonuclear War*, Princeton University Press, 1960.

[30] Luce, R. D. and E. W. Adams: "The Determination of Subjective Characteristic Functions in Games with Misperceived Payoff Functions," *Econometrica*, **24**, 1956, 158–171.

[31] Harsanyi, J. C.: "Bargaining in Ignorance of the Opponent's Utility Function," *The Journal of Conflict Resolution*, **VI**, No. 1, March 1962, 29–38.

[32] Milnor, J.: "Games Against Nature" in *Decision Processes*, R. M. Thrall, C. H. Coombs, and R. L. Davis (Eds.), John Wiley and Sons, 1954, pp. 49–59; see also RAND Memorandum 679, September 1951.

with a submachine gun, he will, in all probability, be killed. If there are enough nonprudent men willing to charge the guard, many may die, but the odds are that the guard will be among them. Thus, paradoxically, statements such as "He is too foolish to give up" or "They do not know enough to see that they are beaten" provide important insights into the role of threats and the policing of social stability. It is in general more costly and difficult to subdue those who do not "understand" that they are beaten.

There are many open questions concerning the role of madmen or individuals whose value systems are importantly different from the norm accepted by one society. The simple game theory models which include such individuals present a pessimistic picture in the sense that they appear capable of doing great damage. In at least one stage of World War II the Japanese kamikaze attacks were effective. On the other hand, it is hard to judge how important a factor political assassination by madmen has been. As weapons become more destructive, more easily decentralized and viable, the greater becomes the danger of accident due to aberrant behavior. There is a trade-off between cross-checks, policing, and viability. Should one man have the responsibility for a declaration of war? How long a time delay can one allow to be introduced by committee decisions? Should there be a direct telephone line from the White House to the Kremlin, or from the White House to every major missile command?

Questions 8, 9, and 10 are closely tied into only partially explored topics in psychology concerning learning and search. Von Neumann and Morgenstern have investigated some of the implications of different degrees of perception on bargaining. In their special example,[33] all the gain available was obtained by the bargainer with the finer perceptions. The memoirs of art dealers such as Duveen are loaded with observations and special comments concerning the paramount importance of special knowledge and perception in art dealing. Generally, in game theory models of human affairs, there is a danger that the explicit aspects of conflict are overemphasized at the expense of under-

---

[33] von Neumann, J. and O. Morgenstern: *op. cit.*

stressing the individual's uncertainties and lack of knowledge about what is at stake.

In politics, in particular, and in life, in general, when an individual is confronted with a choice between A or B, he often searches for or creates C, which he then selects. Simple game models take the environment as specified. Work in heuristic programming and artificial intelligence is directed toward the portrayal and the eventual understanding of the search and "creativity" processes.

GAMES OF SOCIAL AND ECONOMIC SURVIVAL

The length and degree of detail of this introduction do not permit more than a relatively simple example of a dynamic game. This is an extension of the type of game illustrated in Table 4. The basic situation faced each period is shown in Table 8.

The values are suggestive of the relative size of the stakes, relevant to each period. The dynamic game can now be characterized. We draw an abbreviated version of the *game tree*. Figure 7 shows that at each period the two countries commit themselves to follow one of their three short-term policies. The one period game illustrated in Table 8 is denoted by G. In order to keep track of the periods, we denote this game when

TABLE 8

Country 1	No action	"Minor" incident	"Grab"	Country 2
No action	0, 0	−10, 10	−200, 100	
"Minor" incident	50, −20	−5, −5	−150, 10	
War	−1000, −1000	−1000, −1000	−1000, −1000	

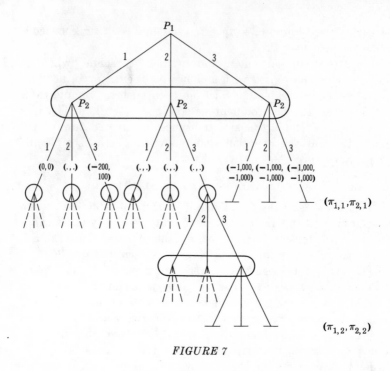

FIGURE 7

played in period t by G_t. We assume that if an atomic war breaks out, not only will it cause great damage to both sides but it will also cause sufficient political and social change that we may regard the game as terminating. For the other situations, the game continues. The information conditions characterized in this (infinitely long) game tree are such that every period there are actions which take place in parallel; after these "tactical" actions have been taken, both sides are informed. There are partial payoffs every period. The payoffs for the first period are denoted by $(\pi_{1,1}, \pi_{2,1})$ and for the second period by $(\pi_{1,2}, \pi_{2,2})$; for example, as is shown in Figure 7, if both select their move 2, the partial payoff will be $\pi_{1,1} = 5$ and $\pi_{2,1} = 5$. The model of human affairs being portrayed here, even though highly simplified, calls for a continuing situation, possibly terminated by disaster but constantly changing inasmuch as the individuals keep receiving partial payoffs and obtain new positions from which to continue. Obviously, as time goes on and resources are developed or obtained, the number of alternatives in the one period subgame may be enlarged. These considerations are of the type that should and can be taken into account by computer calculations. This is further noted in the comments on gaming and simulation in Section 8 below.

In this formulation, we may now explore some of the inter-relations between long- and short-term policies. Using the economists' concept of "income" maximization, we observe that the income stream for the first country is π_{11}, π_{12}, π_{13}, π_{14}, ... Let us suppose that there is some form of discount rate on the future. This may range from "Après moi la deluge" to statements concerning our responsibility and trust for the type of world our grandchildren's grandchildren will live in. As a simple first approximation, we let the discounts on the future for each country be ρ_1, $\rho_2 < 1$. The condition that the numbers "rho" are less than one implies that benefits in the present are valued more highly than the same benefits in the future. "Pie on the plate" is preferred to "pie in the sky." In some cases it might be argued that for a short period, of, say, a few years, the future may be more highly valued; however, over the longer range, this is not so.

Given the discount on the future, we may describe the over-all evaluation of the results of long-term policies for the first country as

$$\pi_1 = \sum_{t=1}^{\infty} \rho_1{}^t \pi_{1,t}$$

or equivalently

$$\pi_1 = \rho_1 \pi_{1,1} + \rho_1{}^2 \pi_{1,2} + \rho_1{}^3 \pi_{1,3} + \cdots + \rho_1{}^t \pi_{1,t} + \cdots$$

We are now in a position to consider the long-run payoffs associated with long-term policies. By using Table 8 for the tactical values, the consequences of several policies are noted.

Policy A for Country 1:
No action under all circumstances.
Policy A for Country 2:

Minor incident to start; if no counterincident takes place, grab; if a counterincident takes place, resume no action for some length of time, then try a minor incident again; if grabbing provokes nothing, keep grabbing; if it provokes counterincidents, go back to minor incidents; if it provokes war, fight.

Given these two strategies, the results will be continued aggression by the second country, and the payoffs will be

$$\pi_1 = \rho_1(-1) + \rho_1^2(-200) + \rho_1^3(-200) + \rho_1^4(-200) + \cdots$$

$$= -\rho_1 - \rho_1^2\left(\frac{200}{1-\rho_1}\right)$$

The payoff to the second country will be

$$\pi_2 = \rho_2(1) + \rho_2^2(100) + \rho_2^3(100) + \rho_2^4(100) + \cdots$$

$$= \rho_2 + \rho_2^2\left(\frac{100}{1-\rho_2}\right).$$

Suppose that the first country places a high value on the future. This would be reflected in a value of ρ_1 near to 1. Let $\rho = 0.99$; then

$$\pi_1 = -0.99 - 0.98\left(\frac{200}{0.01}\right) = -19{,}600 \text{ approximately}$$

This is costlier than war. It is so much costlier than war that under almost any reasonable inference system, if the second country knew only the high value placed by the first country on the long run, it would easily be able to infer that a policy of inaction will not be followed. The discount rate would have to be around $\rho_1 = 0.85$ before "peace in our time" might be preferred to war against the aggressor.

From an examination of the discount rates we arrive at the possibly not very astounding but nevertheless comforting conclusion that the more two countries value their long-run future (and each knows that the other places a high value on the future), if each has strike and counter-strike forces, the less are the chances for war. Furthermore, as the value placed on the future increases, the longer are the chances that even relatively stupid individuals will be able to infer the degree of danger in an overly aggressive policy.

In the example given, a considerable oversimplification has been made in assuming that events occur once each unit of time. In order to account for variable action time, a more complex model would be needed, and it would be desirable to utilize a high-speed digital computer to trace consequences.

Let us consider another, and more complex, policy for the first country. It might reflect a general learning in the sense that, although the initial degree of faith may be high, it is modified by the course of affairs.

Policy B for Country 1:

No action as long as there is no action by the other. No action against the first minor incident; use counterincident on any subsequent incident. If any action is a grab, reply with a counterincident; if the grab continues beyond a certain time, then war; if minor incidents are resumed, employ counterincidents; if no action is resumed, then resume no action.

The Policy B for the first country and Policy A for the second country are, even in this simple situation, relatively complicated. They can be best illustrated in two flow diagrams, Figures 8 and 9, such as are used prior to writing computer programs.

The small circles with numbers in them denote places where actions may be repeated in the course of time; thus, for example, if a grab takes place, the flow diagram indicates that before anything else happens, a check will be made to examine the reaction. If there is none, then the 2 indicates that the program should return to the other 2, which means that the grab will continue. If there is a reaction, the 3 indicates that the program should proceed to 3, where the type of reaction is checked.

With the strategies as outlined above, the second country will cause a minor incident which will go unanswered; it will then try for a grab which will provoke a reply. After this, there will be a series of testing and replies in the form of minor incidents. The same type of calculation as was given before will provide the basis for evaluating the plausibility for inferences concerning parts of each other's strategies. Danger of war will be less, the

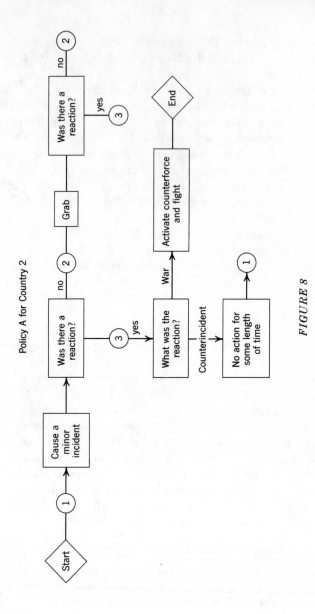

FIGURE 8

Policy B for Country 1

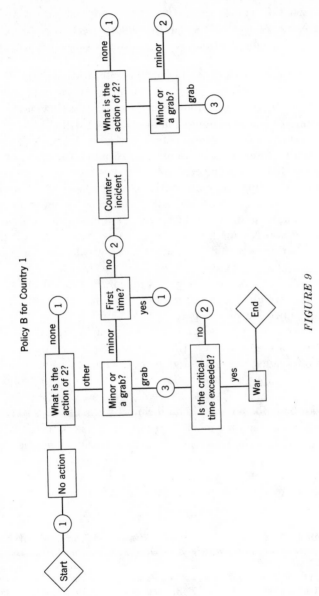

FIGURE 9

more each side values the future, the more accurate are their estimates of each other's strength, and the less random events clutter up communications and provide a basis for incorrect inferences.

In the course of the past few years military estimates of the strengths of the Soviet Union, the United States, China, and others have fluctuated wildly. For the most part they have been overestimates and as such have, if anything, contributed to short-term stability. If a power in fact possesses a first-strike and counterstrike force, it is in its interest to make sure that others can verify that this is the case.

The type of dynamic game outlined above has been described as a "game of economic survival"[34] and could equally well be termed as a game of social survival. It differs from a game as defined by von Neumann and Morgenstern inasmuch as it does not necessarily have a finite end; the payoffs do not come in a lump sum after the game is over but are distributed over its history. There are both payoff and survival problems to be faced. In straight "survival games" which have been studied,[35] the only objective of the players is to survive. The worth of any assets can only be calculated in terms of contribution to the two values of life or death. Here the desire for survival must be traded off against the level of gains obtained while surviving.

When we apply a simple noncooperative equilibrium solution concept to a game of social survival, we find that almost any state can be enforced as an equilibrium by the use of a strategy carrying a sufficiently violent threat. In these dynamic situations, the distinction between cooperative and noncooperative behavior becomes difficult to draw. The participants do not concern themselves with the normalized form of the game. Strategies are not known but must be inferred from behavior observed.

---

[34] Shubik, M. and G. L. Thompson: "Games of Economic Survival," *Naval Research Logistics Quarterly*, **6**, 1959; Shubik, M.: *Strategy and Market Structure*, op. cit.

[35] Milnor, J. and L. S. Shapley: "On Games of Survival" in M. Dresher, A. W. Tucker, and P. Wolfe (Eds.), *Contributions to the Theory of Games*, **III**, Princeton University Press, 1957, 15–45.

The key to the examination of the possible equilibrium states rests with our ability to develop a calculus of plausibility for threats. In order to do this we must characterize measures for the degree of cooperation between individuals (not a dichotomy between cooperative and noncooperative behavior) as well as measures for information, intelligence and social, political and psychological as well as statistical inference. Games of social survival provide a format in which at least some of the simpler preliminary problems can be framed. Furthermore, they may be dealt with naturally by gaming and simulation methods, as is noted in Section 8.

The complexity, machinery, pomp, and apparent high scientific powers of game theory, computer techniques, simulation, and gaming are no substitute for substantive knowledge. Furthermore, there is a danger that a false sense of accuracy and precision will lead to a misemphasis in the study of political, sociological, or psychological problems. For example, game theory is primarily concerned with conscious decision processes. Much of operations research and many of the mathematical applications to industry, the military, and other organizations have been concerned with the sensitivity, optimality, and economy of processes.

Both biological research and socio-political observations indicate that individuals and groups of organisms have large amounts of built-in redundancy. They are also often quite insensitive to changes in the environment. Inertia, administrative convenience, procedures, protocol, and other sociological and cultural factors all appear to play a role in reducing uncertainty and in providing methods for resolving problems of such complexity that they can scarcely be formulated.

It is not a criticism of game theory, simulation, or any other methodology to stress the dangers in attempting to apply new methodologies to problems where empirical knowledge is unclear:

Procedures followed are not always conscious. Optimization is not always a meaningful criterion (as shown by n-person game theory). Insensitivity may be a virtue. Redundancy appears to provide for many different yet satisfactory solutions to the same problem.

The development of an applied mathematics and the science

to which it is applied go hand in hand. The needs of the science must be served by the techniques of the mathematics. In Section 7 several important needs have been noted; the mathematical methods for dealing with them have not yet been adequately developed. A great deal of development in mathematics is needed, as well as in the subjects themselves, before even parts of diplomatic negotiations or a political campaign can be seriously based on calculations derived from models, in the same way as it is possible to calculate the flight of a trajectory. Yet, as is further developed in the article of Wohlstetter on "Sin and Games in America," critics have made claims about and against the theory of games which give little indication that they have mastered the theoretical content. The same critics would seem to confuse the developing of political science or other behavioral sciences with the offering of advice on the "burning questions of the hour."

8. Gaming and Simulation

Game theory and other mathematical methods have added considerably to the methodology of the behavioral sciences. In certain ways, however, they have created a need larger than the one they have filled. There are now techniques for describing and analyzing simple bargaining procedures, arbitration schemes, and so forth. The predictions of many of the mathematical models have been based on highly restrictive assumptions concerning human behavior in special environments. In some instances it has been possible to construct the environments in a laboratory and to test hypotheses about behavior. The growth of the mathematical methodology cannot be separated from the growth of empirical, experimental and observational methods in the behavioral sciences. Once the art has been learned, it is relatively easy to jot down simple, small mathematical models of various aspects of human affairs. It is not easy to show that the models are relevant, and it is even less easy to establish that they are right.

Two new and important techniques have grown along with the development of the use of formal models in the behavioral sciences. They are *simulation* and *gaming*. There is not yet a completely accepted common terminology; hence the reader is forewarned that the definitions of the terms presented here may not coincide with those read elsewhere.

A *simulation* of a system or an organism is the operation of a model or simulator which is a representation of the system or organism. From studying the operation of the model, properties concerning the behavior of the actual system are inferred. Among the reasons for constructing a simulation are that the model is amenable to manipulations which would be too expensive, impracticable, or impossible to perform on the entity it portrays.

The word simulation and the phrase "manipulation of a model" are essentially synonymous except that the latter might be taken to include analytical methods, whereas the former is usually limited to operations by digital computer or analog devices.

Computer simulation, man-machine simulation, and gaming are often all classed as simulation. It is important to clarify the distinctions between these very different methods designed for different purposes. Our major distinction is between gaming and simulation. *Gaming* is an experimental, operational, or training technique which may or may not make use of a simulated environment but is invariably concerned with studying human behavior or teaching individuals. In a simulation, the behavior of the components is taken as given. The actual presence of individuals is not necessary to a simulation, but it is to a gaming exercise.

Although neither gaming nor simulation depends completely on the use of the high-speed digital computer, for most uses beyond the manipulation of highly simplified models of the environment or experimentation with very restricted games, a computer is a necessity.

The advent of the high-speed digital computer is already having a profound effect on the physical sciences, military systems, and economic life, although there is little doubt that its potential has barely begun to be realized. In the behavioral sciences, the role of the computer has not been as apparent as elsewhere. Nevertheless, it will undoubtedly have at least as deep an influence on their development as did the microscope in the biological sciences and the telescope in astronomy. It is a viewing instrument for the behavioral sciences.

Work on artificial intelligence, chess-playing programs, checker-playing programs, problem solving, the simulation of the economy, the simulation of industries, firms or parts of firms, the simulation of traffic flow, neural networks, voting procedures, and air attacks present an array of problems for which simulation using high-speed computers has been able to provide insights into the performance of complex systems.

In Section 7 an example of a dynamic game of social survival was presented. Several relatively simple strategies were suggested. It was difficult to write down even these simple strategies in words. It would have been just as difficult, if not more so, to have written them out mathematically. Their easiest presentation was given in the flow diagrams of Figures 8 and 9. Flow diagrams and certain languages used to communicate with computers, such as FORTRAN,[36] are by themselves highly valuable tools for the behavioral scientist. They are more precise than language and richer and more flexible than mathematical notation. It is not easy to catch in a convenient mathematical notation many of the adjectives, qualifying phrases, and nuances needed to describe a political or social system. It is relatively easy to do so by means of flow diagrams or computer programs.

This book contains no articles on the computer simulation of social, political, or military systems. The topic is both large and technical. It is of sufficient importance, however, that we should be aware of this possibility for describing and manipulating complex systems.

Although it has been common to use the words "gaming" and "simulation" interchangeably, much confusion can be caused by doing so. In general, individuals are referring to gaming in a simulated environment when they use the word simulation in reference to a game. Sometimes the reference is to the simulated roles of the players, when, for example, graduate students fill the role of prime ministers. There are many types of gaming and many purposes for which games can be used.

---

[36] FORTRAN C-28-6054-2, IBM White Plains, New York, 1961.

Three major divisions are for (1) teaching, (2) experimentation, and (3) operational purposes. All three are of interest to the behavioral scientist or policy maker. Many games do not need computers in order to play them. Military games, such as maneuvers, make use of a real rather than a simulated environment. Other military games use an analog simulation for the environment, such as a sand table. Several political gaming exercises have been designed to be played with pencil and paper. Whenever the environment in which the game is to be played becomes complex, however, and when the information to be presented to the players involves many numerical displays, a digital computer becomes a necessity. The gaming exercise of Guetzkow presented in these readings, for example, is about the largest and most complex exercise that can be run without a computer. It is my opinion that even at its current size a computer version would be, in the long run, cheaper and far more useful.

In many behavioral science investigations three major aspects are of interest to the observer. They are (1) an adequate description of the environment in which the activity takes place, (2) an understanding of the plans, strategies, and motivations of the decision makers, and (3) an ability to predict what will happen if the decision makers carry out their plans, given the environment. A simulation takes the first two items as given and provides a method for obtaining the third. Gaming in a simulated environment may be used as a method whereby the first is taken as given, the outcome of the game is observed, and inferences are made concerning the intents and motivations of the players. This is done in experimental gaming.

In operational gaming the environment may be taken as given and the players may then proceed to try out different plans and strategies in order to examine their outcomes. It may be very advantageous to have new diplomats or officers exposed to an intensive period of synthetic experience in this manner. Furthermore, experienced decision makers are afforded an opportunity to try out harebrained schemes that they might want to experiment with but feel would be too dangerous to risk in their real environment.

Other ways in which games may be classified concern the degree of control and formalization in the structure of the game and the levels of richness of the environment. Many of the psychologists' experimental games tend to be extremely impoverished in environmental setting and highly controlled with respect to the rules and manner of play. At the other extreme, games designed as operational exercises for politico-diplomatic negotiations may be very loose in structure. In the latter case, expert referees may decide on rules and permissible strategies as the game progresses. The experimental controls may be few or nonexistent. The exercise may have more in common with a group psychodynamic process than with any formal theory of games.

We stressed earlier that there is no single satisfactory solution concept for an n-person nonconstant sum game. There are many informal conjectures concerning both intent and behavior. The work in experimental gaming is beginning to test some of these conjectures. Rapoport and Orwant's review article, parts of which are reprinted here, indicates the scope of experimentation performed. The experiments were for the major part motivated by a desire to test simple game theoretic models. The insights obtained both from carrying them out and from the results have in turn suggested modifications to the theory of games.

9. About the Readings

The readings are divided into four major groups. The first group (Part 2) is aimed at giving a broad coverage of game theory and indicating its relevance to social analysis. The excerpts from the writings of A. Kaplan, Luce and Raiffa, von Neumann and Morgenstern, and D. Black discuss the general aspects of the theory of games. Marschak's article deals specifically with utility and the measurement of value, a topic which is separate from but necessary to the development of a theory of games. The article by Milnor is in a class of its own. It requires a greater technical background or more patience to read than do the others. It serves to demonstrate the power and importance of the axiomatic approach in the examination and understanding of basic notions concerning behavior under uncertainty.

Part 3 deals with political choice, power, and voting. In all the articles in this part, the values of the participants are assumed to be known and remain unchanged. Excerpts from Arrow's book point out the relationship between political and economic choice mechanisms. Shapley and Shubik suggest a method for constructing an index to measure power in a voting system. A large-scale computation carried out by Mann and Shapley applies this index to the Electoral College. Luce and Rogow suggest modifications to the Shapley-Shubik index which take into account problems of coalitions and the two-party system. Harsanyi offers an alternative method for obtaining a power index and relates this to other discussions concerning the nature of power and influence in the recent literature on political science.

Part 4 is addressed to applications of game theory to bargaining, threats, and negotiations. Wohlstetter's comments on "Sin and Games in America" discuss the role of game theory in studies of arms control and military affairs. His comments point out to several critics (primarily English) their misunderstanding both of the theory of games and the role it plays. The brief excerpt from an article by McDonald and Tukey provides the reader with a very simple example of the actual calculations for the solution of a simple two-person zero-sum game. Although this type of game is usually encountered only in tactical situations and is out of the main stream of game theory, it provides an interesting example for the nonmathematical reader and enables him to obtain a flavor of the sort of computations performed. Ellsberg's "Crude Analysis of Strategic Choices" provides a direct example of the type of broad application noted by Wohlstetter and criticized by Blackett and others. Aumann's "Almost Strictly Competitive Games" points out an important connection between certain types of nonzero sum games and situations in which there is a pure opposition of interests. Only the observation and a few comments are noted here. The work of Aumann is usually highly mathematical but nevertheless directed toward problems of relevance to the behavioral sciences. The paper by Iklé and Leites presents a scheme for political negotiation. In a first draft of these readings it had been my intention to reproduce excerpts from the "Art of War" by the Chinese General Sun Tzu, writing in 500 B.C.[37] This remarkable document is recommended to the reader. In many ways it is a direct precursor to the papers presented here. Finally, attention must be called to the article by Karl Deutsch on "International Politics and Game Theory,"[38] which was also reproduced in a previous book of readings.[39]

Part 5 is devoted to gaming. The first article, "Some Observations on Political Gaming" by Goldhamer and Speier, gives a description and evaluation of the study of foreign affairs by means of political gaming. This is followed by Guetzkow's paper discussing the exploratory runs of a gaming exercise in the study of international relations used in the Program of Graduate Training and Research in International Relations at Northwestern University. Guetzkow notes the use of this type of gaming for both research and teaching purposes. The third article, "Experimental Games: A Review" by Rapoport and Orwant, presents an impressive array of game experiments performed by psychologists, social-psychologists, mathematicians, economists, and others in attempts to test fundamental ideas underlying the various solution concepts. Schelling discusses the use of games for the study of theory in international politics. His work is followed by excerpts from a prize-winning paper in social psychology by Morton Deutsch and Krauss on "Studies of Interpersonal Bargaining." The somewhat different, yet parallel, points of view of the psychologists and social-psychologists when compared with those of political scientists, economists, and mathematical game theorists are brought out both in the article by Deutsch and Krauss and in that by Wilson and Bixenstine (readers should also note the book by Thibault and Kelley[40]).

[37] Sun Tzu: "The Art of War," *Roots of Strategy*, Military Service Publishing Company, Harrisburg, Pennsylvania, 4th printing, March 1955.

[38] Deutsch, K.: "International Politics and Game Theory," *Canadian Journal of Economics and Political Science*, February 1954, pp. 76–83.

[39] Shubik, M.: *Readings in Game Theory and Political Behavior*, Doubleday, 1954.

[40] Thibault, J. W. and H. H. Kelly: *The Social Psychology of Groups*, John Wiley and Sons, 1959.

The latter authors investigate "Forms of Social Control in Two-Person, Two-Choice Games." Finally, in a spirit of good-will the rules for the game "So Long Sucker," which was invented by Hausner, Nash, Shapley, and Shubik, are supplied to provide the reader with a simple easy-to-play parlor game from which he may contemplate some of the problems of social conflict and bargaining.

part 2

GENERAL

2

Mathematics and social analysis

ABRAHAM KAPLAN

The limitations of space in a brief collection of readings prevent the reproduction of an article that should be read completely by anyone seriously concerned with the role of mathematics in the social sciences. The title of the article "Sociology Learns the Language of Mathematics" is a misnomer inasmuch as the topic discussed by Kaplan is far broader than sociology. Only those comments addressed to game theory are presented here. They provide a clear and balanced view of the approach used by von Neumann and Morgenstern. Since the appearance of this article, many papers and books have appeared which, in part, answer several of the questions raised by Professor Kaplan. Much work has been done on utility theory and preferences; many different approaches to n-person games have been followed and some first steps taken in the examination of dynamic processes.

A troubling question for those of us committed to the widest application of intelligence in the study and solution of the problems of men is whether a general understanding of the social

Excerpts from *Commentary*, September 1952, pp. 274, 282–284. Reprinted by the courtesy of the author and *Commentary* magazine.

sciences will be possible much longer. Many significant areas of these disciplines have already been removed by the advances of the past two decades beyond the reach of anyone who does not know mathematics; and the man of letters is increasingly finding, to his dismay, that the study of mankind proper is passing from his hands to those of technicians and specialists. The aesthetic effect is admittedly bad: we have given up the belletristic "essay on man" for the barbarisms of a technical vocabulary, or at best the forbidding elegance of mathematical syntax. What have we gained in exchange?

To answer this question we must be able to get at the content of the new science. But when it is conveyed in mathematical formulas, most of us are in the position of the medieval layman confronted by clerical Latin—with this difference: mathematical language cannot be forced to give way to a vernacular. Mathematics, if it has a function at all in the sciences, has an indispensable one; and now that so much of man's relation to man has come to be treated in mathematical terms, it is impossible to ignore or escape the new language any longer. There is no completely satisfactory way out of this dilemma. All this article can do is to grasp either horn, sometimes oversimplifying, sometimes taking the reader out of his depth; but hoping in the end to suggest to him the significance of the growing use of mathematical language in social science.

To complicate matters even further, the language has several dialects. "Mathematics" is a plural noun in substance as well as form. Geometry, algebra, statistics, and topology use distinct concepts and methods, and are applicable to characteristically different sorts of problems. The role of mathematics in the new social science cannot be discussed in a general way: as we shall see, everything depends on the kind of mathematics being used.

. . . Among the recent applications to the study of man of this whole general body of ideas, one is especially celebrated; the theory of games presented by J. von Neumann and O. Morgenstern in *Theory of Games and Economic Behavior*. Here the focus is confined to problems of economics, but it is hoped that it will be extended to the whole range of man's social relations.

It may seem, superficially, that von Neumann and Morgenstern, in selecting games as a way of approaching the study of social organization, fall into the trap of oversimplification. But unlike Rashevsky, von Neumann and Morgenstern do not so much introduce simplifying assumptions in order to deal artificially with the whole complex social order as *select* relatively simple aspects of that order for analysis. Only after a theory adequate to the simple problems has been developed can the more complicated problems be attacked fruitfully. To be sure, the decision-maker cannot suspend action to satisfy the scruples of a scientific conscience; but neither can the scientist pretend to an advisory competence that he does not have, in order to satisfy practical demands.

While the theory of games does not deal with the social process in its full complexity, it is not merely a peripheral aspect of that process which it studies, but its very core. The aim is "to find the mathematically complete principles which define 'rational behavior' for the participants in a social economy, and to derive from them the general characteristics of that behavior." Games are analyzed because the pattern of rational behavior that they exhibit is the same as that manifested in social action, insofar as the latter does in fact involve rationality.

The theory is concerned with the question of what choice of strategy is rational when all the relevant probabilities are known and the outcome is not determined by one's choice alone. It is in the answer to this question that the new mathematics enters. And with this kind of mathematics, the social sciences finally abandon the imitation of natural science that has dogged so much of their history.

The authors first present a method of applying a numerical scale other than the price system to a set of human preferences. A man might prefer a concert to the theater, and either to staying at home. If we assign a utility of "I" to the last alternative, we know that going to the theater must be assigned a higher number, and the concert a higher one still. But how much higher? Suppose the decision were to be made by tossing two coins, the first to settle whether to go to the theater or not, the second (if necessary) to decide between the remaining alternatives. If the utility of the theater were very little different from that of staying at home, most of the time (three-fourths, to be exact) the outcome would be an unhappy one; similarly, if the theater and concert had comparable utilities, the outcome would be usually favorable. Just how the utilities compare, therefore, could be measured by allowing the second coin to be a loaded one. When it is a matter of indifference to the individual whether he goes to the theater or else tosses the loaded coin to decide whether he hears the concert or stays home, the loading of the coin provides a numerical measure of the utilities involved.

Once utility can be measured in a way that does not necessarily correspond to monetary units, a theory of rational behavior can be developed which takes account of other values than monetary ones. A game can be regarded as being played, not move by move, but on the basis of an over-all *strategy* that specifies beforehand what move is to be made in every situation that could possibly arise in the game. Then, for every pair of strategies selected—one by each player in the game—the rules of the game determine a *value* for the game: namely, what utility it would then have for each player. An optimal strategy is one guaranteeing a certain value for the game even with best possible play on the part of the opponent. Rational behavior, that is to say, is characterized as the selection of the strategy which minimizes the maximum loss each player can sustain.

If a game has only two players and is "zero-sum"—whatever is won by one player being lost by the other, and vice versa—then, if each player has "perfect information" about all the previous moves in the game, there always exists such an optimal strategy for each player. The outcome of a rationally played game can therefore be computed in advance; in principle, chess is as predictable as ticktacktoe.

Not every game, however, is as completely open as chess. In bridge and poker, for example, we do not know what cards are in the other players' hands; and this is ordinarily the situation in the strategic interplay of management and labor, or in the relations among sovereign states. In such cases rationality consists in playing several strategies, each with a mathematically determined probability. Consider a type of matching pennies in which each player is permitted to place his coin as he chooses. If we were to select heads always, we should be quickly found out; even if we favored heads somewhat, our opponent (assuming it is he who wins when the coins match) could always select heads and thereby win more than half the time. But if we select heads half the time—not in strict alternation, to be sure, but at random— then, no matter what our opponent does, we cannot lose more than half the time. Rational play consists in what is actually done in the game· we toss the coin each time to determine, as it were, whether we select heads or tails. Of course, in more complex games our strategies are not always to be "mixed" in equal proportions. The fundamental theorem of the theory of games is that for every two-person zero-sum game, no matter how complex the rules or how great the range of possible strategies open to each player, there always exists some specific pattern of probabilities of strategies which constitutes rational play. It minimizes the maximum loss that each player can sustain, not in every play of the game, but in the long run. And there is a mathematical solution that tells us what this strategy is.

Unfortunately, many games are not "zero-sum": in the game between management and labor, utilities are created in the process of play; in war they are destroyed. It is simply not true in such cases that what one side loses the other gains, or vice versa. In such games, the mathematics of the "zero-sum" game will not apply. Moreover, many games have more than two players: a number of manufacturers may be competing for a single market. Here the mathematics of a two-person game will not hold. The first difficulty, however, can be absorbed into the second. A non-"zero-sum" two-person game can be regarded as a three-person game, where the third person wins or loses whatever is lost or won by the other two together.

But how are we to solve games of more than two persons? Only if coalitions are formed, in effect making the game a two-person one. This is not an unrealistic assumption, since, obviously, if two players can coordinate their strategies against a third, they will enjoy a special advantage: odd-man-out is the simple but fundamental principle in such situations. For such games, however, the theory does not provide a detailed solution, for it cannot determine what is a rational division of the spoils between the members of a coalition in the way it can determine what is a rational strategy for the coalition as a whole. And here, of course, is the great difficulty in politics. The United States and Russia may be conceived of, in this theory, as playing a two-person non-"zero-sum" game with nature as the third player: only nature wins from atomic destruction, only nature loses if resources need not be diverted to military purposes. But the coalition of men against nature still leaves open how the utilities acquired in the game are to be divided between the participants. And here conflicting interests stand in the way of the joint interests that would make rational a coalition strategy.

From our present standpoint, the important outcome of the theory is to show that there exists a rigorously mathematical approach to precisely those aspects of the study of man that have seemed in the past to be least amenable to mathematical treatment—questions of conflicting or parallel interest, perfect or imperfect information, rational decision or chance effect. Mathematics is of importance for the social sciences not merely in the study of those aspects in which man is assimilable to inanimate nature, but precisely in his most human ones. On this question the theory of games leaves no room for doubt.

But a mathematical theory of games is one thing, and a mathematical theory of society another. Von Neumann and Morgenstern, it must be said, never confuse the two. Many fundamental difficulties remain, even within the limitations of the games framework. The theory of games involving many players is in a very unsatisfactory state; there is no way at present of comparing the utilities of different persons; and the whole theory is so far a static one, unable to take account of the essential learning process which (it may be hoped) takes place in the course of the selection of real-life strategies. Yet the theory has already provided enormous stimulation to mathematical and substantive research, and much more can be expected from it. Above all, it has shown that the resources of the human mind for the exact understanding of man himself are by no means already catalogued in the existing techniques of the natural sciences. . . .

3

Games and Decisions

R. D. LUCE AND H. RAIFFA

The following excerpts are from the general introduction to the theory of games, in the first chapter of the outstanding textbook and overview of the basis of the mathematical study of conflict and cooperation. With care, much of this book can be read by those with little formal mathematical training. Luce and Raiffa do not dwell on applications to specific disciplines; rather, they try to provide insight for the social scientist into the processes of model building and the formal analysis of some aspects of multiperson decision making.

In all of man's written record there has been a preoccupation with conflict of interest; possibly only the topics of God, love, and inner struggle have received comparable attention. The scientific study of interest conflict, in contrast to its description or its use as a dramatic vehicle, comprises a small, but growing, portion of this literature. As a reflection of this trend we find today that

Excerpts from R. D. Luce and H. Raiffa, *Games and Decisions*, 1957, pp. 1, 3, 4, 9, 10, and 11. Reprinted with permission of the authors and John Wiley and Sons.

conflict of interest, both among individuals and among institutions, is one of the more dominant concerns of at least several of our academic departments: economics, sociology, political science, and other areas to a lesser degree.

Game theory does not, and probably no mathematical theory could, encompass all the diverse problems which are included in our brief characterization of conflict of interest. In this introduction we shall try to cite the main features of the theory and to present some substantive problems included in its framework. The reader will easily fill in examples not now in the domain of the theory, and as we discuss our examples we shall point out some other important cases which are not covered.

First, with respect to the possible outcomes of a given situation, it is assumed that they are well specified and that each individual has a consistent pattern of preferences among them. Thus, if we ignore the fact that the player is in conflict with others and concentrate only on the outcomes, it is supposed that one way or another it can be ascertained what choice he would make if he were offered any particular collection of alternatives from which to choose. This problem of individual decision making is crucial to the whole superstructure we shall discuss, and it is important that there be no confusion about the assumptions that are made. For this reason we have devoted the whole of Chapter 2 to the topic of modern utility theory. In order that those familiar with the classical, and somewhat discredited, uses of the word "utility" not be misled, we shall expend some effort in establishing how the modern work on utility differs from the earlier ideas. In brief, the current theory shows that if one admits the possibility of risky outcomes, i.e., lotteries involving the basic alternatives, and if a person's preferences can be represented numerically by what is called a utility function. This utility has the very important property that a person will prefer one lottery to another if and only if the expected utility of the former is larger than the expected utility of the latter. Thus, the assumed individual desire for the preferred outcomes becomes, in game theory, a problem of maximizing expected utility.

Second, the variables which control the possible outcomes are also assumed to be well specified, that is, one can precisely characterize all the variables and all the values which they may assume.

As we said earlier, in this type of conflict situation we are interested in only some of the resulting behavior. Actually, our curiosity may encompass all of it—the tensions resulting, suicide rates or frequency of nervous disorder, agressive behavior, withdrawal, changes in personal or business strategy, etc.—but of these, any one theory will, presumably, deal with only a small subset. At present, game theory deals with the choices people may make, or, better, the choices they should make (in a sense to be specified), in the resulting equilibrium outcomes, and in some aspects of the communication and collusion which may occur among players in their attempts to improve their outcomes. Although much of what is socially, individually, and scientifically interesting is not a part of the theory, certain important aspects of our social behavior are included.

Political controversies are still another fertile source of situations involving conflicts of interest. In addition to the difficulties of the economic and military problems with respect to ill-defined domains of action, we know that here there is considerable ambiguity as to the outcome, or payoff, function even over a known domain of possible actions. This is to some extent true in the other situations we have described, but it is overwhelmingly obvious in the political realm, where, for example, the defeat of a candidate has sometimes been attributed (after the fact) to a single sentence out of the hundreds he spoke in a campaign.

A feature suggested by political and economic conflicts is the "social arbiter." Often it is felt that conflicts of interest should not be allowed to resolve themselves in, shall we say, the open market of threats and counter threats, but that there should exist social devices to take into account the preferences and strategic potentialities of each of the players and to arrive at a "fair" resolution of the conflict. Such a conciliation device—be it a voting scheme or an individual classed as an arbiter—must have the property that it is brought forth not to resolve a particular conflict but a wide class which potentially may arise: and its fairness is evaluated in the abstract with respect to this domain of possible conflicts.

Thus you have the compact summary that game theory is a model for situations of conflict among several people, in which two principal modes of resolution are collusion and conciliation. (Several of our colleagues convinced us that we should not use the tempting, but flip, title *Conflict, Collusion, and Conciliation* for this book.)

What then is the significance of game theory to the social scientist? First, because there has not been a plethora of applications in a dozen years, it does not follow that the theory will not ultimately be vital in applied problems. Judging by physics, the time scale for the impact of theoretical developments is often measured in decades. Second, although the present form of the theory may not be totally satisfactory—in part, presumably, because of its so-called normative character—this does not necessarily mean that abandoning it is the only possible course for a social scientist. Much of the theory is of very general importance, but some revision may be required for fruitful applications. Attention to the theory is needed, and not attention from the mathematician alone, as is now the case. Third, game theory is one of the first examples of an elaborate mathematical development centered solely in the social sciences. The conception derived from non-physical problems, and the mathematics—for the most part elementary in the mathematical sense —was developed to deal with that conception. The theory draws on known mathematics according to need—on set theory, on the theory of convex bodies, etc.; furthermore, when known tools were not applicable new mathematics was created. Most other attempts at mathematization (with the exception of statistics which plays a special role) have tended to take over small fragments of the mathematics created to deal with physical problems. If we can judge from physics, the main developments in the mathematization of the social sciences will come—as in game theory—with the development of new mathematics, or significantly new uses of old mathematics, suited to the problem. No one of these theories should be expected to be a panacea, but their cumulative effect promises to be significant.

4

The approach of game theory

JOHN VON NEUMANN AND OSKAR MORGENSTERN

The Theory of Games and Economic Behavior *is a difficult book to read. A measure of its significance is that it is no longer the book to which those wishing to learn about the scope or contributions of game theory should refer. The mathematical and behavioral science aspects of the theory of games have grown considerably beyond the contents of this classical volume. Nevertheless, specifically because of various fundamental questions and criticisms which have been raised, it is of importance to consider both the claims made and the warnings raised in this first book on game theory. The authors warn that they deal exclusively with statics; they indicate why and point out some of the difficulties in going from a static to dynamic analysis. In many parts of political science, in bargaining and negotiation in particular, dynamic models are needed, and recent work has begun to develop these.*

Our approach should be compared with the widely held view that a social theory is possible only on the basis of some precon-

Excerpts from *Theory of Games and Economic Behavior*, pp. 42–45. Reprinted by the courtesy of the authors and the Princeton University Press.

ceived principles of social purpose. These principles would include quantitative statements concerning both the aims to be achieved *in toto* and the apportionments between individuals. Once they are accepted a simple maximum problem results.

Let us note that no such statement of principles is ever satisfactory *per se*, and the arguments adduced in its favor are usually either those of inner stability or of less clearly defined kinds of desirability mainly concerning distribution.

Little can be said about the latter type of motivation. Our problem is not to determine what ought to happen in pursuance of any set of—necessarily arbitrary—*a priori* principles, but to investigate where the equilibrium of forces lies.

As far as the first motivation is concerned, it has been our aim to give just those arguments precise and satisfactory form, concerning both global aims and individual apportionments. This made it necessary to take up the entire question of inner stability as a problem in its own right. A theory which is consistent at this point cannot fail to give a precise account of the entire interplay of economic interests, influence and power.

It may now be opportune to revive the analogy with games, which we purposely suppressed in the previous paragraphs. The parallelism between the solutions in the sense of "game theory" on one hand and of stable "standards of behavior" on the other can be used for corroboration of assertions concerning these concepts in both directions. At least we hope that this suggestion will have some appeal to the reader. We think that the procedure of the mathematical theory of games of strategy gains definitely in plausibility by the correspondence which exists between its concepts and those of social organizations. On the other hand, almost every statement which we—or for that matter anyone else—ever made concerning social organizations, runs afoul of some existing opinion. And, by the very nature of things, most opinions thus far could hardly have been proved or disproved within the field of social theory. It is therefore a great help that all our assertions can be borne out by specific examples from the theory of games of strategy.

Such is indeed one of the standard techniques of using models in the physical sciences. This two-way procedure brings out a significant function of models, not emphasized in their discussion "before."

To give an illustration: The question whether several stable "orders of society" or "standards of behavior" based on the same physical background are possible or not, is highly controversial. There is little hope that it will be settled by the usual methods because of the enormous complexity of this problem among other reasons. But we shall give specific examples of games of three or four persons, where one game possesses several solutions in the sense of "game theory." And some of these examples will be seen to be models for certain simple economic problems. . . .

The next subject to be mentioned concerns the static or dynamic nature of the theory. We repeat most emphatically that our theory is thoroughly static. A dynamic theory would unquestionably be more complete and therefore preferable. But there is ample evidence from other branches of science that it is futile to try to build one as long as the static side is not thoroughly understood. On the other hand, the reader may object to some definitely dynamic arguments which were made in the course of our discussions . . . We think that this is perfectly legitimate. A static theory deals with equilibria. The essential characteristic of an equilibrium is that it has no tendency to change, i.e. that it is not conducive to dynamic developments. An analysis of this feature is, of course, inconceivable without the use of certain rudimentary dynamic concepts. The important point is that they are rudimentary. In other words: For the real dynamics which investigates the precise motions, usually far away from equilibria, a much deeper knowledge of these dynamic phenomena is required.

Finally let us note a point at which the theory of social phenomena will presumably take a very definite turn away from the existing patterns of mathematical physics. This is, of course, only a surmise on a subject where much uncertainty and obscurity prevail.

Our static theory specifies equilibria—i.e. solutions . . . which are sets of imputations. A dynamic theory—when one is found —will probably describe the changes in terms of simpler concepts: of a single imputation—valid at the moment under consideration

—or something similar. This indicates that the formal structure of this part of the theory—the relationship between statics and dynamics—may be generically different from that of the classical physical theories.

All these considerations illustrate once more what a complexity of theoretical forms must be expected in social theory. Our static analysis alone necessitated the creation of a conceptual and formal mechanism which is very different from anything used, for instance, in mathematical physics. Thus the conventional view of a solution as a uniquely defined number or aggregate of numbers was seen to be too narrow for our purposes, in spite of its success in other fields. The emphasis on mathematical methods seems to be shifted more towards combinatorics and set theory—and away from the algorithm of differential equations which dominate mathematical physics.

5

Scaling of utilities
and probability

JACOB MARSCHAK

*The subject of the measurement of utility and preferences among uncertain
events has given rise to a large, important, and highly technical literature
in the past fifteen years. In this article Jacob Marschak presents, in as
nontechnical a manner as is possible, the basic aspects of the measurement
of utility. Although a reader with no mathematical training will have to
read with care, this article is of considerable importance to those wishing to
understand most of the recent work on decision making under uncertainty.
The problems of utility measurement are not dealt with elsewhere in this
volume; and in the literature, in general, it is difficult to find a basic exposition written with the degree of clarity of this one.*

This is a revision in part from Marschak's paper "Mathematical Models
and Experiments on Decision-making" (mimeographed), presented in
February 1954 at a meeting sponsored by the Epidemiological Board, U. S.
Army, and Dunlap and Associates, Inc., and devoted to mathematical
models and human behavior. Other parts give a reformulation of Marschak's "Probability in the Social Sciences," in *Mathematical Thinking in
the Social Sciences,* edited by Paul Lazarsfeld, Glencoe, Ill., The Free Press,
1954. Research undertaken by the Cowles Commission for Research in
Economics under Contract Nonr-358 (OI), NR 047-006 with the Office of
Naval Research. Produced here with the permission of the author.

One strategy is better than another if it brings the player more. More of what? Clearly, one uses some criterion of "utility," of something that is being maximized. Moreover, since the opponent's response or the future in general is uncertain, the player does not know a unique result of his strategy but rather expects various possible results, some with greater, some with smaller degrees of belief or "(subjective) probabilities."

If utilities and probabilities could be merely ranked (like degrees of patriotism) but not also scaled (like degrees of temperature), the theory of games could say rather little. Accordingly, von Neumann and Morgenstern revived the eighteenth century concept of a player who is concerned with his subjective status (so called "moral wealth"—the modern "utility"), a number which, under uncertainty, is a random one, and whose average (the "moral expectation"—the modern "expected Utility") the player tries to maximize. A lively discussion developed.[1] The most elegant restatement of the relevant postulates of rational behavior and a rigorous proof of the implied "Bernoulli theorem" was given by Herstein and Milnor.[2] In this discussion, the necessarily subjective nature of the probabilities was somewhat neglected. But this latter aspect (actually also traceable back to the eighteenth century) was revived by Ramsey and De Finetti and in L. J. Savage's *Foundations of Statistics*.[3]

The following exposition tries to appeal to the reader's intuition and cater to his laziness more than it would be permissible in a mathematical paper. A proof is merely sketched. It may be added, however, that the substance of the proof, too, is simpler than in my earlier papers on the subject.[4]

I shall often use the second person pronoun. In discussing rational behavior as in discussing logic, appeal is made to the

---

[1] For example, at the colloquium on risk in econometrics, held in 1952; its Proceedings published by the Centre National de la Recherche Scientifique, Paris, 1953.

[2] I. N. Herstein and John Milnor, "An Axiomatic Approach to Measurable Utility," *Econometrica*, 1953.

[3] John Wiley and Sons, 1954.

[4] *Econometrica*, 1950; and Second Berkeley Symposium, ed. by J. Neyman, 1951.

reader's reasonable self: given time to think, how would you decide? I don't deal with another, quite a different question (as different as psychology is from logic): how often do you decide hurriedly and foolishly?

The Case of Three Outcomes

Suppose you, the reader, have to choose between two decisions (actions): to build or not to build a bomb-proof shelter for yourself and your family. To make the example drastic, let us suppose that you are rich but that the shelter would cost you practically the whole of your fortune; and that such a shelter is both indispensable and sufficient for life preservation in the case of war. Thus your two alternative decisions and the two alternative states of the world (war or peace) combine into the following "payoff matrix":

| | States of World | |
Decisions	Peace	War
Build shelter	Alive and poor (r_2)	Alive and poor (r_2)
Don't build shelter	Alive and rich (r_3)	Dead (r_1)

This is oversimplified indeed. Especially, we have neglected the difference between being alive and poor in peace, and being alive and poor in war (with shelterless neighbors dead). I need this particular simplification in order to have in my example just three possible outcomes. This will be a convenient introduction to more complicated cases. The three outcomes, or results, I have denoted by $r_1 = $ "dead"; $r_2 = $ "alive and poor"; $r_3 = $ "alive and rich" I suppose you prefer r_3 to r_2 and r_2 to r_1. This ranking of results is sufficient to determine your choice of action if you are certain about the future. If you are certain that there will be war, you choose to build the shelter (because you prefer r_2 to r_1); if you are sure that there will be peace, you choose not to build the shelter (because r_3 is better than r_2).

But suppose you do not know whether there will be war or peace. Yet you have to take a decision! You will still choose not to build a shelter if your *degree of belief* in peace and your *degree of preference* for wealth relative to survival are sufficiently large. (Note that we now speak of degrees and not of mere ranks! Summer is warmer than spring, and spring is warmer than winter: this is ranking; but we can also measure degrees of temperature in each of the three seasons.)

The statement I have just made, about the degrees of your beliefs and preferences that will make you decide not to build a shelter though you are uncertain about the future, must be made more precise. Denote the degrees of belief (also called subjective probabilities) that you assign to peace and war, respectively, by p and $1 - p$. Calibrate your thermometer of preferences, or "utilities" as follows: assign utility zero to the worst of the three outcomes, and utility one to the best. Thus

$$u(r_1) = 0; \quad u(r_3) = 1$$

Then, since r_2 is better than r_1 and worse than r_3,

$$0 < u(r_2) < 1$$

Subject to these inequalities, you are still free to assign any number $u(r_2)$ to the outcome r_2. I now suggest that you can, without incurring any logical contradiction, determine the number $u(r_2)$ in such a way as to satisfy the following principle: "*of any two decisions, the one you (the reader) choose is the one that, in your opinion, results in the higher, or at least not lower, average utility.*" The average utility that results from the decision "don't build" is defined as the weighted average of $u(r_3)$ and $u(r_1)$, the weights being the corresponding degrees of belief, which we have denoted above by p and $1 - p$, respectively. Thus the average utility that results from "not building shelter" is

$$(1) \quad u(r_3) \cdot p + u(r_1) \cdot (1 - p) = 1 \cdot p + 0 \cdot (1 - p) = p$$

On the other hand, the average utility that results from the decision "to build" is

$$u(r_2) \cdot p + u(r_2) \cdot (1 - p) = u(r_2)$$

Now, suppose you have chosen to build. According to the above principle of choosing in favor of the decision that results in the higher average utility, your actual choice will imply that, in your opinion [and still using the scale where one had fixed $u(r_3) = 1$ and $u(r_1) = 0$],

$$u(r_2) \geq p$$

On the other hand, if you had chosen not to build, the above principle would imply [still using the same scale]

$$u(r_2) \leq p$$

You can now perform on yourself a mental experiment, by varying the number p and asking: "with this degree of belief into persistence of peace, do I still prefer to build (or not to build)?" You may come close enough to a value of p, at which you will be *indifferent* between building and not building. Call this hypothetical value: $p = p_0$. Then both statements are true: $u(r_2) \geq p_0$ and $u(r_2) \leq p_0$. That is

$$u(r_2) = p_0$$

You have now attached numerical utilities to all three outcomes considered. You have also attached numerical average utilities to the two alternative decisions, to build and not to build. Call these two decisions (actions) a_1 and a_2, respectively. Thus

$$u(r_1) = 0; \quad u(r_2) = p_0; \quad u(r_3) = 1;$$

average utility if a_1 is taken $= p_0$

average utility if a_2 is taken $= p$

Remember that p is your actual degree of belief in peace; while p_0 is that degree of belief in peace that would make you indifferent between the two decisions. If you have decided to build, this implies that, in your opinion, $p \geq p_0$. If you have decided not to build, this implies that, in your opinion, $p \leq p_0$.

We have had occasion to discuss your preferences between results (for example, better to be alive and poor than to be dead: choice between r_2 and r_1) as well as between decisions (better to build than not to build: choice between a_1 and a_2). It is thus natural to extend the concept of utility accordingly, and speak, not only of a utility of a result, but also of a utility of a decision. In fact a "result" can be regarded as a special case of a "decision," viz., a decision which can have only one result. Such was in fact the decision a_1 in our example; its unique result was r_2. Accordingly we might simply assign to it the utility $u(a_1) = u(r_2)$. On the other hand, decision a_2 is identified with a bundle of results (r_3 and r_1), each with a respective degree of belief (p and $1 - p$). We can call such a bundle a "prospect": it is a (subjective) probability distribution of results, a lottery. A prospect promising— as in the case of a_1—a single result, may be called a sure prospect. It is, in fact, *also* a (subjective) probability distribution, with one of the results having probability one. Thus, when you compared the two decisions, you did, in fact, compare the following two probability distributions (or prospects).

Decision:	Probability of		
	r_1	r_2	r_3
a_1	0	1	0
a_2	$1 - p$	0	p

One can say that, of two decisions (or of two corresponding prospects), you have chosen the one with a higher, or at least not lower, utility. If you choose a_1, then $u(a_1) \geq u(a_2)$. The principle of choosing the decision that results in a higher average utility can, then, be rephrased as follows: "the utility of a decision is the higher, the higher the average utility resulting from it." It will therefore not contradict this principle if you simply equate $u(a_1)$ and $u(a_2)$ with the corresponding average utilities. That is

$$u(a_1) = p_0; \quad u(a_2) = p$$

You have thus scaled the utilities of prospects, sure as well as non-sure ones:

$$u(r_1) = 0; \quad u(r_2) = u(a_1) = p_0; \quad u(a_2) = p; \quad u(r_3) = 1$$

It will prove more convenient to use a notation that unifies the sure and non-sure prospects, by listing the alternative results and their corresponding probabilities. In this notation, the equations just given become

$$u(r_1, r_2, r_3; 1, 0, 0) = 0;$$

$$u(r_1, r_2, r_3; 0, 1, 0) = u(r_1, r_2, r_3; 1 - p_0, 0, p_0) = p_0$$

$$u(r_1, r_2, r_3; 1 - p, 0, p) = p;$$

$$u(r_1, r_2, r_3; 0, 0, 1) = 1$$

It is easily checked that each of these equations satisfies the principle "utility of a prospect equals its average utility," i.e., the average of the utilities of the component outcomes (sure prospects) promised by the prospect in question.

Note that the zero and the unit of the scale of utilities were chosen arbitrarily, by assigning utility 0 to the worst, and utility 1 to the best of the results considered. To this extent, the scale is arbitrary, just as is a temperature scale. If, for example, we had to put $u(r_1) = -10$ and $u(r_3) = +100$, the principle of choosing the decision with the higher average utility would yield [compare equations (1)]:

$$u(r_3) \cdot p + u(r_1) \cdot (1 - p) = 100 \cdot p - 10 \cdot (1 - p)$$
$$= 110p - 10$$

as the average utility for the decision a_2; the latter we have also denoted by $(r_1, r_2, r_3; 1 - p, 0, p)$. Thus if, as before, p_0 denotes the probability of peace that would make you indifferent between the two actions, our new scale will be (using both of the suggested notations):

$$u(r_1) = u(r_1, r_2, r_3; 1, 0, 0) = -10;$$

$$u(r_2) = u(a_1) = u(r_1, r_2, r_3; 0, 1, 0) = u(r_1, r_2, r_3; 1 - p_0, 0, p_0)$$
$$= 110p_0 - 10;$$

$$u(a_2) = u(r_1, r_2, r_3; 1 - p, 0, p) = 110p - 10;$$

$$u(r_3) = u(r_1, r_2, r_3; 0, 0, 1) = 100$$

We see that, to convert from the old to the new utility scale, one has to perform a "linear transformation": that is, to multiply by a constant (110) and to add a constant (-10); just as we do in converting from Fahrenheit degrees to centigrades or from altitudes measured in feet over Lake Michigan level to altitudes in meters over sea level. In this sense, the utility scale that interprets your choices among decisions is "determinate up to an arbitrary linear transformation." (Even measurements of geometrical distances or of physical weights are determinate up to an arbitrary linear transformation, although in those cases only the multiplying constant is arbitrary: the "unit of measurement.")

So far, we have treated a case in which only three alternative outcomes (r_1, r_2, r_3) are possible. What have we shown? We have shown that your decisions are consistent with a scale of utilities that satisfies the following principle: *choose the decision that results, on the average, in the highest utility.* After fixing arbitrarily the utilities of two of the outcomes (assigning a higher utility to the better one), the application of this principle results in a definite utility number for the third outcome, and also in definite utility numbers for all prospects that promise the three outcomes with pre-assigned probabilities.

The General Case: "Bernoulli Norm"

Let us now relax the strait jacket of "three outcomes only." Let there be any (finite) number of outcomes, also called "sure prospects." Let us generalize even further, by considering prospects which promise, with preassigned probabilities, not only certain outcomes, but possibly also prospects. The case where a prospect is a lottery promising certain outcomes rather than a lottery promising certain lotteries is clearly a special one, with certain probabilities shrinking to zeros.

So far, the letters a_1, a_2 stood for decision or action, and each corresponded to a certain prospect. We shall continue to denote prospects by $a_1, a_2, \ldots$, but it will be convenient also to use the subsequent letters of the alphabet ($b, c, \ldots$) and also x. For probabilities, we shall use, as before, p; but q and π will also be needed.

I want to convince the reader that it will be possible for him to set up a scale of his utilities of all prospects, sure and otherwise, this scale satisfying the following property: if a prospect x is a lottery promising the prospects $a_1, a_2, \ldots, a_n$ with subjective probabilities $\pi_1, \ldots, \pi_n$, then

$$(2) \qquad u(x) = \sum_1^n u(a_1)\pi_1$$

That is, again: the utility of a prospect should equal the average of promised utilities.

If it is possible to interpret your behavior as satisfying (2), we shall say that you obey the "Bernoulli Norm": see "Historical Note," below.

The technical term for "average of values of a variable, weighted by probabilities of their occurrences" is "mathematical expectation" of that variable, or, more briefly its "expected value." The expression on the right-hand side of (2) is, then, the "expected value of utility of the prospect x," or, still more briefly, "expected utility of x." What we try to show is: there exists a numerical scale of utility for all prospects, with the following property: the utility of a prospect equals its expected utility. Since you will decide in favor of a prospect with higher utility in preference to one with lower utility, you will choose a decision that maximizes the utility of a prospect; and, by the principle just mentioned (and that we are going to prove), this implies that you maximize the expected utility of a prospect.

Let a and b be two prospects (either sure or uncertain) facing the reader, and let him regard b as better than a. Consider the following classes of prospects:

1. a and b
2. all prospects that promise a or b
3. all prospects that are not better than b and not worse than a [Obviously (1) and possibly (2) are included in (3).]
4. all prospects that are better than b
5. all prospects that are worse than a.

The utilities in class (1) will be assigned arbitrarily, except for the condition that a is worse than b. We put $u(a) = 0$, $u(b) = 1$. [If classes (4) and (5) were empty, a might stand for "agony" and b for "bliss"!]

The utilities in class (2) will all lie between (and excluding) 0 and 1, for the following reason: Let a lottery c promise b if a possible event s happens, and a if it does not happen. Therefore, if you acquire c and s happens, you get something better than a; while if s does not happen you get a. Hence c is better than a. Similarly, c is worse than b. For, if you acquire c and s happens you get b; but if s does not happen you have something worse than b. Hence $u(a) < u(c) < u(b)$ and therefore $0 < u(c) < 1$, i.e., $u(c)$ is some proper fraction.

Moreover compare two lotteries in class (2): c_1 and c_2, where c_1 promises b if the event s_1 happens. Let p_1 be the probability of s_1 and suppose $p_1 < p_2$. Then $u(c_1) < u(c_2)$, for the following reason. The lottery c_2 promises b with larger probability than does lottery c_2; but with smaller probability than does a direct offer of b. Therefore c_2 can be conceived of as a lottery that promises c_1 and b with certain probabilities.[5] Hence, by a reasoning similar to the one made before, c_2 must be better than c_1 and worse than b.

It follows that you will rank the utilities of the various prospects in class (2) by assigning increasing proper fractions as the probability p of getting b increases.

It is permissible therefore to choose as the utility number for a lottery the fraction p if the lottery promises b with probability p. We have thus scaled all prospects of class (2), and this scale fits with the boundary values $u(a) = 0$ and $u(b) = 1$,

---

[5] Let these probabilities be q and $1 - q$, respectively, q is easy to find (though it is not really necessary for our purpose) by posing

$$q \cdot p_1 + (1 - q) \cdot 1 = p_2$$

since p_2, the chance of obtaining b, must be equal to the chance (in the new lottery) of getting it by virtue of having gotten c_1, *plus* the chance of getting it directly. We have $q = \dfrac{1 - p_2}{1 - p_1}$.

since a and b can themselves be called lotteries, with $p = 0$ and $= 1$, respectively.

Before proceeding to the remaining classes of prospects, let us satisfy ourselves that our scale, so far, has the desired property. Let a prospect x be a lottery promising prospects [belonging to classes (1) and (2)] $c_1, \ldots, c_n$ with probabilities $\pi_1, \ldots, \pi_n$. Show that

$$(3) \qquad u(x) = \sum_1^n \pi_1 u(c_1)$$

To prove (3), we replace $u(x)$ by the probability with which the lottery x promises b. This probability is compounded from $p_1, \ldots, p_n$, where p_1 is the probability with which c_1 promises b. Hence $u(x) = \sum_1^n \pi_1 p_1$. But we have seen that $u(c_1) = p_1$. Hence (3) is true.

Consider now the class (3) of prospects. It includes class (1); and we have seen that it also includes class (2); but it includes more. We have covered those of the members of (3) that are a or b or lotteries promising a or b; and we were able to assign to each of these lotteries a utility p equal to the probability with which that lottery promises b. Of course, p ranges from 0 (the utility of a itself) to 1 (the utility of b itself). Now the utility of any member of class (3) must lie between 0 and 1 since it consists of prospects that are not better than b and not worse than a. Hence, any member of class (3)—say, d_1—that is not a lottery promising a or b has a utility that is equal to that of one of those lotteries—call it c_1—i.e., to some p, $0 \leq p \leq 1$. If we now form a lottery y that promises various members $d_1, \ldots, d_n$ of class (3) with probabilities $\pi_1, \ldots, \pi_n$, then y has the same utility as the lottery x considered in equation (3). For, the event s_1 (with probability π_1) will give the subject the prospect d_1 if he had chosen y; and the prospect c_1 if he had chosen x. And so for $s_2, \ldots, s_n$. But since we have seen each d_1 to have the same utility as the corresponding c_1 (this utility being equal to the probability with which c_1 promises b), it follows that the subject is indifferent between y and x. Thus (3) is extended to all members of the class (3), since $u(y)$ can replace $u(x)$ and each $u(d_1)$ can replace $u(c_1)$.

This would complete the proof if we could assume that there exists for each subject a worst and a best prospect, "agony" and "bliss" (a and b). If this is not the case, i.e., utility is not bounded and classes (4) and (5) are not empty, equation (3) still holds good. To show this, it suffices to pick the worst and the best prospect—say, a' and b'—among those composing the particular lottery x [i.e., a' and b' will be among the c_1, . . . , c_n in (3)], and use a' and b' in the same way in which a and b were treated previously; i.e., create a new scale of utilities—say, u'—with $u'(a') = 0$, $u'(b') = 1$, $u'(a) = p < q = u'(b)$, where p and q are certain probabilities; a and b having, respectively, the same utilities as certain two lotteries, each promising a' or b'. We see by former reasoning, that in terms of this new scale, (3) will be valid, that is

$$(4) \qquad\qquad u'(x) = \Sigma \pi_1 u'(c_1)$$

But this latter equation remains valid also if the function u' is replaced by any linear transform of it, $\alpha u' + \beta$ (this can be easily verified by substitution). Now, the functions u' and u are, in fact, linear transforms of each other, with (for any c) $u'(c) = (q - p)u(c) + p$ [i.e., the scale u' is obtained from the scale u by shifting the origin by p and multiplying the utility unit by $q - p$]. Hence the validity of (4) entails the validity of (3) for any prospects,[6] i.e., the validity of (2).

---

[6] With $u(a) = 0$ and $u(b) = 1$, the utility $u(e)$ of a member of class (4) and the utility $u(f)$ of a member of class (5) are easily shown to be

$$u(e) = \frac{1}{q} > 1; \quad u(f) = 1 - \frac{1}{r} < 0$$

where q and r are probabilities defined as follows: the subject is indifferent between b and a lottery promising e or with respective probabilities q and $1 - q$; and he is indifferent between a and a lottery promising f or b with respective probabilities r and $1 - r$. It is easily verified that with these definitions,

$$u(e) \cdot q + u(a) \cdot (1 - q) = u(b) \text{ and}$$
$$u(f) \cdot r - u(b) \cdot (1 - r) = u(a)$$

Historical Note

Suppose that you apply the utility scale just described to various amounts of monetary wealth, and discover that, for you, the utility can be regarded as proportional to money amount. Should your tastes happen to be of this kind then (since you have agreed that your choices are as described by the Bernoulli Norm and you therefore maximize the mathematical expectation of utility) you are a maximizer of the mathematical expectation of monetary wealth. And remember that this mathematical expectation was computed on the basis of your subjective probabilities.

Now, the idea that a consistent decision-maker chooses a bet that gives him the maximum expected monetary wealth, computed on the basis of his subjective probabilities, can be traced back to Thomas Bayes (eighteenth century). Daniel Bernoulli who lived in that same century was not so clear about the subjective nature of the probabilities that can be said to underline human choice. He assumed people to know the true odds in a game, and neglected the case when a man has no sufficient theory or no large sample to compute the odds with precision. But, on the other hand, Bernoulli was emphatic (as Bayes was not: remember that Bayes dealt with money instead of utilities) about the subjective nature of preferences. Unless your tastes are of a peculiar character, utilities are not proportional to money amounts (and moreover they can and should be attached to many other objects of choice besides money!), and one must be careful to state that the consistent decision-maker maximizes his expected utility, not his expected monetary wealth. This is what we called the Bernoulli Norm. In stating it, we did describe the probabilities used as subjective and called them sometimes degrees of belief. But we did not say how they too (like the equally subjective utility numbers) can be derived as characterizing a consistent decision-maker's behavior. This was done by the late Frank Ramsey in 1926, and more recently by De Finetti and by L. J. Savage. Their approach will be outlined in our concluding section.

The Ramsey Norm

I shall now try to convince you that your decisions, if consistent, can be interpreted in the following manner: there exist utility numbers, attached to outcomes of your actions, and there exist degrees of belief, attached to the future states of the world, with the following property: if for each of your possible actions the expected utility (i.e., the mathematical expectation of utility of outcomes) were computed on the basis of your degrees of belief, then the action chosen by you would be the one with the highest expected utility. We may call this the Ramsey Norm.

Imagine that the following eight actions $a_1, \ldots, a_8$ will have one of the two outcomes, Death (D) or Life (L), depending on whether the world will be in the state s_1 or s_2 or s_3 (mutually exclusive), as shown in the following table which, as you can convince yourself, exhausts all possible triplets of L- and D-symbols:

States of World

Actions	s_1	s_2	s_3	Group
a_1	D	D	D	1
a_2	L	D	D	
a_3	D	L	D	2
a_4	D	D	L	
a_5	D	L	L	
a_6	L	D	L	3
a_7	L	L	D	
a_8	L	L	L	4

I assume that you prefer Life to Death. Then you will prefer a_8 to a_7 because a_8 has a better outcome that a_7 in state s_3, and the same outcome as a_7 otherwise. By this reasoning, you will prefer the action a_8 to any of the actions in group 3; you will prefer any action in 3 and any one in 2 to the action a_1.

Now suppose, in addition, that you happen to be indifferent between a_2, a_3, and a_4. If this is the case we shall say that your degrees of belief in the occurrence of each of the states s_1, s_2, s_3 are $\frac{1}{3}$, $\frac{1}{3}$, $\frac{1}{3}$; and we shall assign to the occurrence of the state s_1 *or* s_2 (and similarly: of the state s_1 *or* s_3; and s_2 *or* s_3) the degree of belief $\frac{2}{3}$. Moreover: would it be reasonable for you to be indifferent within group 2 and not to be indifferent within group 3? Would this not mean that you grant the three possible future states of the world an equal degree of belief as long as rewards or punishments are attached to them in a certain way, but revise your beliefs when the rewards and punishments are interchanged? This would be unreasonable.

We thus have:

$$u(a_1) < u(a_2) = u(a_3) = u(a_4) < u(a_5) = u(a_6) = u(a_7) < u(a_8)$$

We now proceed to scale these utilities. We are free to fix the utility of Life (like the utility of "bliss" in an earlier part of the paper) at 1, and the utility of Death at 0. Then the utilities of prospects will also fall in their places, being equal to the probability of Life as promised in a given prospect. That is, we obtain $u(a_1) = 0$; $u(a_8) = 1$; $u(a_2) = u(a_3) = u(a_4) = $; $u(a_5) = u(a_6) = u(a_7) = \frac{2}{3}$. We shall find as before that this utility scale is consistent with your being a maximizer of expected utility.

Thus, not only your utilities but also your degrees of belief can be derived from your behavior—including the indifference which you have shown in choosing within group 2 of actions (and also—as consistency required—within the group 3 of actions).

We have thus shown that it was possible to interpret your choices as consistent with the existence of utilities and subjective probabilities and with the maximization of expected utility. Granted that the example was a special one. It can be easily extended to n (instead of 3) states of the world, and degrees of belief $0, \dfrac{1}{n}, \dfrac{2}{n}, \cdots, \dfrac{n-1}{n}, 1$ can then be defined—if one can catch you as being indifferent within a certain group of decisions. How to arrange for a demarcation of states of the world that would make this possible requires a more complete and rigorous logical analysis. (This has been done by L. J. Savage.) Here we have had to content ourselves with a mere sketch.

6

The unity of political and economic science

DUNCAN BLACK

Although this article is not directly concerned with the theory of games, it is addressed to key problems in committee and community decision making. Analogies between economic and political choice mechanisms are developed, and a case is made for the combined study of a theory of economic and political choice.

This article will put forward the view that Economic and Political Science are the same in kind: that when we do eventually obtain a "satisfactory" Political Science it will have the same distinguishing marks as Walras' *Éléments* or Pareto's *Manuel*—or perhaps Marshall's *Principles*, with the admixture of the rigorously formal and the descriptive treatment—rather than those of the existing texts in Politics.[1] And the core of the treatment, we hold, will consist of a set of formal or mathematical propositions.

---

[1] We distinguish between Politics, the science, and politics meaning political phenomena, by the use of the capital letter; and similarly in other cases.

From *The Economic Journal*, September 1950, pp. 506–514. Reprinted by the courtesy of Duncan Black and The Royal Economic Society.

The main reason which I can give in substantiation of this view is that it is possible, using terms which are precisely those of Economic Science, to construct a Theory of Committee Decisions. In getting a theory of the committee, however, it is clear that we at the same time get a sufficient means to construct a Theory of Politics. All that is needed for this is to construct a theory of the committee that is sufficiently comprehensive. When this has been done we can deduce from the schedules of valuation of the individuals in the community, taken in conjunction with the election law which is initially existent, which Members will be elected to Parliament (and which representatives will be selected for local-government councils). But Parliament is itself a bicameral committee; its workings will therefore be covered, as will those of the cabinet, which is a committee requiring unanimous decisions on the part of its members. The party machines are again committees which help to determine the transactions inside Parliament; and their workings, too, can be examined in terms of a theory of committees. At the highest level, international agreements are reached by committees which again require unanimity in their decisions.

Admittedly the theory which has been given so far would not cover the workings of all committees; but this can be done by an elaboration of the same *kind* of theory, which, in principle, is capable of covering all types of committee action.

A theory of committees seems to be obtainable; and, if so, we argue, a Theory of Politics. And the essential features of a Theory of Politics obtained along these lines will be those of a theory of committees. But, as we will proceed to show, these essential features are precisely those of Economic Science. Indeed, if we accept the view that a Politics can be developed out of the theory of committees, then Political Science and Economic Science would appear quite definitely to be two branches of the same subject. In particular, we can specify that they make use of the same language, the same mode of abstraction, the same instruments of thought and the same method of reasoning—because this is true of the theory of committees and Economic Science.

The use of the same terminology in the two sciences perhaps

goes farther than anything else to prove their fundamental identity: this because one's thinking is largely conditioned by the means of expression at command, and language permeates thinking to its innermost core and in all its recesses. The importance of language is evident enough when the stage has been reached of giving an intelligible formulation to the results arrived at: the degree of success achieved in presenting the system of thought will largely depend on the adequacy of the technical terms employed. But before the stage has been reached of making explicit the results of such thinking as has already been carried out, a language, if it were really suitable to the subject, would direct the mind at the beginning of thought to those elements in the situation which are significant, would suggest to the imagination and intellect the actual or possible inter-relations between the elements, and would enable one to "fumble one's way gently and patiently through the problem." Thus the adequacy of a Political Science developed as we suggest, will depend, among other things, on how far economic language—for the language of the theory of committees comes entirely from Economic Science—can first capture and then make explicit, thoughts which relate to a field other than Economics, viz., to Politics.

Now if Economics and Politics were separate and distinct subjects, such a use of language would certainly be disadvantageous. If, however, Political Science were really one with Economic Science, far from the use of the borrowed vocabulary being a drawback, it would be a help. Economic Science has been built up progressively and continuously over two centuries; it has worked its way through to a language which has laid an always firmer grasp on the concepts necessary for thought; the progress has been made by a succession of distinguished thinkers, each taking over and developing the work of his predecessors. Political Science (though not Political Philosophy), on the other hand, has been little cultivated; its lists contain few names of a lustre similar to those of Economics; it has nothing to show of the same continuity of development as Economics. In the one science the heritage of language is much richer, of greater pliancy and exactitude than in the other.

If it is legitimate for Political Science to make use of this heritage of language and concept, it should be to its immediate and considerable advantage. We ourselves have been led to the belief that it is, by finding that the problems of committees could be resolved by a use of economic language that was quite natural and unforced. From the explanations that we go on to give it will become clear that this means of expression has determined the crucial steps in breaking down the problem into its elements.

To get the very complex materials with which they deal sufficiently simplified to be dealt with in thought, both sciences, Economics and Politics, have to abstract from the situations met with in practice; they must deal only with certain aspects of the situations and disregard the others. First, they must find the answers to the simpler problems; and after that, with a lesser degree of abstraction, they can pass on to consider the more complex problems. In doing this Politics will make use of what, in virtue of its earlier historic development, can be referred to as the *economic mode of abstraction.*

One feature of this is that the treatment is often of the "timeless" variety: times does not enter into the equations used. In the theory of the market or of marginal productivity, for instance, the *data* are assumed to remain unchanged until such period as equilibrium is attained; and after that, with the persistence of the same *data*, the position of equilibrium will remain unaltered. Similarly, in dealing with committees many of the basic theorems are obtainable by assuming *data* that don't alter with time and examining the positions of equilibrium that will be reached.

But in neither subject is this a necessary limitation. Rather it is a simplifying device used to obtain the broad outlines of an answer. When a further degree of approximation to reality is needed, or when certain problems come to be investigated, time must be taken into account. The same means of doing this exist in both subjects, and the same difficulties arise in both.

The most important feature of this mode of abstraction, however, is that in both sciences the individual is represented by his schedule of preferences.

Economic Science looks on the various phenomena with which it deals as the outcome of the valuations placed upon goods and services by the individuals concerned. The number of men employed in a particular factory, their length of working-day and the output of the factory are shown to be related to the scales of valuation of the consumers of the good that it manufactures, to the scales of the members of the board of directors and of the workmen concerned.

If we were to examine the matter further, we might find that the scales of valuations of each individual in any of these classes could be correlated with various other phenomena. The consumer's valuations might be found to be related to his native constitution, physiological and psychological, to the kind of house in which he lived or to his family circumstances. And the firm's output of the commodity would certainly depend on the existing state of technology, e.g., on the existing knowledge of Chemistry. Other branches of Economics or other branches of science may examine the influence exerted by technology on the output of the firm, or the influence of family circumstances on the schedule of preferences of the consumer, but Economic Science itself does not do so. It does not inquire by what events in the realm of fact these preference schedules have come to be what they are.

So also it would be possible to relate the structure of a country's industry, the scale of its engineering, shipbuilding or cotton industries, to the deposits of minerals in it, its climate or its geographical position; and all of this would be enormously important, quite vital, indeed, for an understanding of the country's position. The student of Economics who was without this knowledge would be like the physicist who was born with a knowledge of Einstein's theory but had never had the advantage of walking over fields or seeing tides or measuring a table with a yardstick. It is quite safely assumed that the physicist studying Relativity has in fact measured tables and has seen electric cells and resistances and the other paraphernalia of his science, and that the student of Economics is acquainted with the importance that the existence of coal deposits or the possession a seaboard has for a country's economy. These effects are a proper subject of study, but this part of the study would belong to Descriptive Economics or other branches, and not to Economic Science itself.

The position of Political Science is exactly similar. Political Science, too, accepts the scales of valuation of the individuals concerned as being among the *data* of its problem. A knowledge of the economic system of the country, of its racial composition, its political and social traditions, its complicated political history, would be necessary to an understanding of its political system. But such topics as these would fall within the discussion of other branches of Politics, not of Political Science itself. This is a hard saying. Only the student familiar with the methods of reasoning of the various sciences would agree that the Science of Politics should accept as its *data* the scales of preferences of individuals. Yet it is so.

Consideration of technology lies outside Economic Science as it does outside Political Science, but the technological facts, so far as they are known from the past or guessed at for the future, play their part in the formation of the individual's scales of preferences. Here the issues which arise are not obvious, and we may examine them further.

In economics some of the technological facts are definitely known by the people concerned. The effect of combining specified quantities of iron and coal in producing steel are known from the numerous instances of this which have occurred in the past. The manner in which it is possible to produce a steel plate using different kinds of machinery and different quantities of labour and raw materials can be accurately stated. As a result of the numerous experiments and accumulated experience of the past, the technical possibilities entailed in the production process are often known beyond cavil. So long as we confine ourselves to the realm of the purely technical, the possibilities which are open, and from which one must be selected, will often be definitely enough known to all.

In politics there is rarely or never this measure of agreement. Facts rarely or never recur in the exact form which they had in the past. The ingredients in the situation are usually different, or combined in different proportion from what they were in the past. Taking a simple illustration, if a college curriculum is being revised by a committee, the members will have before their minds a knowledge of past curricula of this and other colleges with which they have been acquainted, but some will have been acquainted with some curricula, others with others; the experience on the basis of which they are choosing will be different for the various members. The committee member who has had the opportunity of witnessing each of two curricula in operation may even be uncertain as to what the effects of one have been by comparison with the other. The effects of political adjustments cannot be specified in terms of lbs. weight, and rarely can be specified definitely in terms of £s of profit or loss or other numerical measures. The individual is left to read general effects as well as he can, when often they are of a type which is difficult to observe correctly, and rarely will he feel that he knows accurately what they have been. When he tries to communicate such knowledge as he has to others, he is unlikely to succeed beyond the first few steps; he cannot specify effects in numerical terms, and his listeners, relying on their own experience of similar instances, may believe that his reading of experience has been mistaken. Beyond that, the milieu in which any proposed changes have to be introduced will be different from the old; and the old ingredients in a new medium might give rise to different effects from those of the past, even if it had been possible to specify these effects correctly and in a way which was accepted as true by all. The facts of political technology, therefore, are much more elusive and less knowable than some of the facts of economic technology.

But the line of demarcation between Politics and Economics is not hard and fast. In economics, too, some facts are difficult to specify and can only be guessed at. If, for example, the proposal is to establish a factory to manufacture a certain good, the costs of manufacture, the quantity of sales and the price of the product will all be uncertain; and if it is a joint enterprise to be undertaken by several people, each person concerned will entertain a different expectation of the outcome, the view taken by each being dependent on his past experience, his intellectual or imaginative abilities and on the degree of optimism of his temperament. The facts lie in the future and must be guessed at: many events which will be of vital importance to the success of the enterprise can only be visualised dimly, if at all. Each person must exercise his choice in a realm in which he can have an opinion as to what the alternatives are as between which he can choose, but he has no definite knowledge of these alternatives. While, therefore, there is often a greater certitude attaching to economic judgments than to political, this is not always the case. There is a difference in the degree of knowledge of the outcome of the various lines of action which might be chosen, this knowledge often being greater in economics than in politics; but there is no difference in principle between the economic and political estimates which people must make. Technological factors play the same role in the formation of preference schedules in both economic and political choice; and both Economics and Politics leave these factors to be discussed outside the pure science which deals with the subject. In either case, for the pure science it is enough that we represent the individual by his schedule of preferences.

Apart from the schedule of preferences, the other main instrument in the two sciences is the conception of equilibrium.

In Economics, from the time of Adam Smith onwards, the question asked has been: What are the characteristics of economic equilibrium in the particular case concerned? Even in asking the question which the science is an attempt to answer, it is presupposed that a concept of equilibrium has been, or can be, found.

In Politics the question which should be asked, so far as I can see, is: What are the characteristics of political equilibrium in particular cases? Or, more exactly: What characteristics of political adjustment can be formulated in terms of a theory of relative valuation and in terms of a concept of equilibrium? If this really is the problem with which the science is concerned, it becomes apparent that the whole nature of Political Science derives from the question asked. But this question is only a minor modification of that asked by Economics; and the answer to it would plainly be the same in kind as that given by Economics. To the extent that we accept this as a satisfactory statement of the problem with which Politics deals, we will expect Political Science and Economic Science to share a common nature; for the nature of a science is predetermined by the question to which it is an answer, and both Politics and Economics seek to answer practically the same question.

It might, of course, have been true that the conceptions of equilibrium in the two sciences were significantly different. After all, equilibrium in Physics or Chemistry means something very different from what it does in Economics.

Let us examine the matter. In Economics, although the conception has been differently treated by different authors, always the underlying idea has been that equilibrium results from the equality of demand and supply.

In Political Science the motions before a committee stand in some definite order on the scales of preferences of the members. Equilibrium will be reached through one motion being selected as the decision of the committee by means of voting. The impelling force towards having one particular motion selected will be the degree to which the members' schedules, taken as a group, rank it higher than the others. The barriers to its selection will be of two kinds. On the one hand, there is the degree to which the group ranks other motions as high as, or higher than, the motion concerned. And on the other, there is the particular form of committee procedure in use; and it can be shown that with a given group of schedules, one procedure will select one motion, while another procedure will select another. If so, equilibrium in Politics is "the resultant of tastes and obstacles"; and these are the words Pareto used of equilibrium in Economics.

Thus each science uses a different definition of equilibrium; but the underlying conceptions are the same in kind. The position is that we get from the one science to the other by the change of a single definition.

This provides us with a criterion to distinguish between economic and political material. If the pure theory appropriate to the case makes use of preference schedules, the phenomena will be either economic or political. If the definition of equilibrium employed relates to equality of demand and supply, the phenomena will be economic in nature; if it relates to equilibrium attained by means of voting, they will be political.

In both sciences the fundamental requisite is to give an account of the relations which, *in conditions of equilibrium*, necessarily hold between the elements; and in both the most general type of theory would be formulated in terms of Mathematics. This has its disadvantages, but it is only by mathematical logic that we are able to deal with a number of interdependent variables, each influencing and being influenced by the others. To begin with, however, progress in the formation of a Science of Politics is likely to take the form of a number of studies in "partial analysis." This would employ only two or three variables, and would be expressible in terms of Geometry.

As in Economics, it would be possible, at least in principle, to fit *data* from actual situations to the theory obtained; and correspondence of the conclusions of the theory with political reality could be tested for empirically.

The pure theory would enable us to work out the effects of any given change in the political circumstances. The initial state of equilibrium, before the change was introduced, would be examined, and when the *data* had been altered so as to incorporate the given change, the new state of equilibrium would be examined. The set of differences between these two states of equilibrium would give the effects of the assumed political change. Here, it must be added, the effects of any given change might be very different according to the context into which it had been introduced. Sometimes a small change in the *data* might give rise to far-reaching changes in the final state of equilibrium; at other times a considerable change in the *data* could be introduced with little or no effect on the resulting equilibrium. The method by which the effects of such political changes would be traced is that familiar in Economics as the method of comparative statics.

Reasoning throughout both sciences, therefore, seems to me to be nothing short of identical in kind, and we draw the conclusion that Economics and Politics really form two branches of the same subject. Each relates to choosing of some kind, and it might seem that a suitable title for the subject that includes both would be the Theory of Choices; but if such a title were used, too much would be brought under it: Ethics, in one aspect, is a theory of choice, and the Theory of Permutations and part of the Theory of Probability is again a theory of choice. On these grounds it would seem preferable to refer to the wider subject, which includes both Economics and Politics, as being the Theory of Economic and Political Choices.

7

Games against nature

JOHN MILNOR

This paper is the most mathematical of the selection presented here. It is nevertheless not inordinately difficult to read and is an excellent introduction to the axiomatic method. Many different criteria for dealing with uncertainty are suggested and examined. They are applied to several examples, and an analysis of the logical implications of the various criteria is given.

Introduction

The object of this paper will be to study games of the following type. A matrix (a_{ij}) is given in which a player must choose a row. A column will be chosen by "Nature," a fictitious player having no known objective and no known strategy. The payoff

The preparation of this paper was sponsored in part by the RAND Corporation. The author was a National Science Foundation fellow during 1952–53. Reprinted by courtesy of John Milnor and John Wiley and Sons from *Games against Nature* in R. M. Thrall, C. H. Coombs, and R. L. Davis (eds.), *Decision Processes* pp. 49–59.

to the player will then be given by the entry in that particular row and column. This entry should represent a numerical utility in the sense of von Neumann and Morgenstern.

It will be shown that several known criteria for playing such games can be characterized by simple axioms. An axiomatic procedure will also be used to criticise these criteria, and to study the possibilities for other criteria.

(Our basic assumption that the player has absolutely no information about Nature may seem too restrictive. However such no-information games may be used as a normal form for a wider class of games in which certain types of partial information are allowed. For example, if the information consists of bounds for the probabilities of the various states of Nature, then by considering only those mixed strategies for Nature which satisfy these bounds, we construct a new game having no information. Unfortunately in practice partial information often occurs in vague, non-mathematical forms which are difficult to handle.)

The following criteria have been suggested for such games against Nature.

Laplace. If the probabilities of the different possible states of Nature are unknown, we should assume that they are all equal. Thus if the player chooses the ith row, his expectation is given by the average $(a_{i1} + \cdots + a_{in})/n$, and he should choose a row for which this average is maximized.

Wald [4] (Minimax Principle). If the player chooses the ith row, then his payoff will certainly be at least $\min_{j} a_{ij}$. The safest possible course of action is therefore to choose a row for which $\min_{j} a_{ij}$ is maximized. This corresponds to the pessimistic hypothesis of expecting the worst.

If mixed strategies for the player are also allowed, then this criterion should be formulated as follows. Choose a probability mixture $(\xi_1, \ldots, \xi_m)$ of the rows so that the quantity $\min_{j} (\xi_1 a_{1j} + \cdots + \xi_m a_{mj})$ is maximized. In other words play as if Nature were the opposing player in a zero sum game.

Hurwicz.[1] Select a constant $0 \le \alpha \le 1$ which measures the player's optimism. For each row [or probability mixture of rows] let a denote the smallest component and A the largest. Choose a row [or probability mixture of rows] for which $\alpha A + (1 - \alpha)a$ is maximized. For $\alpha = 0$ this reduces to the Wald criterion.

Savage [2] (Minimax Regret). Define the (negative) regret matrix (r_{ij}) by $r_{ij} = a_{ij} - \max_k a_{kj}$. Thus r_{ij} measures the difference between the payoff which actually is obtained and the payoff which could have been obtained if the true state of Nature had been known. Now apply the Wald criterion to the matrix (r_{ij}). That is choose a row [or mixture of rows] for which $\min_j r_{ij}$ [or $\min_j (\xi_1 r_{1j} + \cdots + \xi_m r_{mj})$] is maximized.

These four criteria are certainly different. This is illustrated by the following example, where the preferred row under each criterion is indicated.

$$\begin{pmatrix} 2 & 2 & 0 & 1 \\ 1 & 1 & 1 & 1 \\ 0 & 4 & 0 & 0 \\ 1 & 3 & 0 & 0 \end{pmatrix} \begin{matrix} \text{Laplace} \\ \text{Wald} \\ \text{Hurwicz (for } \alpha > \tfrac{1}{4}) \\ \text{Savage} \end{matrix}$$

Axiomatic Characterization of Criteria

In this section we will consider criteria which assign to each matrix (a_{ij}) a preference relation $\gtrsim$ between pairs of rows[2] of the matrix. It will be shown that each of the four criteria of 1 is characterized by certain of the following axioms. The first five axioms are compatible with all four criteria.

---

[1] Suggested by L. Hurwicz in an unpublished paper.

[2] For simplicity, only pure strategies for the player are considered in this section. However the results can easily be generalized to the (more natural) case where mixed strategies are allowed.

1. *Ordering.* The relation $\gtrsim$ is a complete ordering of the rows. That is, it is a transitive relation, such that for any two rows r, r' either $r \gtrsim r'$ or $r' \gtrsim r$.

2. *Symmetry.* This ordering is independent of the numbering of the rows and columns. (Thus we are not considering situations where there is any reason to expect one state of Nature more than another.)

3. *Strong domination.* If each component of r is greater than the corresponding component of r', then $r > r'$ (shorthand for: $r \gtrsim r'$ but not $r' \gtrsim r$).

4. *Continuity.* If the matrices $a_{ij}^{(k)}$ converge to a_{ij}, and if $r^{(k)} > r_1^{(k)}$ for each k, then the limit rows r and r_1 satisfy $r \gtrsim r_1$.

5. *Linearity.* The ordering relation is not changed if the matrix (a_{ij}) is replaced by (a_{ij}') where $a_{ij}' = \lambda a_{ij} + \mu$, $\lambda > 0$.

The following four axioms serve to distinguish between the four criteria.

6. *Row adjunction.* The ordering between the old rows is not changed by the adjunction of a new row.

7. *Column linearity.* The ordering is not changed if a constant is added to a column.

(This can be interpreted as an assertion that Nature has no prejudices for or against the player. It also asserts that the utility is linear, not only with respect to known probabilities but also with respect to unknown probabilities of the type under consideration.)

8. *Column duplication.* The ordering is not changed if a new column, identical with some old column, is adjoined to the matrix. (Thus we are only interested in what states of Nature are possible, and not in how often each state may have been counted in the formation of the matrix.)

9. *Convexity.* If row r is equal to the average $\frac{1}{2}(r' + r'')$ of two equivalent rows, then $r \gtrsim r'$. (Two rows are *equivalent*, $r' \sim r''$, if $r' \gtrsim r''$ and $r'' \gtrsim r'$. This axiom asserts that the player is not prejudiced against randomizing. If two rows are equally favor-

able, then he does not mind tossing a coin to decide between them.)

Finally we will need a modified form of axiom 6 which is compatible with all four criteria.

10. *Special row adjunction.* The ordering between the old rows is not changed by the adjunction of a new row, providing that no component of this new row is greater than the corresponding components of all old rows.

The principal results of this section are all incorporated in the following diagram, which describes the relations between the ten

	Laplace	Wald	Hurwicz	Savage
1. Ordering	☒	☒	☒	☒
2. Symmetry	☒	☒	☒	☒
3. Str. Domination	☒	☒	☒	☒
4. Continuity	X	☒	☒	☒
5. Linearity	X	X	☒	X
6. Row adjunction	☒	☒	☒	
7. Col. linearity	☒			☒
8. Col. duplication		☒	☒	☒
9. Convexity	X	☒		☒
10. Special Row adj.	X	X	X	☒

Diagram 1. X = compatibility.
Each criterion is characterized by axioms marked ☒.

axioms and the four criteria. The symbol "X" indicates that the corresponding axiom and criterion are compatible. Each criterion is characterized by those axioms which are marked "☒."

THEOREM 1. The Laplace criterion is compatible with all of these axioms other than axiom 8; the Wald criterion with all but axiom 7; the Hurwicz criterion will all but 7 and 9; the Savage criterion with all but 6.

The proofs are all completely trivial. Perhaps the following two examples are of interest. In the first matrix the Hurwicz criterion (for $\alpha > 0$) is not compatible with axiom 9 (convexity).

In the second pair the Savage criterion is not compatible with axiom 6 (row adjunction).

$$\begin{pmatrix} 2 & 0 & 0 \\ 1 & 1 & 0 \\ 0 & 2 & 0 \end{pmatrix} \qquad \begin{pmatrix} 2 & 1 \\ 0 & 2 \end{pmatrix} \rightarrow \begin{pmatrix} 2 & 1 \\ 0 & 2 \\ 7 & 4 \end{pmatrix}$$

THEOREM 2. The Laplace criterion is characterized by axioms 1, 2, 3, 6, 7.

It is first necessary to prove the following.

LEMMA 1. Assuming axioms 1, 2, 6 (ordering, symmetry, row adjunction) two rows which differ only in the order of their components are equivalent.

Adjoin a sequence of intermediate rows so that two consecutive rows differ only by a permutation of two components. The result now follows by an application of the symmetry axiom to each pair of consecutive rows.

The proof of theorem 2 follows. Suppose that the average of the components of r equals the average of the components of r'. Alternately perform the following two operations on the matrix:

(a) Permute the elements of r and r' so that they are in order of increasing size. (Permissible by lemma 1, and axiom 6.)

(b) Subtract from each column the component in r or the component in r', whichever is smaller. (Permissible by axiom 7.) After a finite number of steps, all of the components of r and r' will be zero. It follows that $r \sim r'$.

Now using axioms 3 and 6 it follows that $r > r'$ whenever the average of the elements of r is greater than the average of the elements of r'. Thus the criterion is that of Laplace.

THEOREM 3. The Wald criterion is characterized by axioms 1, 2, 3, 4, 6, 8, 9.

Two lemmas are first necessary.

LEMMA 2. Assuming axions 3 and 4 (domination and continuity), if each component of r is greater than or equal to the corresponding component of r', then $r \gtrsim r'$.

The proof is clear.[3]

LEMMA 3. Assuming axions 1, 2, 3, 4, 6, 8, two rows which have the same minimum element and the same maximum element are equivalent.

Let $(a_1, \ldots, a_n)$ be any row having the minimum component a and the maximum component A. From lemmas 1 and 2 it follows that

$$(a, \ldots, a, A) \lesssim (a_1, \ldots, a_n) \lesssim (A, \ldots, A, a).$$

But $(a, \ldots, a, A)$ is equivalent to $(A, \ldots, A, a)$ since the matrix $\begin{pmatrix} a & \cdots & a & A \\ A & \cdots & A & a \end{pmatrix}$ can be obtained from the symmetrical matrix $\begin{pmatrix} a & A \\ A & a \end{pmatrix}$ by column duplication. Therefore any two rows having minimum element a and maximum element A are equivalent.

Proof of Theorem 3. By lemma 3 it is sufficient to consider pairs (a, A) with $a \leq A$ in place of rows. Applying the convexity axiom (9) to the matrix

$$\begin{pmatrix} a & \tfrac{1}{2}(a + A) & \tfrac{1}{2}(a + A) \\ a & a & A \\ a & A & a \end{pmatrix}$$

we have $(a, A) \lesssim (a, \tfrac{1}{2}(a + A))$. By repeated application of this rule, together with the continuity axiom, we have $(a, A) \lesssim (a, a)$, hence $(a, A) \sim (a, a)$. It follows easily that the criterion is that of Wald.

THEOREM 4. The Hurwicz criteria are characterized by axioms 1, 2, 3, 4, 5, 6, 8.

---

[3] Lemma 2 suggests the following criterion. Define $r \gtrsim r'$ if and only if each component of r is $\geq$ the corresponding component of r'. It may be shown that this criterion satisfies all axioms except 1, and is characterized by 2, 3, 4, 6, 7, 8, together with the transitivity portion of 1.

Again it suffices to consider pairs (a, A) with $a \le A$. Let α be the supremum of all numbers α' such that

$$(\alpha', \alpha') \lneqq (0, 1).$$

By the domination axiom it follows that $0 \le \alpha \le 1$. By continuity it follows that $(\alpha, \alpha) \sim (0, 1)$. By linearity

$$(\alpha A + (1 - \alpha)a, \alpha A + (1 - \alpha)a) \sim (a, A),$$

whenever $a < A$. It follows easily that the given criterion is just that criterion of Hurwicz which corresponds to the parameter value α.

THEOREM 5. The Savage criterion is characterized by axioms 1, 2, 3, 4, 7, 8, 9, 10.

A matrix will be called normalized if it contains a row r_0 consisting entirely of zeros, and if it contains no positive components. Any given matrix can be normalized by first subtracting the maximum element from each column, and then adjoining the row r_0. By axioms 7 and 10 these operations do not change the ordering relation between the old rows. In a normalized matrix we are free, by axiom 10, to adjoin any row which contains no positive elements and to delete any row other than r_0. The proof is now completely parallel to the proof of theorem 3. It is only necessary to require that all matrices considered be normalized.

Criticism of the Criteria

There is one fundamental principle which has not yet been mentioned: that of domination (or admissibility). One strategy is said to *dominate* another if it is just as good in all states of Nature and definitely better in at least one. It is natural to require that the following axiom be satisfied.

3′. If r dominates r', then $r > r'$

This axiom is not compatible with the criteria of Wald, Hurwicz, and Savage. Each of these criteria could be modified in a trivial way[4] so as to satisfy 3′, but the result would violate the equally fundamental axiom of continuity. This difficulty is illustrated by the following two examples.

EXAMPLE 1. Consider the family of matrices

$$\begin{pmatrix} 2 & 1 & 1 \\ 2 & 2 & k \end{pmatrix}$$

where $0 \leq k \leq 1$. Mixed strategies are to be allowed. In the case $k = 1$ the second row dominates the first. It is therefore natural to expect that the second row should be chosen exclusively for $k = 1$, and should be chosen with high probability for k close to 1. But according to the Wald and Hurwicz criteria ($\alpha < 1$) the first row should be chosen whenever $k < 1$. (Compare diagram 2). In this example the Savage criterion has the expected behavior, but in the following, more complicated, example, the Savage criterion is also unsatisfactory.

---

[4] Let r be preferred to r' (in the modified sense) if either $r > r'$ in the old sense (of Wald, Hurwicz, or Savage) or r dominates r'.

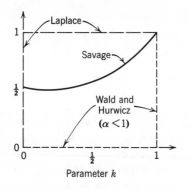 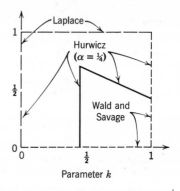

DIAGRAM 2. Probability of choosing second row (Example 1).

DIAGRAM 3. Probability of choosing last two rows (Example 2).

EXAMPLE 2.   Consider the matrices

$$\begin{pmatrix} 1 & 0 & 1 & 0 \\ 0 & 1 & 0 & 1 \\ 1 & 1 & k & 0 \\ 1 & 1 & 0 & k \end{pmatrix}$$

where $0 \leq k \leq 1$. For $k = 1$ the first two rows are dominated, yet according to the Wald and Savage criteria these two rows should be chosen exclusively whenever $k < 1$. (Compare diagram 3.) Only the Laplace criterion gives a satisfactory solution in this example.

The Laplace criterion has been successful under all of the tests which have been made of it, with the single exception of axiom 8 (column duplication). It appears that, if we are willing to sacrifice this axiom, then the Laplace criterion is definitely the best. However in many applications it is desirable to preserve axiom 8. This is particularly true in cases where there is no clear and natural separation of the possible states of Nature into a finite number of distinct alternatives.

Thus all of the criteria under consideration seem unsatisfactory in that they fail to satisfy certain rather basic axioms.

Possibilities for Other Criteria

It has become apparent that no possible criterion can have all of the properties that one would desire. It is therefore natural to try constructing a list of those properties which are most fundamental and important, to see if at least these can be satisfied. The following is the author's attempt to construct such a list. Others would doubtlessly have given rather different lists.

Let S denote the simplex of mixed strategies over the rows of the matrix.

1. To each matrix there corresponds a non-vacuous choice set C contained in S.

(The complete ordering of 2 really gave more information than was necessary.)

2. *Symmetry.* C does not depend on the numbering of the rows and columns.

3. *Domination.* Every element of C is undominated ($=$ admissible).

4. *Continuity.* If $a_{ij}^{(k)} \to a_{ij}$, $s^{(k)} \in C(a_{ij}^{(k)})$, and $s^{(k)} \to s$, then $s \in C(a_{ij})$.

5. *Row adjunction.* The choice set is not changed by the adjunction of a new row which is dominated by some old row. (Some stronger row adjunction axiom would be desirable, but at least this much seems indispensable.)

The following three axioms are also desirable, although not as basic as the first five.

6. *Column duplication.* C is not changed by the adjunction of a duplicate of some column.

7. *Column linearity.* C is not changed by the addition of a constant to a column.

8. *Convexity.* C is convex.

Evidently no criterion which has been mentioned so far satisfies all of these axioms.

THEOREM 6. There exist criteria which simultaneously satisfy the preceding eight axioms.

First consider the following slight modification of the Savage criterion. Let S be a convex polyhedron of mixed strategies for the player, and let $p_1, \ldots, p_n$ be linear payoff functions on S, corresponding to the n possible states of Nature. The negative regret is defined by $r_j(s, S) = p_j(s) - \max_{s' \in S} p_j(s')$. The Savage choice set $C(S)$ consists of the set of all strategies $s \in S$ for which $\min_j r_j(s, S)$ attains its maximum M. Instead we will consider the set $C_\epsilon(S)$ consisting of all $s \in S$ such that

$$\min_j r_j(s, S) \geq M - \epsilon.$$

The required criteria are now constructed as follows. Choose as parameters an infinite sequence of positive numbers $\epsilon_1, \epsilon_2, \ldots$ which converge to zero. Define the sets $S_0 \supset S_1 \supset \cdots$

by $S_0 = S$, $S_i = C_{\epsilon_i}(S_{i-1})$. As choice set $C_{(\epsilon_1, \epsilon_2, \ldots)}(S)$ we take the intersection of the S_i.

The axioms 1 through 8 may now be verified. The proofs will not be carried out, since they are rather involved (at least for domination and continuity). In any case these criteria are probably too difficult computationally to be of practical interest.

A further interesting property which is possessed by these criteria is the following. The n payoff functions are all constant on the choice set. Thus any two elements in the choice set are completely equivalent.

It is interesting to ask if there exist any simple, computable criteria which satisfy all of the preceding conditions.

part **3**

POLITICAL CHOICE, POWER, AND VOTING

8

Political and economic choice

KENNETH J. ARROW

The investigations of Arrow go far in the direction pointed out by Black. The politico-economic bases for a liberal democratic state are examined. Only the introduction on "The Types of Social Choice" is reproduced here. The book, however, contains an examination of the consistency of various social goals and choice systems. The problem which bedevils both economic theory and political science, the constitution of a value system for a society and its relation to individual values, is scrutinized. The reader is also recommended to read Chapter 14 on social choice in Luce and Raiffa's book.

In a capitalist democracy there are essentially two methods by which social choices can be made: voting, typically used to make "political" decisions, and the market mechanism, typically used to make "economic" decisions. In the emerging democracies with mixed economic systems, Great Britain, France, and Scandinavia, the same two modes of making social choices prevail, though more scope is given to the method of voting and decisions

---

From *Social Choice and Individual Values*, pp. 1–6. Reprinted with permission from Kenneth J. Arrow and John Wiley and Sons.

based directly or indirectly on it and less to the rule of the price mechanism. Elsewhere in the world, and even in smaller social units within the democracies, social decisions are sometimes made by single individuals or small groups and sometimes (more and more rarely in this modern world) by a widely encompassing set of traditional rules for making the social choice in any given situation, e.g., a religious code.

The last two methods of social choice, dictatorship and convention, have in their formal structure a certain definiteness absent from voting or the market mechanism. In ideal dictatorship there is but one will involved in choice, in an ideal society ruled by convention there is but the divine will or perhaps, by assumption, a common will of all individuals concerning social decisions, so in either case no conflict of individual wills is involved. The methods of voting and the market, on the other hand, are methods of amalgamating the tastes of many individuals in the making of social choices. The methods of dictatorship and convention are, or can be, rational in the sense that any individual can be rational in his choices. Can such consistency be attributed to collective modes of choice, where the wills of many people are involved?

It should be emphasized here that the present study is concerned only with the formal aspects of the above question. That is, we ask if it is formally possible to construct a procedure for passing from a set of known individual tastes to a pattern of social decision-making, the procedure in question being required to satisfy certain natural conditions. An illustration of the problem is the following well-known "paradox of voting." Suppose there is a community consisting of three voters, and this community must choose among three alternative modes of social action (e.g., disarmament, cold war, or hot war). It is expected that choices of this type have to be made repeatedly, but sometimes not all of the three alternatives will be available. In analogy with the usual utility analysis of the individual consumer under conditions of constant wants and variable price-income situations, rational behavior on the part of the community would mean that the community orders the three alternatives according to its collective preferences once for all, and then chooses in any given case that alternative among those actually available which stands highest on this list. A natural way of arriving at the collective preference scale would be to say that one alternative is preferred to another if a majority of the community prefer the first alternative to the second, i.e., would choose the first over the second if those were the only two alternatives. Let A, B, and C be the three alternatives, and 1, 2, and 3 the three individuals. Suppose individual 1 prefers A to B and B to C (and therefore A to C), individual 2 prefers B to C and C to A (and therefore B to A), and individual 3 prefers C to A and A to B (and therefore C to B). Then a majority prefer A to B, and a majority prefer B to C. If the community is to be regarded as behaving rationally, we are forced to say that A is preferred to C. But in fact a majority of the community prefer C to A. So the method just outlined for passing from individual to collective tastes fails to satisfy the condition of rationality, as we ordinarily understand it. Can we find other methods of aggregating individual tastes which imply rational behavior on the part of the community and which will be satisfactory in other ways?

If we continue the traditional identification of rationality with maximization of some sort (to be discussed at greater length below), then the problem of achieving a social maximum derived from individual desires is precisely the problem which has been central to the field of welfare economics. There is no need to review the history of this subject in detail. There has been controversy as to whether or not the economist *qua* economist could make statements saying that one social state is better than another. If we admit meaning to interpersonal comparisons of utility, then presumably we could order social states according to the sum of the utilities of individuals under each, and this is the solution of Jeremy Bentham, accepted by Edgeworth and Marshall. Even in this case we have a choice of different mathematical forms of the social utility functions in terms of individual utilities; thus, the social utility might be the sum of the individual utilities or their product or the product of their logarithms or the sum of their products taken two at a time. So, as Professor Bergson has pointed out, there are value judgements implicit even at this level. The case is clearly much worse if we deny the possibility of making interpersonal comparisons of utility. It was on the latter grounds that Professor Robbins so strongly attacked the concept that economists could make any policy recommendations, at least without losing their status as economists and passing over into the realm of ethics. On the other hand, Mr. Kaldor and, following him, Professor Hicks have argued that there is a meaningful sense in which we can say that one state is better than another from an economic point of view, even without assuming the reality of interpersonal comparison of utilities. The particular mechanism by which they propose to accomplish the comparison of different social states, the compensation principle, [has been] examined . . .

The controversy involves a certain confusion between two levels of argument. There can be no doubt that, even if interpersonal comparison is assumed, a value judgment is implied in any given way of making social choices based on individual utilities; so much Bergson has shown clearly. But, given these basic value judgments as to the mode of aggregating individual desires, the economist should investigate those mechanisms for social choice which satisfy the value judgments and should check their consequences to see if still other value judgments might be violated. In particular, he should ask the question whether or not the value judgements are consistent with each other, i.e., do there exist any mechanisms of social choice which will in fact satisfy the value judgments made? For example, in the voting paradox discussed above, if the method of majority choice is regarded as itself a value judgment, then we are forced to the conclusion that the value judgment in question, applied to the particular situation indicated, is self-contradictory.

In the matter of consistency, the question of interpersonal comparison of utilities becomes important. Bergson considers it possible to establish an ordering of social states which is based on indifference maps of individuals, and Samuelson has agreed. On the other hand, Professor Lange, in his discussion of the social welfare function, has assumed the interpersonal measurability of utility, and elsewhere he has insisted on the absolute necessity of measurable utility for normative social judgments. Professor Lerner similarly has assumed the meaningfulness of an interpersonal comparison of intensities of utility in his recent work on welfare economics.

In the following discussion of the consistency of various value judgments as to the mode of social choice, the distinction between voting and the market mechanism will be disregarded, both being regarded as special cases of the more general category of collective social choice. The analogy between economic choice and political choice has been pointed out a number of times. For example, Professor Zassenhaus considered the structure of a planned economy by considering the free market replaced by influence conceived generally as a means of distributing the social product. He argued that, under conditions analogous to free competition, the market for exchanging influence for goods would come to equilibrium in a manner analogous to that of the ordinary market, political influence taking the place of initial distribution of goods. His model, however, is expressed only in very general terms, and it is not easy to see how it would operate in a socialist democracy, for example.

Dr. Howard Bowen has considered voting as the demand for collective consumption. In his treatment he regards distribution of income and costs as given, and other simplifying assumptions are made. Close analogies are found with the ordinary market demand curve.

Knight has also stressed the analogy between voting and the market in that both involve collective choice among a limited range of alternatives. He has also stressed certain differences, particularly that there is likely to be a greater tendency towards inequality under voting than under the market; these differences are, however, largely of a socio-psychological type rather than of the formal type which alone is relevant here.

More recently, there has been a series of papers by Professor Duncan Black, dealing with various aspects of the theory of political choice under certain special assumptions and emphasizing the close similarity between the problems of market and electoral choice. . . . There is also a literature on the technical problems of election. The chief relevant point here is that virtually every particular scheme proposed for election from single-member constituencies has been shown to have certain arbitrary features.

The problem of choosing by election one among a number of candidates for a single position, such as the Presidency of the United States or membership in a legislative body when each district returns only a single member, is clearly of the same character as choosing one out of a number of alternative social policies; indeed, selection among candidates is presumably a device for achieving selection among policies.

9

A method for evaluating the distribution of power in a committee system

L. S. SHAPLEY AND MARTIN SHUBIK

The word "power," unfortunately, has many connotations and overtones. When the authors wrote this piece, they were well aware that the index they were suggesting, though possibly of certain theoretical interest, reflected only one facet of the properties of power. Possibly a better name for the article would have been "A Method for Evaluating the a Priori Voting Strength in a Committee System."

In the following paper we offer a method for the *a priori* evaluation of the division of power among the various bodies and members of a legislature or committee system. The method is based on a technique of the mathematical theory of games, applied to what are known there as "simple games" and "weighted majority games." We apply it here to a number of illustrative cases, including the United States Congress, and discuss some of its formal properties.

Reprinted with permission from the authors and the American Political Science Association, from the *American Political Science Review*, **48**, 1954, 787–792.

The designing of the size and type of a legislative body is a process that may continue for many years, with frequent revisions and modifications aimed at reflecting changes in the social structure of the country; we may cite the role of the House of Lords in England as an example. The effect of a revision usually cannot be gauged in advance except in the roughest terms; it can easily happen that the mathematical structure of a voting system conceals a bias in power distribution unsuspected and unintended by the authors of the revision. How, for example, is one to predict the degree of protection which a proposed system affords to minority interests? Can a consistent criterion for "fair representation" be found? It is difficult even to *describe* the net effect of a double representation system such as is found in the U. S. Congress (i.e., by states and by population), without attempting to deduce it *a priori*. The method of measuring "power" which we present in this paper is intended as a first step in the attack on these problems.

Our definition of the power of an individual member depends on the chance he has of being critical to the success of a winning coalition. It is easy to see, for example, that the chairman of a board consisting of an even number of members (including himself) has no power if he is allowed to vote only to break ties. Of course he may have prestige and moral influence and will even probably get to vote when someone is not present. However, in the narrow and abstract model of the board he is without power. If the board consists of an odd number of members, then he has exactly as much power as any ordinary member because his vote is "pivotal"—i.e., turns a possible defeat into a success—as often as the vote of any other member. Admittedly he may not cast his vote as often as the others, but much of the voting done by them is not necessary to ensure victory (though perhaps useful for publicity or other purposes). If a coalition has a majority, then extra votes do not change the outcome. For any vote, only a minimal winning coalition is necessary.

Put in crude economic terms, the above implies that if votes of senators were for sale, it might be worthwhile buying forty-nine of them, but the market value of the fiftieth (to the same customer) would be zero. It is possible to buy votes in most corporations by purchasing common stock. If their policies are entirely controlled by simple majority votes, then there is no more power to be gained after one share more than 50% has been acquired.

Let us consider the following scheme: There is a group of individuals all willing to vote for some bill. They vote in order. As soon as a majority has voted for it, it is declared passed, and the member who voted last is given credit for having passed it. Let us choose the voting order of the members randomly. Then we may compute the frequency with which an individual belongs to the group whose votes are used and, of more importance, we may compute how often he is *pivotal*. This latter number serves to give us our index. It measures the number of times that the action of the individual actually changes the state of affairs. A simple consequence of this formal scheme is that where all voters have the same number of votes, they will each be credited with $1/n$th of the power, there being n participants. If they have different numbers of votes (as in the case of stockholders of a corporation), the result is more complicated; more votes mean more power, as measured by our index, but not in direct proportion (see below).

Of course, the actual balloting procedure used will in all probability be quite different from the above. The "voting" of the formal scheme might better be thought of as declarations of support for the bill, and the randomly chosen order of voting as an indication of the relative degrees of support by the different members, with the most enthusiastic members "voting" first, etc. The *pivot* is then the last member whose support is needed in order for passage of the bill to be assured.

Analyzing a committee chairman's tie-breaking function in this light, we see that in an *odd* committee he is pivotal as often as an ordinary member, but in an *even* committee he is never pivotal. However, when the number of members is large, it may sometimes be better to modify the strict interpretation of the formal system, and say that the number of members in attendance is about as likely to be even as odd. The chairman's index would then be just half that of an ordinary member. Thus, in the U.S. Senate the power index of the presiding officer is—strictly—equal to $\frac{1}{97}$. Under the modified scheme it is $\frac{1}{193}$. (But it is zero under either interpretation when we are considering decisions requiring a two-thirds majority, since ties cannot occur on such votes.) Recent history shows that the "strict" model may sometimes be the more realistic: in the present Senate (1953–54) the tie-breaking power of the Vice President, stemming from the fact that 96 is an even number, has been a very significant factor. However, in the passage of ordinary legislation, where perfect attendance is unlikely even for important issues, the modified scheme is probably more appropriate.

For Congress as a whole we have to consider three separate bodies which influence the fate of legislation. It takes majorities of Senate and House, with the President, or two-thirds majorities of Senate and House without the President, to enact a bill. We take all the members of the three bodies and consider them voting[1] for the bill in every possible order. In each order we observe the relative positions of the straight-majority pivotal men in the House and Senate, the President, and also the $\frac{2}{3}$-majority pivotal men in House and Senate. One of these five individuals will be the pivot for the whole vote, depending on the order in which they appear. For example, if the President comes after the two straight-majority pivots, but before one or both of the $\frac{2}{3}$-majority pivots, then he gets credit for the passage of the bill. The frequency of this case, if we consider all possible orders (of the 533 individuals involved), turns out to be very nearly $\frac{1}{6}$. This is the President's power index. (The calculation of this value and the following is quite complicated, and we shall not give it here.) The values for the House as a whole and for the Senate as a whole are both equal to $\frac{5}{12}$, approximately. The individual members of each chamber share these amounts equally, with the exception of the presiding officers. Under our "modified" scheme they each get about 30% of the power of an ordinary member; under the "strict" scheme, about 60%. In brief, then, the power indices for the three bodies are in the proportion $5:5:2$. The indices for

---

[1] In the formal sense described above.

a *single* congressman, a *single* senator, and the President are in the proportion $2:9:350$.

In a multicameral system such as we have just investigated, it is obviously easier to defeat a measure than to pass it.[2] A coalition of senators, sufficiently numerous, can block passage of any bill. But they cannot push through a bill of their own without help from the other chamber. This suggests that our analysis so far has been incomplete—that we need an index of "blocking power" to supplement the index already defined. To this end, we could set up a formal scheme similar to the previous one, namely: arrange the individuals in all possible orders and imagine them casting *negative* votes. In each arrangement, determine the person whose vote finally defeats the measure and give him credit for the block. Then the "blocking power" index for each person would be the relative number of times that he was the "blocker."

Now it is a remarkable fact that the new index is exactly equal to the index of our original definition. We can even make a stronger assertion: *any scheme for imputing power among the members of a committee system either yields the power index defined above or leads to a logical inconsistency.* A proof, or even a precise formulation, of this assertion would involve us too deeply in mathematical symbolism for the purposes of the present paper.[3] But we can conclude that the scheme we have been using (arranging the individuals in all possible orders, etc.) is just a convenient conceptual device; the indices which emerge are not peculiar to that device but represent a basic element of the committee system itself.

We now summarize some of the general properties of the power

---

[2] This statement can be put into numerical form without difficulty, to give a quantitative description of the "efficiency" of a legislature.

[3] The mathematical formulation and proof are given in L. S. Shapley, "A Value for *N*-Person Games," *Annals of Mathematics Study, No. 28*, Princeton, 1953, pp. 307–17. Briefly stated, any alternative imputation scheme would conflict with either *symmetry* (equal power indices for members in equal positions under the rules) or *additivity* (power distribution in a committee system composed of two strictly independent parts the same as the power distributions obtained by evaluating the parts separately).

index. In pure *bi*cameral systems using simple majority votes, each chamber gets 50% of the power (as it turns out), regardless of the relative sizes. With more than two chambers, power varies inversely with size: the smallest body is most powerful, etc. But no chamber is completely powerless, and no chamber holds more than 50% of the power. To illustrate, take Congress without the provision for overriding the President's veto by means of two-thirds majorities. This is now a pure tricameral system with chamber sizes of 1, 97, and 435. The values come out to be slightly under 50% for the President, and approximately 25% each for the Senate and House, with the House slightly less than the Senate. The exact calculation of this case is quite difficult because of the large numbers involved. An easier example is obtained by taking the chamber sizes as 1, 3, and 5. Then the division of power is in the proportions 32:27:25. The calculation is reproduced at the end of this paper.

The power division in a multicameral system also depends on the type of majority required to pass a bill. Raising the majority in *one* chamber (say from one-half to two-thirds) increases the relative power of that chamber.[4] Raising the required majority in all chambers simultaneously weakens the smaller house or houses at the expense of the larger. In the extreme case, where unanimity is required in every house, each individual in the whole legislature has what amounts to a veto, and is just as powerful as any other individual. The power index of each chamber is therefore directly proportional to its size.

We may examine this effect further by considering a system consisting of a governor and a council. Both the governor and some specified fraction of the council have to approve a bill before it can pass. Suppose first that council approval has to be unanimous. Then (as we saw above) the governor has no more power than the typical councilman. The bicameral power division is in the ratio $1:N$, if we take N to be the number of councilmen. If a

---

[4] As a general rule, if one component of a committee system (in which approval of all components is required) is made less "efficient"—i.e., more susceptible to blocking maneuvers—then its share of the total power will increase.

simple majority rule is adopted, then the ratio becomes $1:1$ between governor and council. That is, the governor has N times the power of a councilman. Now suppose that the approval of only one member of the council is required. This means that an individual councilman has very little chance of being pivotal. In fact the power division turns out to be $N:1$ in favor of the governor.[5] If votes were for sale, we might now expect the governor's price to be N^2 times as high as the average councilman's.

Several other examples of power distribution may be given. The indices reveal the decisive nature of the veto power in the United Nations Security Council. The Council consists of eleven members, five of whom have vetoes. For a substantive resolution to pass, there must be seven affirmative votes and no vetoes. Our power evaluation gives $\frac{76}{77}$ or 98.7% to the "Big Five" and $\frac{1}{77}$ or 1.3% to the remaining six members. Individually, the members of the "Big Five" enjoy a better than 90 to 1 advantage over the others.

It is well known that usually only a small fraction of the stock is required to keep control of a corporation. The group in power is usually able to muster enough proxies to maintain its position. Even if this were not so, the power of stockholders is not directly proportional to their holding, but is usually biased in favor of a large interest. Consider one man holding 40% of a stock while the remaining 60% is scattered among 600 small shareholders, with 0.1% each. The power index of the large holder is 66.6%, whereas for the small holders it is less than 0.06% apiece. The $400:1$ ratio in holdings produces a power advantage of better than $1000:1$.[6]

The preceding was an example of a "weighted majority game."

---

[5] In the general case the proportion is $N - M + 1:M$, where M stands for the number of councilmen required for passage.

[6] If there are two or more large interests, the power distribution depends in a fairly complicated way on the sizes of the large interests. Generally speaking, however, the small holders are better off than in the previous case. If there are two big interests, equal in size, then the small holders actually have an advantage over the large holders, on a power per share basis. This suggests that such a situation is highly unstable.

Another example is provided by a board with five members, one of whom casts two extra votes. If a simple majority (four out of seven votes) carries the day, then power is distributed 60% to the multivote member, 10% to each of the others. To see this, observe that there are five possible positions for the strong man, if we arrange the members in order at random. In three of these positions he is pivotal. Hence his index is equal to $\frac{3}{5}$. (Similarly, in the preceding example, we may compute that the strong man is pivotal 400 times out of 601.)

* * *

The values in the examples given above do not take into account any of the sociological or political superstructure that almost invariably exists in a legislature or policy board. They were not intended to be a representation of present day "reality." It would be foolish to expect to be able to catch all the subtle shades and nuances of custom and procedure that are to be found in most real decision-making bodies. Nevertheless, the power index computations may be useful in the setting up of norms or standards, the departure from which will serve as a measure of, for example, political solidarity, or regional or sociological factionalism, in an assembly. To do this we need an empirical power index, to compare with the theoretical. One possibility is as follows: The voting record of an individual is taken. He is given no credit for being on the losing side of a vote. If he is on the winning side, when no others voted with him, then he is awarded the probability of his having been the pivot (or blocker, in the case of a defeated motion), which is $1/n + 1$. His probabilities are then averaged over all votes. It can be shown that this measure gives more weight than the norm does to uncommitted members who hold the "balance of power" between extreme factions. For example, in a nine-man committee which contains two four-man factions which always oppose each other, the lone uncommitted member will always be on the winning side, and will have an observed index of $\frac{1}{5}$, compared to the theoretical value of $\frac{1}{9}$.

A difficulty in the application of the above measures is the problem of finding the correct weights to attach to the different issues. Obviously it would not be proper to take a uniform average over all votes, since there is bound to be a wide disparity in the importance of issues brought to a vote. Again, in a multicameral legislature (or in any more complicated system), many important issues may be decided without every member having had an opportunity to go on record with his stand. There are many other practical difficulties in the way of direct applications of the type mentioned. Yet the power index appears to offer useful information concerning the basic design of legislative assemblies and policy-making boards.

* * *

Appendix

The evaluation of the power distribution for a tricameral legislature with houses of 1, 3, and 5 members is given below:

There are 504 arrangements of five X's, three O's, and one ϕ, all equally likely if the nine items are ordered at random. In the following tabulation, the numbers indicate the number of permutations of predecessors ( ) and successors [ ] of the final pivot, marked with an asterisk. The dots indicate the pivots of the three separate houses.

$$
\begin{array}{l}
\text{O } \dot{\text{O}} \text{ O X X } \phi \text{ } \dot{\text{X}} \text{ X X} \\
\quad (60) \qquad * \quad [1] \\
\text{O } \dot{\text{O}} \text{ X X } \phi \text{ } \dot{\text{X}} \text{ O X X} \\
\quad (30) \qquad * \quad [3]
\end{array}
\left.\begin{array}{l} \\ \\ \\ \\ \end{array}\right\} \begin{array}{l} 150 \text{ pivots} \\ \text{for X} \end{array}
$$

$$
\begin{array}{l}
\text{O X X } \dot{\text{X}} \text{ X X } \phi \text{ } \dot{\text{O}} \text{ O} \\
\quad (42) \qquad\qquad * \quad [1] \\
\text{O X X } \dot{\text{X}} \text{ X } \phi \text{ } \dot{\text{O}} \text{ O X} \\
\quad (30) \qquad\quad * \quad [2] \\
\text{O X X } \dot{\text{X}} \text{ } \phi \text{ } \dot{\text{O}} \text{ O X X} \\
\quad (20) \qquad * \qquad [3]
\end{array}
\left.\begin{array}{l} \\ \\ \\ \\ \\ \end{array}\right\} \begin{array}{l} 162 \text{ pivots} \\ \text{for O} \end{array}
$$

O O O X X Ẋ X X φ
(56)   *

O Ȯ O X X Ẋ X φ X
(35)   * [1]

O Ȯ O X X Ẋ φ X X
(20)   *   [1]

O Ȯ X X Ẋ X X φ O
(21)   * [1]

O Ȯ X X Ẋ X φ O X
(15)   *   [2]

O Ȯ X X Ẋ φ O X X
(12)   *   [3]

} 192 pivots for φ

Power indices for the houses are $\frac{192}{504}$, $\frac{162}{504}$, and $\frac{150}{504}$, and hence are in the proportion $32:27:25$, with the smallest house the strongest. Powers of the individual members are as $32:9:9:9:5:5:5:5:5$.

10

The a priori voting
strength of the electoral college

IRWIN MANN AND L. S. SHAPLEY

When the concept of "power index" for an n-person game was first suggested, it was natural to apply the idea to an example taken from the real world. One such situation at hand which had the right combination of elements of interest was the Electoral College. But the size of the computation was somewhat beyond feasibility. The first excerpt given here shows an attempt to obtain the answers by a computer technique of approximation known as the montecarlo method. Some years later, a mathematical idea, quite independent of machine technology, resulted in the computation becoming entirely possible. In fact, the computing time is not more than two minutes on existing machines. The later paper with the exact calculation is also excerpted. These papers illustrate the possibility of making investigations in depth of models of political processes. Admittedly, it can be argued that the basic assumptions behind the model are simple; yet, the analysis is sophisticated and provides insights which would have been difficult or impossible to obtain in other ways.

From "Values of Large Games IV: Evaluating the Electoral College by Montecarlo Techniques," RAND RM 2651, September 19, 1960, and RM 3158, May 1962. Reprinted with permission of the authors and the RAND corporation.

Introduction[1]

. . . The game considered here is based on a well-known real institution—the Electoral College of the United States—which presents an attractive object for investigation for several reasons. In the first place it is topical. Two new states have recently been admitted to the Union, a Presidential election is imminent, and the regular decennial reapportionment of electoral votes is due next year. The general interest in these events would seem to imply at least a latent interest in the formal structure that underlies them.

On the technical side, the Electoral College game poses a challenge by its very size. It has twice as many players (50) as the next largest games of its kind that have ever been solved numerically. The "montecarlo" method seems to offer the only feasible way to a solution; even then, some ingenuity must be exercised to keep the amount of computer time required within acceptable bounds, and the results that are obtained are only approximate. The various techniques and shortcuts devised for this particular problem are quite general in nature. Thus, game theory apart, the example of this paper provides a nice illustration of some relatively sophisticated montecarlo techniques in action.

From the standpoint of game theory, the Electoral College problem permits us to exercise our intuition as well as our arithmetical abilities. The structure of the game is both familiar and transparent, but the solution is nontrivial. Reasoning directly from the voting rules we can arrive at some general conclusions and some plausible hypotheses about the distribution of power among the players, but it remains for the actual numerical results to confirm or refute the guesses and to fill in the details. Our present approximations are none too good, and many details of the solution are still unclear. We believe, however, that a study of our results will afford some insight into the mathematical and game—theoretical ramifications of the "power index" idea, as applied to large political games. . . .

---

[1] From "Values of Large Games IV," RAND RM 2651, September 19, 1960.

The Electoral College as a
Weighted Majority Game

The rules of the game are very simple. The fifty states are the players, and each one has a certain number of votes to cast for the candidate of its choice. There are 537 votes in all at the present time; the apportionment is tabulated in the next section. To win an election, a candidate must poll a simple majority, i.e., 269 or more, of the votes. We thus have a 50-person *weighted majority game*, which may be symbolized:

$$[269; 45, 32, 32, 27, \ldots \ldots \ldots, 3, 3, 3]$$

The number 269 is called the "majority quota," and the numbers 45, 32, etc. are called the "weights."[2]

There are a number of rather different analyses that might be carried out on this basic game structure. For example, one might apply the von Neumann-Morgenstern solution theory or the Ψ-stability theory of Duncan Luce to discover which coalitions of states are likely to form or persist under certain assumptions. In this note, however, we shall be concerned only with the "values" or "power indices" of the states—numbers that purport to measure the *a priori* power distribution inherent in the given apportionment of voting strength.

The power index can be defined in several mathematically equivalent ways. For example, it is equal to the chance that a state has of being "pivotal" on a ballot—i.e., of casting the deciding vote for or against a proposal—if we assume that the order of voting is determined by lot and that each state has an identical probability of voting "aye."[3] Another approach is to view the power indices as measures of the relative bargaining positions of the different states. They can also be interpreted monetarily, if

---

[2] There is historical justification for regarding the individual Electors as mere functionaries, although this is not the Constitutional view, and treating the states as the decision-making units.

[3] The exact value of this probability turns out to be irrelevant to the definition. In numerical work it is convenient to assume that all states always vote "aye," and to define the pivotal state as the one that clinches the majority.

we please, as indicating how much it is worth to *be* a particular state (in terms, perhaps, of one's expected share of the spoils), the unit of measurement being the total money value of the prize at stake.[4]

It is obvious that all these interpretations rest on *ceteris paribus* assumptions; in particular we are forced to insist that the players (i.e., the states) all be independent agents, free from prior commitments and uninfluenced by considerations outside the stated objectives of the game. These unrealistic assumptions would at once invalidate any attempt to apply the power indices in an actual Presidential campaign. The only conceivably valid direct application of these numbers would be to a study of the electoral vote system itself, as a timeless, Constitutional entity.

Intuitively, one might expect "power" to be proportional to voting strength, or very nearly so. For the Electoral College, our numerical results will bear this out to a fair degree of approximation: We shall observe no more than about 10 per cent variation in the amount of power per vote between different states. The student of politics will find that our analysis requires no major readjustments in his attitude toward the electoral vote system; without serious error he may continue in the belief that Texas, for example, with 24 votes is twice as likely to be decisive as Virginia, with 12.[5]

To illustrate how the naive approach that equates voting strength with intrinsic power might easily lead one astray, how-

---

[4] The power index, suitably extended to cover a wider class of games than we are here considering, might also be recommended as an equitable formula for arbitration purposes—e.g., in the division of assets in bankruptcy proceedings. It can be shown to be the only such formula that is perfectly "fair," in a certain abstract sense.

[5] The true ratio in this case proves to be approximately 24.6/11.8, or 2.09. To quote from *The Politics of National Party Conventions* in which some of our early results are reproduced, "the data reported . . . support the conclusion that the power indices of the states in the Electoral College are *not* out of accord, to any noteworthy extent, with the voting strength actually accorded them." Note that the presidential nominating conventions or the major parties have very nearly the same structure as the Electoral College, provided that the "unit rule" is enforced in all the state delegations.

ever, let us consider a few imaginary Electoral Colleges. For the first one, suppose that more than a simple majority were required to win. In the extreme case of a unanimity rule, namely:

$$[537; 45, 32, \ldots \ldots, 3] \qquad \text{(Ex. 1)}$$

it is clear that all states are equal in power. The differences in nominal voting strength are meaningless because of the excessive majority quota. The same levelling effect would probably be found if the quota were reduced to nine-tenths, or even to two-thirds, of the total vote, but it would be much less distinct and would require a laborious computation to confirm. The point of this initial example is merely to suggest that the way in which the distribution of power depends on the elements of the game may be very complicated; it is not just some trivial function of the nominal voting strengths alone.

Returning to the simple majority rule, suppose that one state, say Texas, is allowed to cast 100 votes, and all the other states only five votes apiece. Symbolically:

$$[173; 100, 5, 5, \ldots \ldots, 5] \qquad \text{(Ex. 2)}$$

A relatively simple calculation then shows that Texas's power index would be 32.7 times as great as the power index of any 5-vote state. This is considerably more than the 20:1 ratio in weights, and illustrates a fairly typical phenomenon of large weighted majority games: a disproportionate power advantage to the big players. Indeed, it is a theorem that if a state's power index is averaged over all possible majority quotas, the result is exactly proportional to the state's voting strength. Thus it is not surprising that the "leveling" associated with extreme quotas (see Ex. 1) should be balanced by a "big state bias" in the case of a simple majority rule.[6]

---

[6] The principle is not universal. In the presence of two big players who are evenly matched, the advantage may go the other way, with the smaller players benefiting as a result of their "balance of power" position.

In such games an intermediate quota, such as two-thirds of the total vote, would presumably produce a big-player bias.

For a third example, much closer in outward appearance to the real thing, consider the following apportionment of weights:

$$[268; 48, 36, 30, \ldots \ldots, 6, 6, 4, 3] \qquad \text{(Ex. 3)}$$

Here it is assumed that the intermediate weights are all multiples of six, and that the total weight is 535 votes. After a little study of the possibilities, we see that the smallest state can never hope to swing an election, even a very close one, since the other states can only build up vote totals of the form 6n or 6n + 4—numbers like 264, 268, 270, etc. Three votes will never push a candidate over the top. Hence the three-vote state has no real power. In contrast, the four-vote state is as powerful as the six-vote states. This can be seen from the fact that no election outcome would be changed if two votes were taken from one of the latter and given to the former. It follows that its four votes are 50 per cent more efficient, in terms of power, than those of its next larger neighbor, and infinitely more efficient than those of its next smaller neighbor. This example serves to show that abrupt and unintended biases can be concealed in a voting system that on its surface appears to be quite "fair," and that is entirely transparent in operation.

At this point we should emphasize that the peculiar effects we are describing do not depend on any particular definition of "power," but are inherent in the voting rules themselves. Our definition, by accurately reflecting these effects, thereby gains a sort of confirmation.

Continuing the discussion of Ex. 3, let us introduce an additional state, having just two votes, and raise the majority quota to 269 to preserve the simple-majority rule. A similar analysis of the possible vote totals would show that the three smallest states, with 4, 3, and 2 votes, now have *equal* amounts of power—greater than zero, but less than the power of a six-vote state. The relative efficiencies of their votes will thus be in the proportion 3:4:6. The favored status of the four-vote state has been upset. This example is intended to demonstrate that the profile of power distribution may have a very complex "fine structure," based on the numerical peculiarities of the weights of *all* the states—a fine structure that can be completely overturned by an apparently minor change in the parameters.

Although such abrupt irregularities may never occur in practice, it is impossible to rule them out completely. As we shall see in the next section, the fine-structure irregularities illustrated by Ex. 3, though undoubtedly present in the real Electoral College, are so small as to be almost obscured by the "statistical error" introduced by our method of calculation. On the other hand, the bias in favor of bigness, illustrated by Ex. 2, is definitely visible in our results for the actual Electoral College apportionments, though it is not large enough to be very significant as a practical matter.[7]

The Numerical Results

In Table 1 we have assembled the best numerical estimates of the Electoral College power indices that we have so far been able to obtain. The values for the 48-state game (before Alaska and Hawaii) were obtained in 1955 by Herman Kahn together with the present authors. They are included because of their greater accuracy, and because comparison with the 50-state case may possibly be of interest.

It is customary to scale power indices so that their sum is 1, since they are interpreted as pivot probabilities. In this case, however, we have multiplied them by the total number of electoral votes, 531 or 537, in order to facilitate the comparison between the powers and the voting strengths of the individual states. These factors should be borne in mind when making comparisons. For example, the actual pivot probability for New York goes down, as would be expected, with the addition of the two new states; our estimates give 0.08916 before, 0.08843 after. . . .

In examining the results, it is interesting to watch how the amount of power per vote varies from state to state. In both

---

[7] Our use of the term "bias" is not intended to convey any kind value judgment. We only point out that the power distribution is not quite what it *seems* to be; we express no opinion as to what it *should* be.

TABLE 1 ESTIMATED POWER INDICES IN THE ELECTORAL COLLEGE

States	Electoral Votes	Power Index × 531 (48-state game)		Power Index × 537 (50-state game)	
New York	45	47.35	±0.31	47.49	±0.49
Calif./Penn.	32	32.97	±0.20	32.44	±0.66
Illinois	27	27.44	±0.25	27.32	±0.52
Ohio	25	24.98	±0.24	25.97	±0.61
Texas	24	24.03	±0.23	24.64	±0.56
Michigan	20	20.28	±0.21	20.49	±0.43
Mass./N. J.	16	16.04	±0.12	14.76	±0.46
North Carolina	14	13.92	±0.15	13.48	±0.42
Ind./Mo.	13	12.94	±0.15	12.94	±0.45
Ga./Va./Wis.	12	11.58	±0.14	11.82	±0.35
Ala./Minn./Tenn.	11	10.79	±0.13	11.24	±0.31
Fla./Ia./Ky./La.	10	9.95	±0.12	9.90	±0.27
Md./Wash.	9	8.83	±0.11	8.79	±0.37
Ark./Conn./Kan./ Miss./Okla./ S. C./W. Va.	8	7.88	±0.10	7.84	±0.18
Colo./Neb./Ore.	6	5.96	±0.08	5.90	±0.26
Maine	5	5.05	±0.07	4.75	±0.17
Ariz./Id./Mont./ N. H./N. M./ N. D./R. I./ S. D./Utah	4	3.85	±0.05	3.83	±0.12
Del./Nev./Vt./ Wyo.	3	2.87	±0.04	2.88	±0.13
Alas./Haw.	3	—	—	2.88	±0.13

cases there is clear evidence that increased size generally means greater power per vote, although the total variation is not much more than 10 per cent. The relationship here may even be approximately linear. . . .

One might wonder whether the "big-state bias" in the power indices is a significant counteragent to the well-known bias in the opposite direction—deliberately written into the Constitution— whereby electoral votes are granted to the small states far out of proportion to their populations. The answer is no. The boost given the voters of the very small states by the two extra "senatorial" votes in the Electoral College is several orders of magnitude greater than the very minor power penalty shown in our indices. To take the most extreme case, New York has 15 times as many electoral votes as Nevada, and their power indices are in the ratio $16\frac{1}{2}:1$, reflecting the big-state bias. But the number of Congressmen (the nominal measure of population) of the two states are in the ratio $43:1$, and the actual populations (1950 census) are in the ratio $93:1$. At best, the two biases cancel each other only for the half-dozen or so most populous states.[8] . . .

The New Results[9]

. . . The formula for the power index of the ith state, denoted by ϕ_i, is simple in appearance:

$$\phi_i = \sum \frac{(\bar{S} - 1)!(n - \bar{S})!}{n!}$$

The summation is extended over all winning coalitions S in which the ith state is essential. (The notation "$\bar{S}$" means the number of states in S.)

In our present application, with n as large as 51, the number of such coalitions is so large that the problem of enumerating them efficiently seemed, until recently, insurmountable. Methods of approximating the power indices were used instead. The new technique circumvents this obstacle, and the exact values have now been obtained for several cases of interest.

. . . The states and their number of votes in the Electoral Col-

---

[8] A proper exploration of this effect would demand a more elaborate game model of the Electoral College, in which the players would be all the voting citizens of all the states. A qualitative argument shows that all the citizens of a big state in this 100,000,000-person game would have *more* power together than the corresponding state-player has in the original 48- or 50-person game, with the situation reversed for a small state. This would constitute an additional big-state bias; we do not know how significant it would be.

[9] From "Values of Large Games VI: Evaluating the Electoral College Exactly," RAND RM 3158.

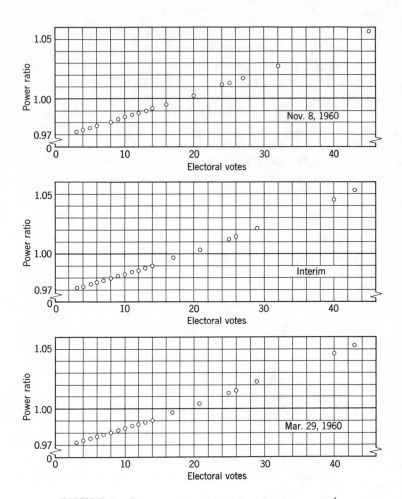

FIGURE 1. Power ratio as a function of voting strength.

lege are given in Table 1. The first column gives the voting weights actually used in the 1960 presidential election. They are based on the 1950 census, with the addition of three votes each for Alaska and Hawaii. The second column gives the distribution votes based on the 1960 census, with the further addition of three votes for the District of Columbia, as provided by the 23rd

Amendment to the Constitution (ratified March 29, 1961).   In our computation, we have determined the power indices for both cases, as well as for the interim case (50 "players" and 535 electoral votes) that existed for a few weeks early in 1961, after the reapportionment but before the inclusion of the District of Columbia.

. . . Table 3 shows for each player the power indices, scaled to be directly comparable to the voting weights.   The right-hand column is the current situation.   Figure 1 gives the ratios between the rescaled power indices and the voting weights, and shows that these two measures of strength differ by little more than five per cent.   There is, however, a systematic bias giving an advantage to the larger states.   This effect is quite smooth and almost linear. . . .

The big-state bias had been revealed by our previous work, but not the extremely high degree of regularity.   (Parabolic fits can be made to the plots in Fig. 1 with a maximum error of the order of 0.0001.)   This might have been expected, given the wide distribution of different voting weights, but until the calculations were made, the number-theoretical possibilities of the voting weights remained in doubt.

It is clear that the mathematical properties discussed here are not very important in the total consequences of the Electoral College.   But in any discussion of the electoral college and its implications, these results, though small in their effect, can meaningfully be included.

TABLE 1 ELECTORAL VOTES

November 8, 1960		March 29, 1961	
New York	45	New York	43
California	32	California	40
Pennsylvania	32	Pennsylvania	29
Illinois	27	Illinois	26
Ohio	25	Ohio	26
Texas	24	Texas	25
Michigan	20	Michigan	21
New Jersey	16	New Jersey	17
Massachusetts	16	Massachusetts	14
North Carolina	14	Florida	14
Indiana	13	North Carolina	13
Missouri	13	Indiana	13
Georgia	12	Missouri	12
Virginia	12	Georgia	12
Wisconsin	12	Virginia	12
Tennessee	11	Wisconsin	12
Alabama	11	Tennessee	11
Minnesota	11	Alabama	10
Florida	10	Minnesota	10
Louisiana	10	Louisiana	10
Iowa	10	Maryland	10
Kentucky	10	Iowa	9
Maryland	9	Kentucky	9
Washington	9	Washington	9
Connecticut	8	Connecticut	8
Oklahoma	8	Oklahoma	8

November 8, 1960		March 29, 1961	
South Carolina	8	South Carolina	8
Kansas	8	Kansas	7
Mississippi	8	Mississippi	7
West Virginia	8	West Virginia	7
Arkansas	8	Arkansas	6
Colorado	6	Colorado	6
Oregon	6	Oregon	6
Nebraska	6	Nebraska	5
Maine	5	Arizona	5
Arizona	4	Maine	4
Idaho	4	Idaho	4
Montana	4	Montana	4
New Hampshire	4	New Hampshire	4
New Mexico	4	New Mexico	4
North Dakota	4	North Dakota	4
Rhode Island	4	Rhode Island	4
South Dakota	4	South Dakota	4
Utah	4	Utah	4
Hawaii	3	Hawaii	4
Alaska	3	Alaska	3
Delaware	3	Delaware	3
Nevada	3	Nevada	3
Vermont	3	Vermont	3
Wyoming	3	Wyoming	3
		District of Columbia	3
	537		538

TABLE 2   RESCALED POWER INDICES

Electoral Votes	November 8, 1960 $\phi \times 537$		Interim $\phi \times 535$		March 29, 1961 $\phi \times 538$	
45		47.593780		—		—
43		—		45.232495		45.226568
40		—		41.790440		41.786804
32	(2)	32.882591		—		—
29		—		29.589537		29.591194
27		27.459216				
26			(2)	26.366383	(2)	26.368783
25		25.322717		25.301217		25.303807
24		24.261247		—		—
21		—		21.084998		21.088085
20		20.059178		—		—
17		—		16.937171		16.940359
16	(2)	15.924559		—		—
14		13.881517	(2)	13.869164	(2)	13.872193
13	(2)	12.865895	(2)	12.854401	(2)	12.857334
12	(3)	11.854146	(4)	11.843514	(4)	11.846331
11	(3)	10.846224		10.836458		10.839140
10	(4)	9.842088	(4)	9.833191	(4)	9.835718
9	(2)	8.841693	(3)	8.833669	(3)	8.836024
8	(7)	7.844999	(3)	7.837854	(3)	7.840015
7		—	(3)	6.845701	(3)	6.847652
6	(3)	5.862553	(3)	5.857174	(3)	5.858896
5		4.876723	(2)	4.872232	(2)	4.873709
4	(9)	3.894437	(10)	3.890837	(10)	3.892051
3	(6)	2.915657	(5)	2.912953	(6)	2.913888
	(50)	536.999843	(50)	534.999825	(51)	537.999790

11

Congressional power distributions for a stable two-party system

R. D. LUCE AND A. A. ROGOW

This article represents a direct extension of the work of Shapley and Shubik. The authors introduce an explicit (even if highly simplified) model of a legislature which captures some of the specific information of Congress. This contrasts with the approach of Shapley and Shubik in which institutional information is consciously ignored. An examination is made of the effect of defections on the stability of a two-party voting system. This article together with the recent books of Riker: The Theory of Political Coalitions and Buchanan and Tullock: The Calculus of Consent provide a start to the introduction of specific content of interest to political scientists into game theoretic models pertaining to political behavior.

The theory of games is a mathematical model for conflict of interest among intelligent and motivated agents; it is, therefore, not surprising that attempts are being made to apply it to some polit-

---

Excerpts from "A Game Theoretic Analysis of Congressional Power Distributions for a Stable Two-Party System," *Behavioral Science*, **1** and **2**, April 1956, 83–95. Reprinted with permission from the authors and *Behavioral Science*.

ical science problems. The present paper outlines another application, which is in a sense a natural successor to the Shapley-Shubik work.

We must emphasize that this is an outline, for we do not view the content as a serious attempt to study Congress as such; rather, it is a purposely oversimplified illustration of how a part of game theory may be applied to such studies.

To this end, we have taken pains to point out the nature of the assumptions made, the extent to which they are inherent in the model, and the extent to which they are simply matters of convenient exposition. We hold that a much more serious attempt must be made to abstract the central features of a legislature than we have undertaken before one can decide whether the particular model recommended is useful or not. In apparent contrast to our doubts that the formulation will sustain careful scrutiny by students of Congress, we have formulated a group of generalizations that summarize some of our detailed results and we have discussed these in the light of prevailing generalizations and some data. This should not be misinterpreted; it is only intended to demonstrate how it is possible to go from the mass of detail generated by the model to the types of generalization more familiar to a political scientist. We hope that our discussion will stimulate others to use these mathematical tools in deeper analyses of legislative bodies—studies in which data are related more closely to theory than we have done.

A legislature, as a voting body, can be viewed as having two inherently different aspects: a formal body of rules, called the legislative scheme, which establish the conditions under which a bill is passed, and the various peculiarities and limitations characteristic of a particular legislature working within the given scheme. Included in these limitations are such realities as the party structure, party discipline, the effects of pressure groups, etc. Following Shapley and Shubik, it appears that the scheme is usefully identified with one of the central notions in n-person game theory: the characteristic function. It is suggested that many of the "realities" of a legislature can be identified with another notion central to one of the several equilibrium theories. This theory is concerned with those couplings of a "power distribution" to a division of the participants into coalitions such that no changes occur. Since it is striking that the two-party system—a division of the participants into two disjoint coalitions—has remained stable for a long time, we shall assume that it *is* stable and inquire as to the theoretically necessary location of power in Congress and the presidency for such stability. We shall not attempt to discuss the much more profound question as to why the two-party system has evolved and why it is stable, but only what conditions are theoretically necessary on the power distributions in order that the system be stable. As will be seen, the theory is simply a formalization of the usual verbal discussions about the location of power—a formalization that can be readily extended to more complicated models of Congress where many of us would find it difficult or impossible to extend a nonsymbolic analysis.

Our work relates to the Shapley-Shubik paper in the following way: They ignored any information one might have about specific legislatures and confined their attention to legislative schemes. Given such a scheme, they inquired into the possibility of a priori statements about the power distributions implied by the scheme. If one is willing to accept certain conditions as to the nature of such an a priori distribution, they establish that it is uniquely determined by the voting scheme. For the study of existing legislatures this is obviously insufficient and one must take into account some of the known realities and attempt to deduce from them other—known or unknown—assertions and to investigate the empirical truth of these consequences. Our purpose is to begin to deal with this problem.

1. A Mathematical Representation of a Legislative Scheme

For the purposes of this paper, we shall suppose that the only function of a legislative body is to vote on bills which are presented to it; of course, this is not actually the case, but it may prove to be a suitable first approximation to a legislature and, at the least, it should be of interest to see what consequences can be drawn from it. For the moment, we shall not consider how a legislature may be divided into chambers nor how it may be partitioned into parties; rather, we will simply think of it as a body of undifferentiated men who vote. Let us denote this set (the terms "class" or "collection" are also used) of men by the symbol L (which stands for "legislators"). Consider any subset S of the set L (for example, if L denotes the set of men in the United States Congress on January 1, 1955, then the Southern Democratic Senators form a well-defined subset of L). The rules of the legislative scheme under consideration must determine whether or not this set S is able as a voting coalition to pass a bill. Indeed, one way to prescribe the voting rules of the body is to list for each possible subset S whether or not it can pass a bill. Let us call those coalitions which can pass a bill *winning* and those which cannot *losing*.

The legislative scheme with which we shall be concerned is that of the United States. It involves two sets of men: Congress, which we shall denote by the symbol C, and the President, whom we shall denote by P. For our purposes, it will not prove necessary to take into account that Congress is divided into two houses, for we shall not be concerned here with the origination of bills, with committee activities, or with treaties, and we shall always assume similar majorities in both houses. A coalition in this scheme is winning if and only if either

1. it consists of a majority (in both houses) of Congress and the President, or
2. it consists of a two-thirds majority (in both houses) of Congress.

All other possible coalitions are losing. It should be noted that by ignoring the possibility of ties, we have made a minor idealization: this is not essential to the model and it can be eliminated at the cost of more *routine* labor later on.

Returning to the general case, we may assume that as a result of passing or defeating a bill, there are certain rewards accruing to those involved. These may range from outright money payments to individuals, through various forms of indirect compensation, to changes in relative prestige. Each of the individuals in the legislature is assumed to have a pattern of preferences among these outcomes. While it is very difficult to ascertain these preferences in practice, they may still be postulated. If they are defined over all risky outcomes, i.e., outcomes consisting of chance distributions over the basic outcomes, and if they satisfy certain axioms, then the theory of utility establishes how the preferences may be represented by numbers.

Since there is an extensive literature on this subject, brevity dictates that we cannot delve into it deeply. Nonetheless, it must be emphasized that the theory is controversial and that many authors do not feel that people can be expected to exhibit the consistency demand by the axioms. On the other hand, the axioms do have a certain compelling plausibility. One important difficulty in the theory, as it is now developed, is that the numbers representing preferences are not uniquely determined—the choice of both the zero and the scale unit is arbitrary. The important ambiguity is that of the unit, for it is impossible to say what changes in the underlying outcomes result in the same utility change for two different people. This is the famed problem of interpersonal comparisons of utility.

With the assumption of the power equality of all winning coalitions and of all losing ones, there is no loss of generality in setting the power of a winning coalition equal to 1 and that of a losing one equal to 0; this we shall do. If S is any subset of L, we denote by $v(S)$ the power of S acting as a coalition, i.e., $v(S) = 1$ if S is winning and $= 0$ if S is losing.

Of course, it is a theoretical fiction to speak of the power of a coalition. True, the power results from the collection of men acting as a coalition, and so in that sense it is associated with the coalition, but the rewards it represents must actually be rewards to individuals in the legislature. We cannot even say "rewards to just the members of the coalition which passes the bill," for the coalition may find it expedient to turn over some of the rewards to men not in the coalition. At least this is an a priori possibility and though it will not actually occur under the assumption of equality of power for winning and for losing coalitions, with more general assumptions it can. We, therefore, suppose that the distribution of total power to the different legislators can be represented by a collection of n numbers x_i, where i is an index running over the n legislators. For example, if we number the legislators from 1 to n, then x_{10} denotes the power accruing to the legislator

numbered 10.   We shall stipulate that *all* the power is distributed
to the legislators, i.e.,

$$x_1 + x_2 + \cdots + x_n = 1$$

and that the smallest amount of power is 0, i.e.,

$$x_i \geq 0 \quad \text{for } i = 1, 2, \ldots, n$$

(In the vocabulary of the theory of games, such a distribution is
called an imputation.)

We shall suppose, subject to some limitations to be given later,
that during the prevote haggling and threatening each of the legislators is attempting to achieve as large a portion of this distribution of power as he can.   The purpose of our analysis, among
other things, will be to establish which, if any, of the distributions
of power are in equilibrium in the sense that further haggling will
not result in a modification of the distribution.

Our purpose is to go beyond the Shapley-Shubik analysis of a
legislative scheme to an analysis of a legislature.   This will, of
course, necessitate a model of what we mean by a legislature.   In
the next section, we shall present a model for Congress, which is
illustrative of a class of models for legislatures.   (The general
class is discussed in the Appendix.)   These models must attempt
to capture some of the realities of specific legislatures—realities
which are not part of the voting scheme.   In the case of Congress,
we mean by realities such facts as the party structure, the committee roles, the liberal-conservative dichotomy, the individual
loyalties to party, personal animosities, etc.   We shall not, by
any means, attempt to deal with all of these in this illustrative
example, but only with the party structure and an approximation
to party loyalty.   This will permit a plausible first approximation which is sufficiently simple to render the analysis fairly transparent.   The effect of introducing other factors is only to increase
the details of analysis without modifying the basic procedure.

2. A Model of Congress

We shall start with the fact that every legislator is identified with
one of two nonoverlapping political parties.   We shall assume for

simplicity, and with little practical loss of generality, that which-ever party has a majority in one chamber of Congress has a majority in the other. Let us label the majority party as number 1 and the minority party as number 2, and let us denote by C_1 the set of congressmen in the majority party and by C_2 the set in the minority party.

An arresting fact about Congress is the stability of the two-party system, i.e., the simple fact that it has not split into more than two parties or reduced to one. One of the major questions to which we shall address ourselves is whether there exist distributions of power for our model of Congress which permit a stable two-party system. Thus, if the President is a member of the majority party, we shall be interested in the stability (in a sense yet to be defined) of the partition of the voting body (which includes the President) into C_2 on the one hand and C_1 plus P on the other. Let the set consisting of C_1 and P be denoted by $C_1 \cup P$. Let τ_1 denote this partition, $(C_1 \cup P, C_2)$. Similarly, if the President is in the minority party, we shall be interested in the partition

$$\tau_2 = (C_1, C_2 \cup P)$$

While the two-party structure is known to be stable, it is equally clear that some, if not most, bills are passed by coalitions different from the party coalition. The conservatives of the two parties may join as a temporary coalition to pass a single bill without causing the disruption of the party structure. However, given a particular bill and a particular Congress, there are certain coalitions which could not conceivably form. If we restrict our attention to the partitioning of Congress by parties, these limitations on the formation of coalitions (to pass a bill) are, therefore, limitations on defections from the parties. Such limitations are produced by a number of factors such as pressure from constituents, party discipline, pressure from lobbies, the particular issue at stake, etc. However they may be generated, they can be described in terms of the set of Congressmen who can be induced to defect to the other party. Here we make two simplifying assumptions: first, that there are no abstentions from voting and, second, that the only defections are from one party to the other.

Actually, the second of these omits the important possibility of defectors from both parties joining to form a winning coalition. Again, as will be seen, there is no inherent reason for making this assumption: it only reduces the amount of routine calculation and the amount of space needed to present the results.

Because of the nature of the legislative scheme, there are only two groups of defections which are of interest: a defection which swells the ranks of the other party to a two-thirds majority in each house, in which case a presidential veto can be overridden, and a defection which fails to achieve a two-thirds majority in at least one house but does result in a simple majority in each, in which case a coalition of the majority and the President can pass the bill. In either case, the party in question theoretically will only be interested in defections which just produce the desired majority—all other votes are technically superfluous. Now, at the time of any given vote, it does not seem too implausible to suppose that in principle the potential defectors in each party can be graded from the most to least willing to defect from their party. If so, and if the defectors are added to a coalition in order of decreasing willingness to defect, then there is a unique set of defectors which will just create a simple majority, if that is possible, and a unique set which will just create a two-thirds majority, if that is possible. So, when we speak of a set of defectors which create a certain majority, we shall mean that minimal set of congressmen, drawn from among those most willing to defect, which is just necessary to form the majority.

With this assumption, then, we may divide the congressmen of parties 1 and 2 into two non-overlapping sets: C_1' and C_2' will denote the sets of *potential defectors* from parties 1 and 2 respectively and C_1'' and C_2'' the remaining members of each party, who will be called the *diehards*.

There are a number of different cases which can occur in this idealized Congress. Since there is no a priori reason to exclude any of these we shall examine each of them separately, and on the basis of this exhaustive examination, we shall draw some general qualitative conclusions from the model (section 5).

First, there are four basically different partitions of Congress into the two-party system: either party 1 (which by assumption has a majority) fails to have a two-thirds majority in at least one chamber, or it has a two-thirds majority in both, and either the President is a member of party 1 or of party 2.

Second, there are twelve different possible limitations on coalition changes from the two-party partition. These twelve arise from a selection of one of the alternatives in each of the following three classes of alternatives:

1. either the President is (or feels) free to defect from his party, or he is not.
2. party 1 plus the defectors from party 2 either form only a simple majority, or they form a two-thirds majority in both houses.
3. party 2 plus the defectors from party 1 either fail to form a simple majority in at least one house, or they form a simple majority in both houses but not a two-thirds majority in at least one, or they form a two-thirds majority in both houses.

We observe that not all these limitations are compatible with all the coalition partitions, e.g., it is not possible for the majority party to have a two-thirds majority in both houses and for the addition of defectors from the other party to reduce this to a simple majority. If such cases are excluded, then there are a total of 36 cases to be examined.

3. Equilibrium Power Distributions in a Special Case

To introduce the equilibrium notion we shall use and to illustrate the typical calculations involved, we shall choose one of the 36 cases; it matters little which one we take. Let us suppose the President is in party 1 and that party 1 has only a simple majority in Congress. Thus, we shall be concerned with the partition $\tau_1 = (C_1 \cup P, C_2)$, where C_1 does not form a two-thirds majority. As the system of limitations on changes from τ_1, let us choose the case where

1. the President is free to defect.
2. party 1 plus the defectors from party 2 form only a simple majority.

3. party 2 plus the defectors from party 1 form only a simple majority.

Now, from these assumptions, we see that a two-thirds majority does not exist among the possible changes; thus any winning coalition that can form must include the President. It is easy to see that there are only three such coalitions:

$$C_1 \cup P, \ C_1 \cup C_2' \cup P, \text{ and } C_2 \cup C_1' \cup P,$$

where, as before, if A and B are sets, $A \cup B$ is the set whose elements consist of those in A and those in B. One of these three will have to form to pass the bill; we shall not concern ourselves with which (there are certainly not enough assumptions even to begin to answer that question), but rather with the location of power in such a Congress under the assumption that the two-party system is stable.

Consider a power distribution x_i, $i = 1, 2, \ldots, n$, which is offered as being compatible in this Congress with the two-party partitioning of Congress. If any legislator i not in $C_1 \cup P$ has $x_i > 0$, then we know that the sum of the x_j for j in $C_1 \cup P$, must be less than 1. But since $C_1 \cup P$ is winning it can command power of 1, and so it can form and each of its members can receive more than they did in the arrangement x_i, $i = 1, 2, \ldots, n$. Since we are assuming each legislator is out to better his gains of power, we must conclude that if anyone outside $C_1 \cup P$ has power, then the combination of the two-party partition and the given power distribution cannot be in equilibrium. A similar argument applies to $C_1 \cup C_2' \cup P$ and to $C_2 \cup C_1' \cup P$, but not to any other set of legislators for either they are losing, and so can offer no power gains, or they are not among the admissible changes. Thus a power distribution x_i, $i = 1, 2, \ldots, n$, is in equilibrium with τ_1 only if $x_i = 0$ for any legislator i not in *each* of the three coalitions. Thus, the power must be distributed over those who are in *all* three of the winning coalitions, i.e., over $C_1' \cup P$. In other words, in this situation the power is distributed over the defectors from party 1 and the President. Exactly how it is distributed over these men is not determined in this simple model: it presumably depends upon factors which we have not taken into account. If we were to extend the model to include such things as the actions of committees, the origins of the bill, and so on, we could then expect a much more detailed determination of the power distributions.

4. The Equilibrium Power Distributions for the Two-party System

In order that there shall be no ambiguity in our definition of equilibrium, we shall be somewhat more formal than we have been up to now. Let $v(S)$ denote the number representing the power accruing to the set S if it forms a voting coalition. Let X stand for the distribution of power x_i, $i = 1, 2, \ldots, n$. Let τ denote a partitioning of the legislature into coalitions (while we have assumed partitions into only two coalitions, this assumption is by no means necessary). Let the symbol $\psi(\tau)$ stand for the class of coalitions which can form, if there is any reason to do so, when the legislature is partitioned according to τ. Then, we shall say that the pair (X, τ) is ψ-stable (which is simply the name assigned to this particular definition of equilibrium) if for each set S in $\psi(\tau)$.

$$v(S) \leq \sum_{i \text{ in } S} x_i$$

(The last symbol, $\Sigma_{i \text{ in } S} x_i$, simply means the sum of the values x_i for each legislator i in the coalition S.)

A re-examination of the analysis of the special case discussed above shows that it is just a special case of this definition.

Actually, the definition we have given here is slightly different from that presented in the mathematical literature (3, 4). There it was stipulated that if a legislator receives no power at all, i.e., if $x_i = 0$, then he shall not be involved in a coalition with any other legislators. The argument for imposing this condition arises simply from asking why he should cooperate with others if this cooperation does not result in any gain for him. This is a powerful argument in situations which occur only once, but it seems less convincing in a legislature where one bill is but part of an on-going process.

Now, while we have in fact been ignoring the on-going process

TABLE 1   THE POWER DISTRIBUTIONS FOR A STABLE TWO-PARTY SYSTEM UNDER THE GIVEN CONDITIONS

No.	Presidential Defection	Party of President	Size of Party 1 Majority	Size of Party 1 plus Party 2 defectors	Size of Party 2 plus Party 1 defectors	Locations of Power
1.a.i	Possible	Either	simple	simple	less than majority	Party 1, President
ii					simple	Party 1 defectors, President
iii					two-thirds	Party 1 defectors
1.b.i				two-thirds	less than majority	Party 1
ii					simple	Party 1 defectors
iii					two-thirds	Party 1 defectors
2.a			two-thirds	two-thirds	less than majority	Party 1
b					simple	Party 1 defectors
c					two-thirds	Party 1 defectors
3.a.i	Not Possible	1	simple	simple	less than majority	Party 1, President
ii					simple	Party 1, President
iii					two-thirds	Party 1 defectors
3.b.i				two-thirds	less than majority	Party 1
ii					simple	Party 1
iii					two-thirds	Party 1 defectors
4.a.i		2	simple	simple	less than majority	Impass-no winning coalitions
ii					simple	Party 2, Party 1 defectors, President
iii					two-thirds	Party 2, Party 1 defectors
4.b.i				two-thirds	less than majority	Party 1, Party 2 defectors
ii					simple	Party 1 defectors, Party 2 defectors
iii					two-thirds	Party 1 defectors, Party 2 defectors
5.a		1	two-thirds	two-thirds	less than majority	Party 1
b					simple	Party 1
c					two-thirds	Party 1 defectors
6.a		2	two-thirds	two-thirds	less than majority	Party 1
b					simple	Party 1 defectors
c					two-thirds	Party 1 defectors

we shall at least take it into account to the extent of waiving the second condition. It may also be worth noting that from the mathematical point of view this does not constitute a very serious change in the definition for the second condition has not played an important role in most of the theorems proved.

We may now give (Table 1) the power distributions which coupled with the party partitioning of Congress are stable in each of the 36 cases described in Section 2. The conclusion in each case arises by an argument like that given in Section 3 (that case is number 1.a.ii in Table 1).

5. Conclusions

By examining the summary of results in Table 1, certain generalizations implied by the model are clear. We may list six which seem interesting:

1. In all cases the arrangement of Congress into two opposed party coalitions is stable provided the power is distributed as indicated. In very many cases, however, it is necessary to form coalitions other than along party lines in order to produce a winning coalition, i.e., to pass a bill. In only one case (4.a.i) are the limitations so stringent that no working majority can form: this is when the President is of the minority party and will not defect to the majority, the majority party has only a simple majority even with the defectors from the minority, and the minority does not have a simple majority even with the defectors from the majority. What is interesting is that in only one case of the 36 can such an impasse result.

2. In all circumstances, the President is weak when the majority party—whether he is a member of it or not—has a two-thirds majority. If this model has any relation to reality, we must conclude that a President should fear a real Congressional landslide for *either* party.

3. The President possesses power (from voting considerations) only when neither party can muster more than a simple majority even with the help of the defectors from the other party.

4. The only circumstances when the minority party is the

holder of any power is when the President is in the minority party and he is unwilling to defect to the majority.

5. Under all conditions, if the defectors from party 1 added to party 2 fail to form a majority, then the diehards of party 1 possess power. The only other case in which they possess power is when the President is a member of party 1, he is unwilling to defect, and party 2 plus the defectors from party 1 form only a simple majority (cases 3.a.ii, 3.b.ii, and 5.b).

6. The only case when the party 2 diehards possess any power is when the President is a member of their party, he is unwilling to defect, party 1 has only a simple majority, and party 2 plus the defectors from party 1 form either a majority or a two-thirds majority (cases 4.a.ii and iii).

In connection with these last two statements, we note that there are a large number of situations where the diehards are not in a position to command power in a stable two-party system, and those situations in which they do have power appear to be ones not likely to occur often in practice. Recall that when we introduced the concept of a ψ-stable pair (section 4) we noted that in the original mathematical definition it was stipulated that a nontrivial coalition would not exist if its members did not benefit from their participation in the coalition. While we waived this condition for our work in this paper, there is still some force to the argument if we think of the long-term existence of a legislature. Thus, if voting coalitions tend to stabilize in time and if consideration is not given to the diehards by the other party members, it should not be too surprising to find a sudden change in their behavior. Of course, it must be understood that this is not a conclusion from the model but an extrapolation, for the model (as a special case of game theory) is inherently static and does not attempt to deal with such changes in time.

Despite the various limitations of the model, which we have already noted, the generalizations we have drawn from it do not appear to be seriously inconsistent with a number of political science "findings" concerning Congress, and in several cases they appear to emphasize aspects of congressional power which may not have been given adequate attention. The sorts of statements with which the model is not in serious contradiction are:

The President, as a legislator, is weak when either

1. his party is in the minority.
2. his party is in the majority but is not committed to his program or
3. either party can muster sufficient strength to overturn a veto:

and the President, as a legislator, is strong when either

4. his party is in the majority and is committed to his program.
5. his party is in the majority, whether or not it is committed to his program, provided that it cannot muster sufficient strength to overturn a veto.
6. supporters from his own party and defectors from the opposition party constitute a pro-administration majority coalition.

Such statements as these are not in all cases fully acceptable generalizations from the model, e.g., the first one must be qualified by the condition that one or another congressional coalition has a two-thirds majority, for if not the President possibly does possess power (see cases 1.a.i, 1.a.ii, 3.a.i, 3.a.ii, and 4.a.ii). A careful examination of our results will show that several others of these statements need some qualification before one can say that they coincide with the results of the model, but the spirit of them is much the same. It would be of some interest to know how stable these generalizations are under slight changes in the assumed limitations on coalition changes (as given by $\psi(\tau)$): for example, one might examine the effect of including as possible coalitions those made up from the defectors of the two parties. This would result in many more cases to examine, but none would be any more difficult to deal with than those above.

Let us emphasize once again that both these statements and the generalizations arrived at using game theory refer only to one aspect of Executive-Legislative relations. They do not deal with the crucial power position of committees and party leaders, the special position of the Rules Committee in the House, the filibuster power in the Senate, or a number of other important factors. Consequently, no claim can be made that our generalizations would not be substantially modified were the model refined.

On the other hand, they do emphasize several factors which are sometimes neglected or which are occasionally minimized in political science literature. One of these is concerned with the power position of diehards vis-à-vis defectors. As V. O. Key, Jr.[1] and James M. Burns (1, see also 2), among others, have noted party defectors often constitute either the effective working majority or the effective opposition, irrespective of whether or not they are members of the nominal majority party. The model suggests that in only a relatively few (and relatively unlikely) cases do the party diehards possess effective power. In the majority of the 36 cases, party defectors hold the balance of power.

This observation suggests that more attention needs to be paid to the analysis of Congress not in terms of nominal party majorities or minorities but in terms of cross-party groupings which might be tentatively classified as we have done. Thus far, empirical research does not provide a clear answer to the question of the extent of party cohesion,[2] let alone answers to such questions as: who are the diehards and defectors, from what areas of the country do they come, why do they operate as such, and is the theoretically greater power of the defectors reflected in the legislation which finally gets to a vote, in committee assignments, or in other kinds of prestige and influence?

Our game theory generalizations also point up a number of inherent features of Executive-Legislative relations. It is clear

---

[1] "In the American Congress the weak ties of the majority encourage the minority to wean away followers from the majority party and to determine the outcome of at least some and at times many legislative issues. It is not uncommon for the working 'majority' to be composed of a substantial part of the minority plus a sector of the nominal majority . . . the genuinely effective 'opposition' often consists, not of the minority, but of recalcitrant members of the majority who hold a balance of power within the House or Senate" (6, p. 706).

[2] The failure is reflected in the differing views held of the matter. Thus Burns' view that "Party cohesion is still slight today," (1, 40) confirming A. Lawrence Lowell's analysis of fifty-four years ago, is similar to that advanced in the American Political Science Association's report "Toward a More Responsible Two-Party System." But a diametrically opposite position has been taken by a number of other political scientists. See, for example, (10).

from the model that the President, under the prevailing system of loose party discipline, does not necessarily gain when his party is returned to Congress with an overwhelming majority. Although most students of legislative behavior are of the view that the party of the President should have the main responsibility for the organization of Congress, our analysis suggests that the President is not much advantaged when his party elects two-thirds or more of the Senators and Representatives. Other things being equal, the President's power as a legislator appears to be great when his own party controls between 51% and 66% of Congressional seats, and when no cross-party combination of diehards and defectors can total more than two-thirds of the membership. Tactically, this means that his party should have only about 55% of the seats.[3]

Rather paradoxically, the President's power can also be great even when his own party is in the minority, provided that he is still in control of a bloc of his party possessing at least 35% of the Congressional votes. For in such cases, and so long as the 35% is loyal to the party chief, the majority (and opposition) party can initiate legislation, but it cannot subdue the veto power. The President, therefore, holds effective power as either party diehard or defector; in the former role, he can bring about a legislative

---

[3] These generalizations are not contradicted by the record of Presidential vetoes cast during the Roosevelt Administration. As the following table shows, 69% of the vetoes cast by Roosevelt were cast during the three Congresses in which one or both houses were controlled by a two-thirds or better Democratic majority.

President	Year	Congress	House		Senate		Vetoes
			D	R	D	R	
Hoover	1931–33	72nd	220	214	47	48	18
Roosevelt	33–34	73rd	310	117	60	35	73
Roosevelt	35–36	74th	319	103	69	25	148
Roosevelt	37–38	75th	331	89	76	16	117
Roosevelt	39–40	76th	261	164	69	23	167
Roosevelt	41–42	77th	268	162	66	28	79
Roosevelt	43–44	78th	218	208	58	37	45
Roosevelt	45–46	79th	242	190	56	38	76

stalemate, and in the latter role, he can transform an opposition which is impotent, so far as positive power is concerned, into a governmental party.

In closing, we must once again return to the limitations of the present version of the model. Whether or not this game theoretic analysis can provide us with any illumination of the Congressional power structure depends very largely on its potentialities of refinement to include factors which are known to be of importance. Thus, the question reduces to our ability to determine the power of coalitions, $v(S)$, and the limitations on coalition change, $\psi(\tau)$, for more complex real situations. More sophisticated models may very well necessitate the collection of empirical data in an attempt to determine these quantities. Presumably, the limitations on coalition defections, etc., can be assessed from obtainable data, in which case there seems to be no reason to assume, a priori, that the model must remain in its present elementary state. Equally, there seems no reason to suppose, if the generalizations deduced from the present model are at all interesting, that future refinements will not produce results of similar but more subtle interest.

12

Measurement of social power

JOHN HARSANYI

This article by Harsanyi discusses the concept of power from a game-theoretical viewpoint. His work fits naturally as an extension of the recent work of Simon, March, and Dahl. The word "power" has many meanings and implications. In order to appreciate more fully the limitations of the scope of power as discussed here, the reader is referred to "Types of Power and Status" by H. Goldhamer and E. Shils, The American Journal of Sociology, **45** (1939), 171–182.

One of the difficulties with this measure and that suggested here by Shapley and Shubik is that they are defined statically for a point of time. Statements such as "he was stripped of his power" are difficult to reconcile with these measures. It would be necessary to change and enlarge the set of assumptions on which they are based and to attempt to construct a more general measure.

The concept of power is so basic and all pervading, it is not surprising that at our present state of knowledge many different theories exist, each

From "Measurement of Social Power, Opportunity Costs, and The Theory of Two-Person Bargaining Games," *Behavioral Science*, vol. 7, No. 1, January 1962. Reprinted with the permissions of the author and *Behavioral Science*.

*illuminating only part of the properties we wish to ascribe to power. There
is a close relationship between the concepts of power and solution to an
n-person game; as has already been noted, there are several dozen competing
solution concepts.*

*Harsanyi's paper lays stress on the proposition that an adequate measure
of power must take into account "opportunity costs—the costs to A of acquiring or using his power over B . . . and the costs to B of noncompliance."
This paper deals with relationships between two individuals; another and
somewhat more technical paper extends his work to the general n-person
situation.*

Introduction

Recent papers by Simon, by March, and by Dahl have suggested
measuring person A's power over person B in terms of its actual
or potential *effects*, that is, in terms of the changes that A causes
or can cause in B's behavior. As Dahl puts it, A has power over
B to the extent to which "he can get B to do something that B
would not otherwise do."

As Simon and March have obtained very similar results, I shall
restrict myself largely to summarizing Dahl's main conclusions.
Dahl distinguishes the following constituents of the power
relation:

(a) the *base* of power, i.e., the resources (economic assets, constitutional prerogatives, military forces, popular prestige,
etc.) that A can use to influence B's behavior.

(b) the *means* of power, i.e., the specific actions (promises,
threats, public appeals, etc.) by which A can make actual
use of these resources to influence B's behavior.

(c) the *scope* of power, i.e., the set of specific actions that A, by
using his means of power, can get B to perform.

(d) the *amount* of power, i.e., the net increase in the probability
of B's actually performing some specific action X, due to
A's using his means of power against B.

If A has power over several individuals, Dahl adds a fifth
constituent:

(e) the set of individuals over whom A has power—this we
shall call the *extension* of A's power.

Dahl points out that the power of two individuals can be compared in any of these five dimensions. Other things being equal, an individual's power is greater: (a) the greater his power base, (b) the more means of power available to him, and the greater (c) the scope, (d) the amount, and (e) the extension of his power. But Dahl proposes to use only the last three variables for the formal definition and measurement of social power. He argues that what we primarily mean by great social power is an ability to influence many people (extension) in many respects (scope) and with a high probability (amount of power). In contrast, a large power base or numerous means of power are not direct measures of the extent of the influence or power that one person can exert over other persons; they are only instruments by which great power can be achieved and maintained, and are indicators from which we can normally *infer* the likely possession of great power by an individual.

Among the three variables of scope, amount, and extension, amount of power is the crucial one, in terms of which the other two can be defined. For the scope of A's power over B is simply the set of specific actions X with respect to which A has a nonzero amount of power over B, i.e., the set of those actions X for which A can achieve a nonzero increase in the probability of these actions actually being performed by B. Similarly, the extension of A's power is the set of specific individuals over whom A has power of nonzero scope and amount.

While the amount of power is a difference of two probabilities, and therefore is directly given as a *real number*,[1] all other dimensions of power are directly given as lists of specific objects (e.g., a list of specific resources, a list of specific actions by A or by B, or a list of specific individuals over whom A has power). But Dahl and March suggest that at least in certain situations it will be worthwhile to develop straight numerical measures for them by

---

[1] But as the probability that B will actually perform a specific action X suggested by A will in general be different for different actions X and for different individuals B, the total amount of A's power (or even the amount of A's power over a given individual B) will also have to be described by a vector rather than by a single number, except if some sort of aggregation procedure is used.

appropriate aggregating procedures—essentially by counting the number of comparable items in a given list, and possibly by assigning different weights to items of unequal importance (e.g., we may give more "marks" for power over an important individual than for power over a less important one). In other cases we may divide up a given list into several sublists and may assign a separate numerical measure to each of them, without necessarily aggregating all these numbers into a single figure. That is, we may characterize a given dimension of power not by a single number, but rather by a set of several numbers, i.e., a vector. (For instance, we may describe the extension of President de Gaulle's power by listing the numbers [or percentages] of deputies, of army officers of various ranks, of electors, etc., who support him, without trying to combine all these figures into one index number.)

Two Additional Dimensions of Social Power

A quantitative characterization of a power relation, however, in my view must include two more variables not mentioned in Dahl's list:

(f) the opportunity costs to A of attempting to influence B's behavior, i.e., the opportunity costs of using his power over B (and of acquiring this power over B in the first place if A does not yet possess the required power), which we shall call the *costs* of A's power over B; and

(g) the opportunity costs to B of refusing to do what A wants him to do, i.e., of refusing to yield to A's attempt to influence his behavior. As these opportunity costs measure the strength of B's incentives for yielding to A's influence, we shall call them the *strength* of A's power over B.[2]

More precisely, the *costs* of A's power over B will be defined as the *expected value* (actuarial value) of the costs of his attempt to influence B. It will be a weighted average of the net total costs

---

[2] Of course, instead of taking the opportunity costs (i.e. the net disadvantages) associated for B with noncompliance, we could just as well take the net advantages associated for him with compliance—they both amount to the same thing.

that A would incur if his attempt were successful (e.g., the costs of rewarding B), and of the net total costs that A would incur if his attempt were unsuccessful (e.g., the costs of punishing B).

Other things being equal, A's power over B is greater the smaller the costs of A's power and the greater the strength of A's power.

Both of these two cost variables may be expressed either in physical units (e.g., it may cost A so many bottles of beer or so many working hours to get B to adopt a given policy X; and again it may cost B so many bottles of beer or so many years' imprisonment if he does not adopt policy X), in monetary units (e.g., A's or B's relevant costs may amount to so many actual dollars, or at least may be equivalent to a loss of so many dollars for him), or in utility units. (In view of the theoretical problems connected with interpersonal comparisons of utility, and of the difficulties associated with utility measurement even for one individual, in practice the costs and the strength of power will usually be expressed in physical or in monetary units.[3] But for the purposes of theoretical analysis the use of utility costs sometimes has important advantages, as we shall see.)

Unlike the power base and the means of power, which need not be included in the definition of the power relation, both the costs of power and the strength of power are essential ingredients of the definition of power. A's power over B should be defined not merely as an ability by A to get B to do X with a certain probability p, but rather as an ability by A to achieve this at a certain total cost u to himself, by convincing B that B would have to bear the total cost v if he did not do X.

The Costs of Power

One of the main purposes for which social scientists use the concept of A's power over B is for the description of the policy

---

[3] A good deal of recent experimental work shows that it is possible, at least under certain conditions, to measure the utilities that a given individual assigns to various alternatives. Interpersonal comparisons of utility can also be given operationally meaningful interpretation (Harsanyi). Note, however, that the main conclusions of this paper, in particular Theorems I and II, do not require interpersonal utility comparisons.

possibilities open to A. If we want to know the situation (or environment) which A faces as a decision-maker, we must know whether he can or cannot get B to perform a certain action X, and more specifically how sure he can be (in a probability sense) that B will actually perform this action. But a realistic description of A's policy possibilities must include not only A's ability or inability to get B to perform a certain action X, but also the *costs* that A has to bear in order to achieve this result. If two individuals are in a position to exert the same influence over other individuals, but if one can achieve this influence only at the cost of great efforts and/or financial or other sacrifices, while the other can achieve it free of any such costs, we cannot say in any useful sense that their power is equally great. Any meaningful comparison must be in terms of the influence that two individuals can achieve at comparable costs, or in terms of the costs they have to bear in order to achieve comparable degrees of influence.

For instance, it is misleading to say that two political candidates have the same power over two comparable constituencies if one needs much more electioneering effort and expenditure to achieve a given majority, even if in the end both achieve the same majorities; or that two businessmen have the same power over the city government if one can achieve favorable treatment by city officials only at the price of large donations to party funds, while the other can get the same favorable treatment just for the asking.

Of course, a power concept which disregards the costs of power is most inaccurate when the costs of using a given power become very high or even prohibitive. For instance, suppose that an army commander becomes a prisoner of enemy troops, who try to force him at gun point to give a radio order to his army units to withdraw from a certain area. He may very well have the power to give a contrary order, both in the sense of having the physical ability to do so and in the sense of there being a very good chance of his order being actually obeyed by his army units—but he can use this power only at the cost of his life. Though the scope, the amount, and the extension of his power over his soldiers would still be very great, it would clearly be very misleading in this situation to call him a powerful individual in the same sense as before his capture.

More generally, measurement of power merely in terms of its scope, amount, and extension tends to give counterintuitive results when the possessor of power has little or no real opportunity to actually use his power. For example, take the case of a secretary who has to compile various reports for her employer, according to very specific instructions which leave her little actual choice as to how to prepare them. Suppose that her employer then uses these reports as a basis for very important decisions.[4] Physically she could exert considerable influence on her employer's policies by omitting certain pieces of information from her reports, or including misleading information. In this sense, the scope and the amount of her power over her employer is considerable. But normally she will have little opportunity for using this power, and social scientists would hardly wish to describe her as a powerful individual, as they would have to do if they used Dahl's power concept without modification.

In terms of our own power concept, however, the secretary in question has little real power if all dimensions of her power are taken into account. Though she does have power of great scope and great amount over her employer, this fact is normally more than offset by the very high costs of using her power. If she intentionally submits misleading reports she probably will be found out very soon and will be dismissed and/or punished in other ways. Moreover, if she is a loyal employee such flagrant violation of her instructions would in itself involve very high disutility costs to her.

To conclude, a realistic quantitative description of A's power over B must include, as an essential dimension of this power relation, the costs to A of attempting to influence B's behavior.

The Strength of Power

While the costs of power must be included in the definition of our power concept in order to ensure its descriptive validity, the variable of *strength* of power must be included to ensure the usefulness of our power concept for explanatory purposes.

As March has pointed out about the concept of influence, one

---

[4] I owe this example to Professor Jacob Marschak.

of the main analytical tasks of such concepts as influence or power (which essentially is an ability to exert influence) is to serve as *intervening variables* in the analysis of individual or social decision-making. Therefore we need a power or influence concept which enables us in the relevant cases to explain a decision by a given private individual or by an official of a social organization, in terms of the power or influence that another individual or some social group has over him. But fundamentally, the analysis of any human decision must be in terms of the variables on the basis of which the decision-maker concerned actually makes his decision—that is, in terms of the advantages and disadvantages he associates with alternative policies available to him. In order to explain why B adopts a certain policy X in accordance with A's wishes, we must know what *difference it makes* for B whether A is his friend or his enemy—or more generally, we must know the *opportunity costs* to B of not adopting policy X. Hence, if our power concept is to serve us as an explanatory intervening variable in the analysis of B's decision to comply with A's wishes, our power concept must include as one of its essential dimensions the opportunity costs to B of noncompliance, which measure the strength of B's incentives to compliance and which we have called the strength of A's power over B.

For instance, if we want to explain the decision of Senator Knowland to support a certain bill of the Eisenhower administration we must find out, among other things, which particular individuals or social groups influenced his decision, and to what extent. Now suppose that we have strong reasons to assume that it was President Eisenhower's personal intervention which made Senator Knowland change his mind and decide to support the bill in question. Then we still have to explain *how* the variables governing the Senator's decision were actually affected by the President's intervention. Did the President make a promise to him, i.e., did he attach new *advantages*, from the Senator's point of view, to the policy of supporting the bill? Or did the President make a threat, i.e., did he attach new *disadvantages* to the policy of opposing the bill? Or did the President supply new information, pointing out certain already *existing* advantages and/or disadvantages associated with these two policies, which the Senator had been insufficiently aware of before? In any case we must explain how the President's intervention increased the opportunity costs that Senator Knowland came to associate with opposing the bill.

If we cannot supply this information, then the mere existence of an influence or power relationship between President Eisenhower and Senator Knowland will not *explain* the latter's decision to support the bill. It will only pose a *problem* concerning this decision. (Why on earth did he comply with the President's request to support the bill, when it is known that he had many reasons to oppose it, and did actually oppose it for a while?)

There seem to be four main ways by which a given actor A can manipulate the incentives or opportunity costs of another actor B:

1. A may provide certain *new* advantages or disadvantages for B, subject to *no condition*. For instance, he may provide certain facilities for B which make it easier or less expensive for B to follow certain particular policy objectives desirable to A. (For example, country A may be able to induce country B to attack some third country C, simply by supplying arms to B, even if A supplies these arms "without any strings attached"—and in particular without making it a condition of her arms deliveries that B will actually attack C.) Or A may withdraw from B certain facilities that could help B in attaining policy objectives undesirable to A. More generally, A may provide for B goods or services complementary to some particular policy goal X, or competitive to policy goals alternative to X, so as to increase for B the net utility of X, or to decrease the net utility of its alternatives; or A may achieve similar results by depriving B of goods or services either competitive to X or complementary to its alternatives.[5]

2. A may set up *rewards* and *punishments*, i.e. *new* advantages

---

[5] Case 1 is discussed in somewhat greater detail because power based on providing services or disservices without any conditions attached is often overlooked in the literature. For our purposes, the distinction between unconditional advantages or disadvantages on the one hand, and conditional rewards or punishments on the other hand, is important because the latter lend themselves to *bargaining* much more easily than the former do.

and disadvantages subject to certain *conditions* as to B's future behavior.

3. A may supply *information* (or misinformation) on (allegedly) already *existing* advantages and/or disadvantages connected with various alternative policies open to B.

4. A may rely on his legitimate *authority* over B, or on B's personal *affection* for A, which make B attach *direct disutility* to the very act of disobeying A.

Of course, in a situation where A has certain power over B, either party can be mistaken about the true opportunity costs to him of various alternatives. Therefore both in discussing the costs of A's power over B, and in discussing the strength of his power, we must distinguish between *objective* costs and *perceived* costs—between what these costs actually are and what the individual bearing these costs thinks them to be. For the purpose of a formal definition of the power relation, the *costs* of A's power over B have to be stated as the *objective* costs that an attempt to influence B would actually entail upon A, while the *strength* of A's power over B has to be stated in terms of the costs of noncompliance as *perceived* by B himself. The reason is that the costs of A's power serve to describe the objective policy possibilities open to A, whereas the strength of A's power serves to explain B's subjective motivation for compliant behavior. (Of course, a full description of a given power situation would require listing both objective and perceived costs for both participants.)

The Strength of Power, and the Amount of Power in Dahl's Sense

Clearly, in general the greater the *strength* of A's power over B, the greater will be A's

$$u_2 - p_2 x \geq u_1 - p_1 x \tag{1}$$

that is, if

$$\Delta p = p_2 - p_1 \leq \frac{u_2 - u_1}{x} = \frac{\Delta u}{x} \tag{2}$$

This gives us:

THEOREM 1. The maximum *amount* of power that A can achieve over B with respect to action X tends to be equal to the *strength* of A's power over B (as expressed in utility units) divided by the disutility to B of doing action X—except that this maximum amount of power cannot be more than the amount of power corresponding to B's doing action X with probability *one*.

The strength of A's power over B divided by the disutility to B of doing X may be called the *relative strength* of A's power over B. Accordingly, we obtain:

THEOREM 2. The maximum *amount* of power that A can achieve over B with respect to action X tends to be equal to the *relative strength* of A's power over B with respect to action X (except that, again, this maximum amount of power cannot be more than the amount of power corresponding to B's doing action X with probability one).

Of course, in the real world we seldom observe B to use a randomized mixed strategy of form $s[p]$, in a literal sense. What we do find is that, if we watch B's behavior over a series of comparable occasions, he will comply with A's wishes in some proportion p of all occasions and will fail to comply in the remaining proportion $(1 - p)$ of the occasions. Moreover, the disutility to B of compliant behavior will vary from one occasion to another. Hence if B wants to comply with A's wishes in pn cases out of n then, other things being equal, he will tend to select those pn cases where compliance is associated with the smallest disutility to him. For example, suppose that a U.S. senator, with political attitudes rather different from the administration's, decides to vote for the president's legislative program often enough to avoid at least an open break with the administration. Then he is likely to select for his support those administration bills which are least distasteful to him and to his constituents. This means that the total disutility to B of a given strategy $s[p]$ (which now has to be defined as a strategy involving compliance in *proportion p* of all cases) will tend to increase somewhat more than proportionally as p increases, because should B decide to increase the frequency of his compliant behavior he would have to include a higher fraction of "difficult" cases.

Accordingly, if we restate our model in terms of empirical *frequencies*, rather than theoretical *probabilities*, we must expect that the maximum *amount* of power that A can achieve over B will increase somewhat less than in proportion to increments in the *strength* of A's power over B (measuring this strength now in terms of the *average* utility value of B's incentives for compliance over all occasions). But our Theorem 1 is likely to retain at least its approximate validity in most empirical situations.[6]

Power in a Schedule Sense

We have just seen that the greater the strength of a person's power over other persons the greater the amount of his power over them tends to be. But likewise, the greater the strength of a person's power over other people, the greater both the scope and the extension of his power over these people. That is, the stronger incentives he can provide for compliance, the larger the number of specific actions he can get other people to perform for him will be, and the larger the number of individuals he can get to perform these actions.

But while the scope, the amount, and the extension of his power are all functions of the *strength* of his power over all individuals, the strength of his power is itself a function of the *costs* of power he is prepared to bear. The greater efforts and sacrifices he is prepared to make, the stronger incentives for compliance he will be able to provide and the greater will be the strength of his power over them.

Therefore, a given individual's power can be described not only by stating the specific values of the five dimensions of his power (whether as single numbers, or as vectors, or as lists of specific

---

[6] More exactly, in most unilateral power situations. The distinction between unilateral and bilateral power situations will be discussed below.

Note that in empirical applications based on a *frequency* interpretation, a further complication may arise owing to the fact that the utilities to A, and the disutilities to B, of a set of several compliant actions $X_1, \ldots, X_k$ by B may *not* be simply *additive* (as they may have the nature of complementary or of competitive "goods" from A's point of view, and/or the nature of complementary or of competitive "evils" from B's point of view).

items), but also by specifying the mathematical *functions* or *schedules* that connect the costs of his power with the other four dimensions. When power is defined in terms of the specific values of the five power variables we shall speak of power in a *point* sense, and when power is defined in terms of the functions or schedules connecting the other four power variables with the costs of power we shall speak of power in a *schedule* sense.[7]

Power in a schedule sense can be regarded as a "production function" describing how a given individual can "transform" different amounts of his resources (of his working time, his money, his political rights, his popularity, etc.) into social power of various dimensions (of various strengths, scopes, amounts, and extensions). The commonsense notion of social power makes it an *ability* to achieve certain things—an ability that the person concerned is free to use or to leave unused. It seems to me that this notion of power as an ability is better captured by our concept of power in a schedule sense than it is by the concept of power in a point sense. (The latter seems to better correspond to the commonsense notion of actually exerted *influence*, rather than to that of power as such.)

If a person's power is given in a mere schedule sense, then we can state the specific values of his five power dimensions only if we are also told how much of his different resources he is actually prepared to use in order to obtain social power of various dimensions—that is, if besides his power schedules we know also his *utility function*. Whereas his power defined in a schedule sense indicates the conditions under which his environment is ready to "supply" power to him, it is his utility function which determines his "demand" for power under various alternative conditions.

Bilateral Power and the "Blackmailer's Fallacy"

So far we have tacitly assumed that, in situations where A has power over B, A is always in a position to determine, by his unilateral decision, the incentives he will provide for B's compliance,

---

[7] In analogy to the distinction in economic theory between demand or supply in a point sense and in a schedule sense.

as well as the degree of compliance he will try to enforce. Situations in which this is actually the case may be called unilateral power situations. But it very often happens that not only can A exert pressure on B in order to get him to adopt certain policies, but B can do the same to A. In particular, B may be able to press A for increased rewards and/or decreased penalties, and for relaxing the standards of compliance required from him and used in administering rewards and penalties to him. Situations of this type we shall call bilateral or reciprocal power situations. In such situations, both the extent of B's compliant behavior (i.e., the scope and the amount of A's power over B) and the net incentives that A can provide for B (i.e., the net strength of A's power over B) will become matters of explicit or implicit *bargaining* between the two parties.

Of the four ways in which A can increase his strength of power discussed previously, we tend to obtain unilateral power situations in cases 1, 3, and 4, where A's power over B is based on providing *unconditional* advantages or disadvantages for B, on conveying information or misinformation to him, or on having legitimate authority over B and/or enjoying B's personal affection (though there are also exceptions where these cases give rise to bilateral power). For example, it is usually largely a matter for A's personal discretion whether he provides certain facilities for B, whether he discloses certain pieces of information to him, or whether he gives him an order as his legitimate superior. In case 2, on the other hand, when A's power over B is based on A's ability to set up rewards and/or punishments for B *conditional* upon B's behavior, normally we find bilateral power situations (though again there are important exceptions). Here B can exert pressure on A by withholding his compliance, even though compliance would be much more profitable than noncompliance. He may also be able to exert pressure on A by making the costs of a conflict (including the costs of punishing B for noncompliance) very high to A.

For bilateral power situations Theorem 1 and Theorem 2 do not hold true. For these conclusions have been completely dependent on the assumption that if a certain strategy s_1, involving some given degree of compliance by B, is more profitable to B than any alternative strategy s_2 involving a lesser degree of compliance (or none at all), then B will always choose strategy s_1 and will never choose strategy s_2—not even as a result of dissatisfaction with the terms A offers in return for B's co-operation. While in unilateral power situations this assumption is perfectly legitimate (as it amounts to no more than assuming that B tries to maximize his utility or expected utility), in bilateral power situations this assumption would involve what I propose to call the "blackmailer's fallacy."

A would-be blackmailer A once argued that as he was in a position to cause damage worth \$1,000 to a certain rich man B, he should be able to extract from B *any* ransom r short of \$1,000, because after payment of $r < \$1,000$, B would still be better off than if he had to suffer the full \$1,000 damage.

But this argument is clearly fallacious. By similar reasoning, B could also have argued that A would accept *any* ransom r larger than nil, because after accepting a ransom $r > \$0$, A would still be better off than if no agreement were reached and he did not receive anything at all. What both of these arguments really show is that in any bargaining between two rational bargainers, the outcome must fall between what may be called the two parties' *concession limits*, which are defined by each party's refusal to accept any agreement that would make him actually worse off than he would be in the conflict situation. But the two arguments in themselves say nothing about where the two parties' agreement point will actually lie *between* these two limits. They certainly do not allow the inference that this agreement point will actually coincide or nearly coincide with one party's concession limit.[8] (Only if we know the two parties' attitudes towards risk-taking, and in particular towards risking a conflict rather than accepting unfavorable terms, can we make any predictions about where their agreement point will lie between the two concession limits.)

Either party's actual behavior will be a resultant of two oppos-

---

[8] Only in ultimatum games, including all unilateral power situations, is it generally true that one party can extract any degree of concession or compliance from the other party up to the latter's actual concession limit point.

ing psychological forces. On the one hand, for example, B will admittedly have some incentive for agreeing to any ransom payment less than \$1,000. But B will also know that A will likewise have some incentive for accepting any ransom payment greater than zero, and this fact will make B expect to get away with a ransom payment of much less than \$1,000. This expectation in turn will provide B with some incentive to resist any ransom payment too close to \$1,000. Any realistic theory of B's behavior must take full account of *both* of these psychological forces—both of B's motives for compliance, and of the reasons which make him expect some concessions on A's part which will render full compliance on his own part unnecessary.

The Zeuthen-Nash Theory and the Strength of Power in Bilateral Power Situations

For analysis of the two parties' behavior in bilateral power situations, and in particular for quantitative assessment of the two opposite psychological forces governing each party's degree of compliance, we shall use the Zeuthen-Nash theory of the two-person bargaining game. Our analysis will be based on the following model.[9]

Just as in the model discussed earlier, A wants B to perform action X. But B associates disutility x with doing X. Nevertheless B would perform X with probability p_1, i.e., would use the mixed strategy $s(p_1)$, even in the absence of A's intervention. This would happen because if B completely refused to do X (i.e., if he adopted strategy $s[0]$) he would obtain only the utility payoff u_0—while if he did X with probability p_1 (i.e., if he adopted strategy $s[p_1]$) then he would obtain the higher utility payoff u_1, making his total expected utility $u_1 - p_1 x > u_0$.

If B completely refused to do X, then A's utility level would be u_0^*. If B did perform X (with probability 1), then A's utility would increase by the amount x^*. Accordingly, if B did X only with probability p_1 then A's expected utility would be $u_0^* + p_1 x^*$.

Now A intervenes and offers B a reward R if B will increase the

---

[9] See Footnotes 7 and 8 in original text.

probability of his doing action X from p_1 to some mutually agreed figure p_2 (i.e., if B adopts strategy $s[p_2]$). In utility units, this reward R would represent a gain r for B, while providing this reward would cost A the amount r^*. Hence, if the two parties can agree on some probability p_2, then A's total expected utility will be

$$u_2{}^* = u_2{}^*(p_2) = u_0{}^* - r^* + p_2 x^* \tag{3}$$

whereas B's total expected utility will be

$$u_2 = u_2(p_2) = u_1 + r - p_2 x \tag{4}$$

A also sets up the penalty T for B if B refuses to sufficiently increase the probability of his performing action X. In utility units, this penalty T would cause a loss t to B, while enforcing this penalty would cost A the amount t^*. Hence, if the two parties could not agree on the value of p_2, A's total expected utility would be

$$u_3{}^* = u_0{}^* - t^* + p_1 x^* \tag{5}$$

(assuming that B would still perform X with probability p_1), whereas B's total expected utility would be

$$u_3 = u_1 - t_1 - p_1 x \tag{6}$$

More generally, we may assume that in a conflict situation *both* parties would use retaliatory strategies against each other, A using strategy T_A and B using strategy T_B. In such a case t should be redefined as the *total loss* that B would suffer in the conflict situation, including both the damages caused to him by his opponent's retaliatory strategy T_A, and the costs to him of his own retaliatory strategy T_B. Similarly, t^* should be redefined as the *total loss* that A would suffer in the conflict situation. But otherwise our conclusions retain their validity.

Now, what will be the equilibrium value of the probability p_2 which tends to be agreed upon in bargaining between two rational bargainers?

We already know that it must lie between the p_2 values corresponding to the two parties' concession limits. A's concession limit is reached when $u_2{}^* = u_3{}^*$. By (3) and (5), the corresponding p_2 value is

$$p_2{}^A = p_1 + \frac{r^* - t^*}{x^*} \tag{7}$$

With $p_2 = p_2{}^A$, A's total expected utility would be

$$u_2{}^*(p_2{}^A) = u_3{}^* = u_0{}^* - t^* + p_1 x^* \tag{8}$$

while B's total expected utility would be

$$u_2(p_2{}^A) = u_1 + r - \frac{x}{x^*}(r^* - t^*) - p_1 x \tag{9}$$

On the other hand, B's concession limit is reached when $u_2 = u_3$. By (4) and (6) the corresponding p_2 value is

$$p_2{}^B = p_1 + \frac{r + t}{x} \tag{10}$$

With $p_2 = p_2{}^B$, A's total expected utility would be

$$u_2{}^*(p_2{}^B) = u_0{}^* - r^* + \frac{x^*}{x}(r + t) + p_1 x^* \tag{11}$$

while B's total expected utility would be

$$u_2(p_2{}^B) = u_3 = u_1 - t - p_1 x \tag{12}$$

It is easy to see (Fig. 1) that in the utility plane $\{u^*, u\}$ for the two parties, all possible agreement points $U(p) = [u_2{}^*(p_2), u_2(p_2)]$ must lie on the straight-line interval connecting the two parties' concession limit points, $L = U(p_2{}^A) = [u_2{}^*(p_2{}^A), u_2(p_2{}^A)]$ and $M = U(p_2{}^B) = [u_2{}^*(p_2{}^B), u_2(p_2{}^B)]$. (The two parties' payoffs in the conflict situation are indicated by the conflict point $C = [u_3{}^*, u_3]$.)

When the locus of all possible agreement points U is a straight line, the Zeuthen-Nash solution takes a particularly simple mathematical form; it is located simply at the mid-point of the distance between the two concession-limit points L and M (i.e., at S).[10]

---

[10] This is obviously true in the special case where the game is perfectly symmetric with respect to the two players. Generally the result follows from the invariance of the Zeuthen-Nash solution with respect to order-preserving linear transformations.

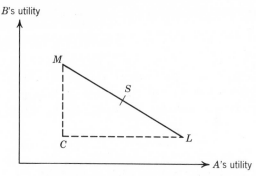

FIGURE 1.   Zeuthen-Nash utility plane

Hence, at the solution point S, A must obtain the expected utility

$$u_4{}^* = \frac{1}{2}\left[u_2{}^*(p_2{}^A) + u_2{}^*(p_2{}^B)\right]$$

$$= u_{01}{}^* - \frac{r^* + t^*}{2} + \frac{x^*}{2x}\,(r + t) + p_1 x^* \quad (13)$$

where the last equality follows from (8) and (11); while B must obtain the expected utility

$$u_4 = \frac{1}{2}\left[u_2(p_2{}^A) + u_2(p_2{}^B)\right]$$

$$= u_1 + \frac{r - t}{2} - \frac{x}{2x^*}\,(r^* - t^*) - p_1 x \quad (14)$$

If we set $u_4{}^* = u_2{}^*(p_2)$ and $u_4 = u_2(p_2)$, by (13) and (3) (or by [14] and [4]) we obtain, as the equilibrium value of p_2 corresponding to the solution point S, the expression

$$p_2 = p_1 + \frac{r + t}{2x} + \frac{r^* - t^*}{2x^*} \quad (15)$$

subject, of course, to the requirement that always

$$p_2 \leq 1 \quad (15a)$$

The Zeuthen-Nash theory also tells us that A will choose the reward R he offers B in such a way as to maximize the expression

$$\Delta r = \frac{r}{x} - \frac{r^*}{x^*}$$

which measures, from A's point of view, the value of R as an incentive, less the cost of providing R for B. Moreover, A will select the penalty T in such a way as to maximize the expression

$$\Delta t = \frac{t}{x} - \frac{t^*}{x^*}$$

which again measures, from A's point of view, the value of T as a deterrent, less the cost of administering T to B. This is so because, according to (13), A will maximize his own final utility payoff $u_4{}^*$, by means of maximizing Δr and Δt.

In the more general case where both parties would use retaliatory strategies in the event of a conflict, A (in order to maximize his own final payoff $u_4{}^*$) would again try to select his own retaliatory strategy T_A so as to *maximize* Δt when B's strategy T_B is given. On the other hand, B (in order to maximize his own final payoff u_4) would try to select his own retaliatory strategy T_B so as to *minimize* Δt when A's strategy T_A is given. Hence the equilibrium choice of T_A and T_B will be such as to make Δt take its maximum value.

Now clearly, if B adopts strategy $s[p_2]$ corresponding to the p_2 value defined by (15), then the *amount* of A's power over B with respect to action X will become

$$\Delta p = p_2 - p_1 = \frac{1}{2}\left(\frac{r + t}{x} - \frac{t^* - r^*}{x^*}\right) \tag{16}$$

But of course the value of Δp must be consistent with (15a). Hence (16) is subject to the restriction that

$$\Delta p \leq 1 - p_1 \tag{16a}$$

Let X^* denote A's action of *tolerating* B's failure to perform action X on one occasion. (We shall call action X^* the complementary action to action X.) Now suppose that A and B agree that B will perform action X with probability p_2, i.e., that B will *not* perform action X, with probability $(1 - p_2)$. This will mean that A will have to tolerate B's not performing action X, i.e., that A will have to perform action X^*, with probability $(1 - p_2)$. That is, technically, A and B will agree on a *jointly randomized* mixed strategy under which, with probability p_2, B will perform action X while A will *not* perform the complementary action X^*—whereas, with probability $(1 - p_2)$, A will perform action X^* while B will *not* perform action X.

Thus, while A's power over B will primarily consist in A's ability to get B to perform action X with a certain probability p_2; B's power over A will primarily consist in B's ability to get A to perform the complementary action X^* with probability $(1 - p_2)$.

On any given occasion where A performs action X^* (i.e., tolerates B's *not* performing action X), A will lose the utility gain x^* that he would derive from B's performing action X. Therefore A will associate disutility x^* with performing action X^*.

In equation (16), the sum $(r + t)$ is the sum of the *reward B* would obtain for compliance, and of the *penalty* he would suffer for noncompliance, both expressed in utility terms. This sum measures the *difference it would make* for B to have A as his enemy instead of having him as his friend. It represents the total opportunity costs to B of choosing noncompliance leading to the conflict situation instead of choosing compliance, i.e., some strategy $s[p_2]$ acceptable to A. In brief, it represents the *opportunity costs of a conflict*, from B's point of view. In our terminology, it measures the (gross) *absolute strength* of A's power over B. Accordingly, the quotient $(r + t)/x$ measures the *gross relative strength* of A's power over B with respect to action X.

The difference $(t^* - r^*)$ is the difference between the costs to A of *punishing B* and the costs to A of *rewarding B*, both again expressed in utility terms. This difference measures the difference it would make for A to have B as an enemy instead of having him as a friend. It represents the net opportunity costs to A of choosing the conflict situation rather than performing action X^* with a probability $(1 - p_2)$ acceptable to B, i.e., rather than tolerating B to follow some strategy $s[p_2]$ acceptable to B. (In computing these opportunity costs, r^* has to be deducted from t^*, because in case of a conflict, A of course would save the costs of rewarding B.) In brief, this difference measures the *opportunity* *costs of a conflict*, this time from A's point of view.　In our terminology, it measures the *gross absolute strength* of B's power over A. Moreover, as x^* is the disutility to A of performing action X^*, the quotient $(t^* - r^*)/x^*$ measures the *gross relative strength* of B's power over A with respect to action X^*.

Finally, the difference $[(r + t)/x - (t^* - r^*)/x^*]$ is the difference between the gross relative strength of A's power over B with respect to action X, and the gross relative strength of B's power over A with respect to the complementary action X^*.　It may be called the *net strength* of A's power over B with respect to action X.　This gives us:

THEOREM 3.　If both parties follow the rationality postulates of the Zeuthen-Nash theory of the two-person bargaining game, then in bilateral power situations the *amount* of A's power over B with respect to some action X tends to be equal to *half* the *net strength* of A's power over B with respect to the same action X— this net strength being defined as the difference between the gross relative strength of A's power over B with respect to action X and the gross relative strength of B's power over A with respect to the complementary action X^*.　(But this theorem is subject to the qualification that the amount of A's power over B cannot be so great as to make the probability of B's performing action X become greater than *unity*.)[11]

Of course, in empirical applications the amount-of-power concept in Theorem 3 (and in Theorem 1) must be reinterpreted in terms of empirical *frequencies*, instead of theoretical *probabilities* (see the preceding discussion of this point).

Simon has pointed out that in bilateral power situations—at least, when none of the participants seriously misjudge the situation—it is impossible to disentangle directly by empirical methods what is due to A's power over B, and what is due to B's power over A, so that we cannot measure separately A's power over B and B's power over A.　But of course this does not mean that, given a sufficiently rich theoretical framework, we cannot disentangle, and separately measure, these two power relations by theoretical analysis.　In effect, our Theorem 3 does provide us—at

---

[11] In other words, Theorem 3 is subject to conditions (15a) and (16a).

least in principle—with separate measures for the gross strength of each of these two power relations, and with a theory about how these two separate measures have to be combined in order to explain the end result.

Relationships of Our Strength-of-power Measures to Alternative Measures for Social Power

Theorems 1 (or 2) and 3 describe how the strength-of-power measures described in this paper are related to Dahl's probabilistic measure for the amount of power, in unilateral and in bilateral power situations. As March's probabilistic measure differs from Dahl's only in taking the absolute value of the difference $(p_2 - p_1)$ rather than the difference itself, these conclusions equally apply to March's measure.

The measure for the net strength of A's power over B in bilateral power situations is also related to the field-psychological measure for social power in small groups, proposed by French, French and Raven, and Cartwright.

It was previously argued that B's (as well as A's) behavior must be explained in terms of two opposing psychological forces, one pressing B for more compliance with A's wishes in view of the rewards and penalties set up by A, and one pressing for less compliance in view of the concessions B expects A to make in enforcing his demand for compliance. Theorem 3 now suggests that the strength of these two psychological forces can be measured by the *gross relative strength* of A's power over B, and of B's power over A, respectively. According to Theorem 3, the strength of the resultant force, the *net strength* of A's power over B, equals the *difference* between the separate strength of the two forces.

Similarly, French defines his measure for social power as "the maximum force which A can induce on B minus the maximum resisting force which B can mobilize in the opposite direction." However, while the *compliance-inducing* force of French's model is closely related to the one of our own model (as both depend on B's incentives to compliance), the *compliance-resisting* force of French's model does not seem to be connected with B's expectation of obtaining concessions as to the degree of compliance that

A requires from him, as is the case in our own model. Moreover, it is not clear whether the two opposing psychological forces of French's model are supposed to follow the same quantitative laws as those of our own model. But in any case the relationship between the two models would be worth further investigation.[12]

Finally, our measure for the net strength of A's power over B in bilateral power situations is also related to the *game-theoretical* measure for power in a committee system proposed by Shapley and Shubik, in that both our and their measures are special cases of the *same* general game-theoretical measure for power in n-person situations.

Our measure for the net strength of power is based on the Zeuthen-Nash theory of the two-person bargaining game. In the following paper I shall discuss how this measure can be generalized for n-person reciprocal power situations, where all n participants mutually possess some power over one another and over the joint policies of their group as a whole. This generalization will be based on my bargaining model for the n-person co-operative game which is itself an n-person generalization of the Zeuthen-Nash theory. This generalized measure for power in n-person situations will be found to contain the Shapley-Shubik measure as a special case.

---

[12] Cartwright mentions the fact that while he himself defines social power as a *difference* of two opposing forces, Lewin proposed to measure it as a *quotient* of two opposing forces. According to Theorem 3, in bilateral power situations the net force that A can exert on B is proportional to the *difference* of two psychological forces. More generally, if a person has both incentives for and incentives against doing a certain action, then the net strength of his incentives will be the difference between the strength of his positive and negative incentives. (For instance, if B's doing X yields him both rewards and penalties, then his net incentive will be the total value of the rewards less the total value of the penalties.) But note that in the former case Theorem 3 brings in a coefficient $\frac{1}{2}$, which does not occur in the latter case. On the other hand, both in unilateral and in bilateral power situations the gross strength of the force moving B toward compliance is the *quotient* of the strength of his incentives to compliance, and of the disutility to B of performing the required action X. Here the quotient formula arises because the disutility of doing X enters into the definition of B's expected utility as a *multiplicative* factor (it multiplies the probability of B's actually doing X).

part **4**

BARGAINING, THREATS,

AND NEGOTIATIONS

13

Sin and games in America

A. WOHLSTETTER

This is a stimulating, popular, and provocative article addressed both to the professional and to the intelligent layman. Wohlstetter points out the degree of misunderstanding that exists with respect to the uses and abuses of game theory to further the discussion of the very "ungamelike" subjects of deterrence, nuclear war, international diplomatic and military policies. Most of the footnotes have been left in so that the reader who is interested in the "burning issues" of the day may see for himself. As a classical example of a profound misunderstanding of either the content or the application of game theory methods, Sir Solly Zuckermann's paper: "Judgment and Control in Modern Warfare," Foreign Affairs, *January 1962, provides a splendid sample of what can happen when a distinguished scientist decides to write on a topic about which he has apparently read (or absorbed) next to nothing. Most other examples of this phenomenon are amply illustrated by Wohlstetter.*

. . . a new profession has been created in the United States, the profession of war gamester. His job is, by the severest and most abstract

---

This chapter is part of a longer essay, with the same title, to be published separately. Published here with the permission of Albert Wohlstetter. Copyright 1963, Albert Wohlstetter.

kind of hypothetical logic, to work out the possible moves and counter-moves of nuclear war and on this basis to suggest to the politician and the practical soldier what strategic decisions they should take. The qualifications of a war gamester combine those of a chess player and a soothsayer. He needs a clear mathematical mind, which can abstract itself from all human considerations, assimilate facts like an adding machine, and then, with absolute predictability and accuracy, produce the logical conclusions from the particular sets of facts which have been fed into his thinking machine. The war gamester, in fact, is a human computer.[1]

Much the same has been said in many recent articles in England about a rather diverse and frequently divergent list of American writers on arms and arms control.[2] Professor Blackett thinks "the theory of games has been almost wholly detrimental" to what he calls the "new school of academic military strategists" in America, and detects that this is how they have reached their false conclusions.[3] Mr. C. P. Snow thinks:

Professor Blackett is absolutely right in saying that for any sane people there is a point at which we should not think of analytic thought. In the circumstances mentioned, I should give up thinking of military things and think of something more practical, such as assassination. There are real dangers in this particular kind of theory of games . . . [4]

Sir Solly Zuckerman, the widely respected Professor of Anatomy at the University of Manchester, and the Scientific Adviser to the Minister of Defence, stated recently that:

. . . the more abstract form of operational analysis which has emerged over the postwar years . . . deals with what has been called "the mathe-

---

[1] R. H. S. Crossman, "Western Defence in the 1960s," *Journal of the Royal United Services Inst.*, August 1961, p. 325.

[2] Besides myself, Bernard Brodie, Alain Enthoren, Charles J. Hitch, Herman Kahn, W. W. Kaufmann, Henry Kissinger, Klaus Knorr, R. N. McKean, Henry S. Rowen, Thomas Schelling.

[3] P. M. S. Blackett, "Critique of Some Contemporary Defence Thinking," *Encounter*, April 1961, p. 16. Professor Blackett suggests shrewdly that if the theory were useful for practical predictions, even in much simpler situations than war, it would have made fortunes in poker or the like.

[4] "Discussion," following "Operational Research and Nuclear Weapons," by P. M. S. Blackett, *Journal of the Royal United Services Institution*, August 1961, p. 324.

matizing of thought processes," and is based upon "game theory," which burst upon the world a few years ago. Protagonists believe that this form of operational analysis can contribute materially to 'decision making' in the fields of strategy and tactics. The issues with which it deals, then, are among the most important which face Western man today—deterrent strategy and nuclear warfare in particular. Upon its conclusions—so we are told—are based certain of the most important decisions which have been taken in determining the defense posture of the United States in the strategic field, as well as some of the predetermined decisions which would be taken if deterrence ever failed.[5]

While he does not pretend to understand the intricacies of game theory, he believes ". . . game theory burst upon a too-generous military world . . ."[6]

According to Prof. Robert Neild "strategic analysis of the modern American School," influenced by the theory of games, deals, perhaps without saying so, with a world in essence populated only by two hostile amoral gambling robots.[7] Mr. Neild says so. And so have many other recent English writers. It would seem that a rather abstruse subject, the mathematical theory of games, has had some devastating practical effects.

Fortunately, so far, the practice of this aberration, if not its effects, has been largely confined to America.

Here in Britain, thank goodness, "Mr. Crossman says," we still realize that, although scientific and technological development may substitute the machine and the computer for human activity, it still remains true that the final decisions must be taken by human beings, and the humble study of human nature still remains the criterion of wisdom, whether in a general or a politician.

In this country we still believe that no war gamester, thinking in the abstract, can teach us much about the decisions which Presidents, Premiers and Chiefs of Staff have to take.[8]

And Professor Michael Howard says that the logic of certain "brilliant" arguments on the stability of the balance of terror is

---

[5] Sir Solly Zuckerman, "Judgment and Control in Modern Warfare," *Foreign Affairs*, January 1962, pp. 209–10.

[6] *Ibid.*, p. 212.

[7] "Cheating in a Disarmed World," Adelphi Papers No. 2, p. 5.

[8] Crossman, p. 325.

generally considered, in this country at least, to be that of war gaming and not of political life.[9]

Nonetheless Professor Blackett and some of the others cited are much concerned with the wide and baleful influence of these American writings on American political figures and in particular on some Englishmen. I have a feeling that in their minds the Inglese Italianato of Elizabethan times has been succeeded as a devil incarnate by the Americanized Englishman. John Strachey, Hedley Bull, Alastair Buchan and several others are suspect. Even Denis Healey has wavered. The 19th century image of the American as a rather simple, straightforward child of nature, exposed to the excessive sophistications of the European, is amusingly reversed by Blackett's picture in which the excessively sophisticated theorizing of the American tends to corrupt the intuitive common sense of English thinkers on military policy. This kind of reversal seems to be very much in the air. In several recent novels and movies made in Europe some theorizing Americans (whatever happened to American pragmatism?) are barely prevented from lousing things up by the natural *sagesse* of some apparently primitive old-world Europeans.

I can very well understand that Mr. Crossman is "frankly horrified by the thought that the strategy and the foreign policy" of Britain's strongest ally should be strongly influenced by such theorizing. Yet we are not all bad. "To be fair to the Americans," Sir Charles has cited an article in *Commentary* with much the same point of view as Mr. Blackett's, though nothing like as penetrating. Indeed, there have been similar comments in quite a few American periodicals. David Riesman and Michael Maccoby, writing in *Commentary*, refer with distaste to the "polished rationality of game theory."[10] In the same vein, Stuart Hughes in describing the "cool and ultraprofessional assessment of risk taking" in "some American strategic studies" says "they deal with thermonuclear war in the context of contemporary game, decision

---

[9] He attributes these arguments in part to me. This is, in a way, flattering, but I confess I cannot recognize the argument.

[10] M. Maccoby and D. Riesman, "The American Crisis," Commentary, June 1960, p. 462.

and communication theory."[11]   Amitai Ezioni, applauded by Lord Russell,[12] points to the belief on the part of one American strategist that those directing nuclear war will behave like men engaged in chess.   Erich Fromm says that

. . . arms control like the invulnerable deterrent demands that we and our opponent act with a super-rationality, as though we were in a game.[13]

Arthur Waskow finds the trouble with the strategists and game theory to be that the latter assumes "governments competing for high stakes in periods of great crisis would remain rational,"[14] and James Newman sums up game theory succinctly as the "Higher Incoherence."   Taking a smack at games and game theory, in short, is a fashionable game on both sides of the Atlantic.

It wasn't always so.   Not very long ago Mr. Newman, for example, wrote:

The theory of games can fairly be said to have laid the foundation for a systematic and penetrating mathematical treatment of a vast range of problems in social science.

and

The theory of Games is today regarded as the most promising mathematical tool yet devised for the analysis of man's social relations.[15]

Game theory was widely praised, on the whole—some of us thought—in spite of its great theoretical achievements, rather overpraised.   And many felt the need for systematic thought on the problems of arms and arms control.   The hostile flood of criticism has rather puzzled game theorists, and even more, most of the writers on arms and arms control under attack.   For game theorists and these strategists of arms and arms control are quite distinct.

---

[11] *An Approach to Peace*, Athenaeum, New York, 1962, p. 53.

[12] "Letter" by Bertrand Russell, *Columbia Review* (Winter) 1962, p. 3.

[13] *May Man Prevail*, Anchor Books, Doubleday and Co., New York, 1961, p. 203.

[14] "This Game of Strategy," *New Republic*, Feb. 26, 1962, pp. 15–17.

[15] *The World of Mathematics*, Vol. 2, p. 1265, Simon and Schuster, New York, 1956.

It is not at all clear that the critics who have made these attacks have read very much either of the "strategists" who, they suppose, all use game theory, or of game theory itself. However, it is very clear that they have read each other.

In fact these critics give few and only vague indications of what they suppose game theory to be and just what they think the "strategists" are doing with it or what they believe the "strategists" do at all. Much of the criticism endows game theorists, players of operational games and "American strategists," all of whom are confounded, with a curious set of beliefs: (1) That conflicting interests are limited to two—as in a "two-person game;" (2) That the behavior of parties in major conflicts is completely rational and perhaps even possible to program on electronic computers; (3) That the interests in such conflicts are completely opposed, in the sense that what one side loses the other side necessarily wins—as in a "zero-sum" game.

It is fairly safe to say that no one competent who is concerned with either the theory of games or with the quite different activity of analysing or evaluating alternative military policies would recognize these beliefs as his own. Most obviously, many of the "strategists" cited have been concerned with many-nation alliance problems and with such problems as the spread of nuclear weapons to many countries, the explosive political and military possibilities inherent in this spread, the possibilities of nuclear "accidents," unauthorized, or irrational acts of war, and the interrelation between the need to reduce the risks of "accidents" and the need to deter a deliberate attack. Their central focus on the problem of deterring a major war is based on the premise that such a war would leave all major participants worse off than they are today. For myself, I have worked some at each of the problems just described, though not at game theory. I am, in particular, perfectly willing to admit the existence of irrationality, even among Nobel prize winners.

But these strictures are also wide of the mark when applied to the abstract discipline of game theory. Some 400 of the 600 or so pages in the early classic on game theory[16] were devoted to games

---

[16] John Von Neumann and Oskar Morgenstern, *Theory of Games and Economic Behavior*, Princeton University Press, 1947.

with more than two persons, the so-called "n-person games." Theoretical advance here is much harder than for two-person games, but that after all is to be expected and may explain why popular accounts stick to the parts of the theory that are simpler as well as more successful. As for taking irrationality into account, again the classic work was not unaware of this:

. . . the rules of rational behavior must provide definitely for the possibility of irrational conduct on the part of others.[17]

Finally, while there are simple games in which the losses of some are always exactly balanced by the gains of other (called, since the totality of gains and losses comes to zero, "zero-sum"), game theory was never limited to these. It was designed to model situations in which the outcome could be either negative or positive. It might be negative, for example, not only from the standpoint of the participants as a whole, but for each one of them—as in a nuclear war. Or it could be positive, as in the case of participants in a productive process. Game theory in fact was developed as a theory of economic behavior, a very paradigm of human acts which are not "zero-sum." The production of useful goods can benefit some without taking anything away from anybody. So also for partners in a trade. That is why they are called partners, rather than simply opponents. Much of the theory in any case has always been concerned with the analysis of coalitions. Luce and Raiffa, authors of a recent volume on game theory, define it tersely:

game theory is a model for situations of conflict among several people, in which two principal modes of resolution are collusion and conciliation.[18]

T. C. Schelling, who has been the butt of some of the least informed of these critics, has used some game-theoretic distinctions in a series of illuminating conceptual analyses of international affairs. But his interest in game theory has been almost all in games in which conflict is at most partial; in fact it extends to "pure coordination" games in which no interests diverge. He thinks of "game theory" simply as the theory of interdependent behavior, in which the outcome for each participant depends not

---

[17] *Ibid.*, p. 32.
[18] Luce and Raiffa, *Games and Decisions*, Wiley, New York, 1957, p. 10.

only on his own behavior but also on that of others whom he cannot completely control.[19] Most game theorists,[20] however, would add the proviso that at least some interests conflict. And in fact define "a person" for this purpose as a set of parties with coincident interests. The theory of games analyzes situations that are both cooperative and conflicting as well as those that are only conflicting. In the purely cooperative case of course there are no conflicting interests; the game is then a one-person game, and as mathematicians would say, a simple maximum problem, a "degenerate case" in which the most characteristic features of the subject matter do not appear. For the characteristic features there must be *some* opposing interests.

As I shall discuss, I think that the assumption of conflicting interests is the one feature of game theory which these recent critics correctly though dimly perceive and, mild though it seems, is essentially responsible for their outcry. This situation has its ironies. For while game theory, like all theory, makes some drastic simplifications, on the other hand it was an attempt to supplant a still simpler kind of theory—one that treated all interests as convergent: Robinson Crusoe, for example, taken as the model for an economic society. Von Neumann's main point was that economic behavior was more complicated than simply getting the most satisfaction of a single interest. It was not a simple maximum problem but a complicated and rather subtle problem of conflicting maxima. If game theory took all conflicts to involve at most two persons, it would be excessively simple, as some of these less informed critics suggest. But some of these same critics, I believe, resent any attention whatever to conflict of national interests. They would reduce our problem then to the degenerate case of a one person game. I am quite sure that chess is an extremely inadequate model of real-life conflicts. Nonetheless it compares very favorably with solitaire. It seems that many of the critics who mistakenly think that game theorists cannot count beyond the number two have themselves yet to reach it.

---

[19] *The Strategy of Conflict*, Thomas C. Shelling, Harvard University Press, Cambridge, Mass., 1960, p. 86 ff.

[20] See, e.g., Luce and Raiffa, *op. cit.*, p. 59, J. C. C. McKinsey, *Introduction to the Theory of Games*, McGraw-Hill, New York, 1952, p. 6.

But just how is game theory related to the writings of the American strategists on the practical issues of policy on arms and arms control? A very good question, and one I may not be the ideal man to answer; for I have never been an enthusiast for game theory. On the other hand it may be useful to have an answer from someone who has had a rather temperate view. I am not, for that matter, an enthusiast for linear programming or queuing theory or differential equations or any of many techniques that are at one time or another used and sometimes are useful in the analysis of broad questions of military policy. I certainly do not oppose game theory. The problems of defense and arms control policy today are too difficult to deprecate any aid, even if it were only mildly promising. For myself, I believe that game theory is simply one among many techniques and one which has been useful, not in empirical study, but mostly in the analysis of basic concepts. Let me distinguish briefly between three sorts of activity related to defense and arms control or disarmament research.

First is the empirical study of tactical alternatives—such as the choice of effective search patterns for a given destroyer force to use in locating submarines along specified routes, or improved methods of releasing a nuclear bomb at low altitude, or efficient methods of sampling in certain specified inspection schemes for arms control arrangements, in which complete inspection is politically infeasible or undesirable.

Second is the empirical study of strategic alternatives. An example of this might be the choice of a strategic force several years off and its strategy of operation. For the purpose of assuring a second-strike capability, how should we allocate the budget for such a force between buying more vehicles or more protection for such vehicles and their control?

A third sort of study might stand in relationship to these two more empirical sorts as utility theory or price theory stands to empirical econometrics and work in the theory and practice of income determination. It would consider, in other words, very pervasive traits of conflicts. At its most basic, it might study characteristics that are common to such diverse fields as the deterrence of nuclear attack, criminal behavior and child care.

There is of course no sharp dividing line among any of these three sorts of study. "Strategic," for example, contrasts with "tactical" pretty much the way "big" contrasts with "small," or "tall" with "short." Empirical work focussing on quantative data and issues of policy, uses and may sometimes illuminate basic concepts.

I would say that game theory has been useful in some conceptual studies,[21] of trivial use in the empirical analysis of tactics and, as a theory, hardly used at all in the complex empirical work on strategic alternatives. I have said as much in several writings, most recently in 1960, "Game theory is helpful conceptually, but so far as its theorems are concerned, it is still a long way from direct application to any complex problem of policy."[22] One would never guess it from the chorus of critics who have supposed game theory to be the foundation of all the structures erected by the "new" military writers, but the majority of the small number of these writers who have been interested enough in game theory to mention it at all, have stressed its present inapplicability. And so have the game theorists. So C. J. Hitch: "Game theory must be developed considerably in several different directions before it becomes a very practical or useful tool for aiding decision-makers."[23] And Alex Mood: the theory of games "has developed a considerable body of clarifying ideas and a technique which can analyze quite simple economic and tactical problems . . . these techniques are not even remotely capable, however, of dealing with complex military problems."[24] E. S. Quade: "Only an occasional problem associated with systems analysis or operations research is simple enough to solve by actually com-

---

[21] E.g., those of T. C. Schelling, Daniel Ellsberg, and Kenneth Boulding. On the other hand, analysts such as C. J. Hitch, McKean, and myself have quite self-consciously made no practical use of the theory. And Bernard Brodie, Henry Kissinger, Klaus Knorr, and W. W. Kaufman have not so far as I know bitten the apple at all.

[22] "Defense Decisions: Design vs. Analysis," *National Decisions Concerning Defense*, Aix en Provence, 1960 (Proceedings of Second International Conference on Operational Research).

[23] *Operations Research*, Vol. 8, No. 4, July–August, 1960.

[24] "War Gaming as a Technique of Analysis," The RAND Corporation Paper, P-899, September 3, 1954, pp. 3–4.

puting the game theory solution—and some of these are only marginally related to the real world."[25]

Such statements are quite consistent with the intentions of the original formulators of game theory, as stated in *The Theory of Games and Economic Behavior*. "The aim of this book lies not in the direction of empirical research . . . We shall attempt to utilize only some *commonplace experience* concerning human behavior which lends itself to mathematical treatment and which is of economic importance."[26] It is surely stretching matters to say that either the theory of games or operational gaming has played a key role in the empirical work done by any of the writers cited. An equally temperate view of the modest uses of operational gaming, the actual playing out of an exercise simulating a military problem, could be shown to prevail among these "new" and "academic" writers on arms and arms control problems.

On the other hand, among the professional military, Mr. Crossman would evidently be surprised to learn, war gaming is hardly regarded as a new profession, even in the United States. War games have been cultivated by military men at least since military chess in the 17th century, and Venturini's map exercises at the end of the 18th. (In fact it seems chess may have had a military origin long before then in India.) Moreover such exercises have not been entirely academic. The Japanese played a many-person political-military game[27] as a preface to the Pearl Harbor attack. Besides Japan which was treated as a coalition of several competing interests, there were 11 other countries. The Germans in the last war prepared for both the Western campaign and the Barbarossa operations against Russia with war games.[28]

In stressing that those military writers who have had occasion

---

[25] "Methods and Procedures," in *Essays on Systems Analysis*, The RAND Corporation study (to be published), p. 198 of blueline copy.

[26] Von Neumann and Morgenstern, *op. cit.*, p. 5 (my italics).

[27] See R. M. Wohlstetter, *Pearl Harbor: Warning and Decision*, Stanford University Press, 1962.

[28] See Rudolf Hofman, General der Infanterie et al., *Kriegspiele*, tr. as *War Games*, by P. Leutzkendorf, MS No. P-094, Historical Division, HQ U. S. Army, Europe, 1952.

to use game theory or gaming have been very conscious of the limitations of both, I don't want to give the impression that these techniques have no use at all. They do and their utility might increase with time. Anyone familiar with the wishfulness and substantial neglect of enemy countermoves that have characterized the design of many weapon systems, arms control arrangements and military plans, would understand the statement that I made following the one I last quoted on the lack of direct application of the theory. I added that as for the empirical work of policy design and analysis, it is not the theorems but "rather the *spirit* of game theory and the way it focuses attention on conflict with an intelligent and live, reacting opponent that is useful."[29]

On this subject I would say that physical scientists have been in particular need of such reminders. And here I may quote Professor Blackett, who unfortunately has forgotten that he once wrote

Some armchair strategists (including some atomic scientists) tend to ignore the inevitable counter-moves of the enemy. More chess-playing and less nuclear physics might have instilled a greater sense of the realities.[30]

Professor Blackett's polemical style and imputation of professional impracticality to his opponents remain constant. It's just that *before* he felt that they lapsed into error because they had not played games, and *now* it is because they have.

It is clear from the foregoing why both game theorists and writers on military policy who have been attacked have been puzzled by the violence of the attacks. One of game theory's conceptual values has been to clarify very pervasive traits of conflicts. It has made it possible to discuss much more lucidly and precisely than before some of the very distinctions which these recent critics of game theory assume the game theorists have ignored. Surely since the elaboration of the basic terms of game theory, it has become possible to state more clearly and more succinctly than ever before the fact that complex activities such

---

[29] "Defense Decisions: Design vs. Analysis," *op. cit.*, p. 4.

[30] P. M. S. Blackett, *Military and Political Consequences of Atomic Energy*, London: Turnstile Press, 1948, p. 72.

as wars are not situations in which whatever one opponent loses his adversary wins.

Many of these comments exhale a faint but distinct odor of invidious comparison: the British against the Yanks, the older against the "new" military writers, World War II operational researchers against contemporary strategists and systems analysts, military against civilians, practical men against professors, followers of the heart against those relying on their heads. There are differences, of course, between the members of each of these pairs. However, they are hardly the differences between Truth and Error, or Virtue and Sin. Some of the differences, I think, are valuable, the contributions complementary. In any case, I am disabled from defending to the death the second member of each pair against the first, since, for example, I have learned much from some military writers like Liddell Hart who are both older and English and I greatly admire such young men working in England as Hedley Bull and Alastair Buchan. In particular, since I have a poor opinion, unhappily, of Professor Blackett's influential polemics on contemporary strategic thought, I should add that I, and anyone else who attempts to do empirical work on defense problems, owe him homage for his pioneering work in applying scientific method to tactical choices during the last war.

That is part of the paradox. Some of the men attacking the use of analysis today in solving the complex problems of our uneasy peace gained their reputation by using analysis, sometimes in remotely related fields like mathematical logic or physics, but sometimes, as in Blackett's case, in the related field of World War II operational research. Blackett once said, "You can't run a war on gusts of emotion." It is even clearer that you cannot keep the peace on gusts of emotion.

Given the substantial irrelevance of most of the comments on game theory and operational gaming and given their tenuous connection with the strategists, why all the hostility? Here of course one can only conjecture. The hostility derives in the first place, I believe, from a distaste for coolness, detachment, and calculation (all of which are connected with games) as against warm-heartedness, commitment, and intuition. The "icily strategic style" of discussion is felt to be "inhuman."[31] In the extreme these critics may stress the importance of being committed rather than right.

For instance, the prime importance, in any crisis of action, of being positive what you want to do and of being able to explain it. It is not so relevant whether you are right or wrong. That is a second-order effect. But it is cardinal that you should be positive.[32]

More usually the distaste for detachment as distinct from commitment is linked to the notion that it is easy to be right: the facts speak plainly to the heart.

In the second place, therefore, the hostility is connected with a distaste for the complicated, the arcane, fancy jargon, anything sophisticated.[33] And this in turn is associated with the feeling that the problem isn't really complicated at all. Aren't these simple moral issues clear to all decent men? Sometimes this praise of simplicity is accompanied by the notion that arguments must be simple "because they must be readily intelligible to the political and military leaders who have the responsibility . . ."[34]

Third, the name "games" suggests frivolity; frivolity in this context about serious matters, matters of life and death.

Fourth and worst, it suggests pleasure: here sadistic pleasure in calculations about enormously painful and cataclysmic events. Professor Blackett talks about the "nauseating inhumanity" of the methods and terminology of these writers and apologizes for having to use them himself in analyzing the stability of the strategic balance. C. P. Snow describing Lindemann's (though

---

[31] Riesman and Maccoby, *The Liberal Papers*, p. 22.

[32] C. P. Snow, *Science and Government*, p. 73.

[33] Professor Blackett complains about the "arduous labor" of studying the intricate arguments of these writers, p. 15, *Critique*. Sir Solly does not "pretend to understand the intricacies of either the mathematics or the logical symbolism one finds in the writings of the game theorists." Both Professor Blackett and Professor Zuckerman's deprecations of the intricate arguments of civilian experts were delivered to military audiences, and pleased them.

[34] *Ibid.*, Blackett *Critique* p. 10, cf. Snow, *op. cit.*, p. 73–74.

evidently not Tizard's and Blackett's) calculations of the effects of strategic bombing on German urban population exclaims

Such calculations on a much larger scale are going on at this moment in the most advanced societies we know. What will people of the future think of us? Will they say, as Roger Williams said of some of the Massachusetts Indians, that we were wolves with the minds of men.[35]

Fifth, the deliberateness of moves in a game are sometimes taken as a model and reduction to absurdity of preparations for self-restraint or deliberation in time of war.[36] Scornful references to "gamesters" have become the stock in trade, then, on the one hand, of those who would paint the picture of war in as apocalyptic a fashion as possible in the hope that thereby the world will adopt at an early date a totally pacifist solution; and, on the other hand, of those who advocate a wartime response without restraint in the case of attack. That is to say, fantasies about the theory of games and gaming have supplied the invective used by people who oppose relying on deterrence altogether and those who are for relying only on deterrence with no preparation in case of its failure.

Some of the hostility described above is associated with the accident of the names "game theory" or "war game." At worst it stems from a quite wrong-headed view of the method of science itself, that is, a kind of romantic antagonism to systematic thought.

The sixth point I would make is related to an essential trait of the theory of games which it seems would make the theory obnoxious in its own right and not just because of its odd name. This is true, even though these critics tend to perceive only vaguely the source of their irritation. I have already indicated the trait that is the trouble-maker. Game theory deals with situations in which some interests conflict. It might seem that a recognition

---

[35] Snow, *op. cit.*, p. 49.

[36] "All this theorizing presupposes that wars can be governed by gentlemen's agreements, and converted from deadly conflicts between deeply aroused nations into chess games between military leaders, using living figures." Eugene Rabinowitch, "Defenders or Avengers?" *Bulletin of the Atomic Scientists*, Nov. 1960, p. 357.

of the existence of hostility in the world is rather innocuous, a first step towards abating conflict, as well as surviving in spite of it. Nonetheless the context of many of these criticisms suggests that the hostility to game theory and to the work of the strategists is based on an antagonism to the fact of hostility itself.

In the view of many critics of game theory, there are no basic interests in conflict between the East and the West. This has been expressed in many ways, by Russell and by many others. The most frequent way is to talk of the overriding common interest between East and West in staying out of World War III. The key word here is not "common"—all the writers criticized recognize vital interests in common including the interest in avoiding World War III—; the key is the word "overriding." To call this interest overriding boils down to saying that all other interests are unimportant, that they can and should be neglected.

Such a statement has a kind of double hortatory meaning. To each adversary it says: (1) "don't press your opposing interests; concentrate just on this one of avoiding World War III perhaps by general and comprehensive disarmament"; and it also suggests to each of the adversaries: (2) "ignore it if the other chap presses his opposing interests. Even if he does, this is less important by far than the avoiding of World War III."

The notion that the conflicts between the adversaries are unimportant simplifies the problem greatly. In fact, such simplicity is related to another less obviously drastic simplification which is performed by these same people on the objectives of each of the adversaries. Each party has many objectives. Some of these objectives overlap; some conflict. Some actions are hard to reconcile with varied objectives. They require a great deal of analysis. However, anyone capable of the heroic simplification of ignoring all conflicts between the East and West finds it fairly easy to ignore the complexities incurred by considering the conflicting objectives of the East and in particular the internally conflicting objectives of the West.

The result of such simplification is to regard nuclear policy as a matter of sturdy simple common sense. In the United Kingdom, perhaps even more than here, "Common Sense and Nuclear War" or "Common Sense and Nuclear Policy," titles used respectively by Russell and Stephen King-Hall, are just about standard.

This view that the right course on nuclear affairs and on matters of defense are very simple and obvious is naturally coupled with the notion that statesmen, political scientists, and other scoundrels such as game theorists are simply insincere or possibly insane; and the arguments *ad hominem* which have become, unfortunately, the most familiar blemish on discussions of nuclear policy are related to this. Here, in a neat inversion of the view that what is good for General Motors is good for the country, a mere dark reference to strategies that further the interests of "the military-industrial complex," is taken as proof of evil. All complicated chains of reasoning on this subject seem so much sophistical mystification. And men who have earned their reputation by their ability to think, at least in some narrow professional field, call for reliance on intuition.

It is not surprising then that those who feel international violence is clearly obsolete are rather violent in their criticism of strategists and gamesters. There may be no essential interests in conflict between nations. But on the domestic scene the Enemy is clear: the bad guy inside the country who suggests there may be bad guys outside. For the heated critics of the cool strategists, while their picture of international order resembles solitaire, their domestic view is quite different. It is rather like, you might say without stretching it excessively, a zero-sum, two-person game.

14

Colonel Blotto:
a problem of military strategy

JOHN McDONALD AND JOHN W. TUKEY

*This very simple example of a two-person zero-sum game is given to provide
an instance of the type of computation used in one part of game theory.
Although, as has already been stressed, two-person zero-sum games are of
minor interest to political scientists, they provide a fertile source for experimental games for social-psychology and they are also of considerable applied
value in military work on weapons evaluation. The reader is also strongly
recommended to browse in the book* The Compleat Strategist *by John
Williams; this provides many more instructive and amusing examples and
serves as an excellent means for providing the nonmathematician with
insight into the construction and analysis of mathematical models.*

The "Colonel Blotto" game is a military deployment problem,
found in Caliban's *Weekend Problems Book*. The version shown
here illustrates in elementary, graphic form the basic idea of von
Neumann's theory of games. With patience it is not too difficult
for the layman to follow.

From *Fortune*, June 1949, p. 102. Reprinted by the courtesy of John W.
Tukey, John McDonald, and *Fortune* magazine.

The problem is given to Colonel Blotto by his general as a test of competence. Blotto has four units of armed force with which to oppose an enemy of three units. Between the opposing forces is a mountain with four passes; in each pass is a fort. War is declared in the evening. The issue will be decided in the morning. Decisions are based on who outnumbers the other at each pass. One point is scored for each fort taken, and one point for each unit taken. In the original form of this game the opponent's units turn up where they do in the night as a matter of luck. Blotto thus deployed his forces against a known probability that his opponent's forces would be grouped as follows: one unit in each of three passes, two in one and one in another, or all three in one pass.

In Princeton during World War II, two mathematicians, Charles P. Winsor and John W. Tukey, working on practical military problems, spent odd moments bringing Colonel Blotto's problem closer to reality. They allowed the units of Blotto's opponent to communicate and employ counterstrategies. Figure 1, shown here by courtesy of Professor Tukey, indicates the solution. Here is the way it goes:

Blotto has available four forms of "pure" strategy (pure as distinguished from mixed): he may deploy his four units singly, one to a pass; or three and one; or two and two; or all four in one pass. To simplify the problem for the purposes of this illustration, a special rule is introduced forbidding Blotto to send all four units into one pass. This leaves him three possible pure strategies. His opponent likewise has three possible pure strategies.

Beginning at the left-hand side of the graph, Blotto's pure strategy "4-1's" (one in each pass) is tried against his opponent's pure strategy "2 and 1." They would meet in the mountain passes like this: 1   1   1   1
                                          2   1

In the first pass Blotto will lose one fort and one unit for a loss of two points; the second, one against one, is a standoff; in the third Blotto will gain a fort for one point and in the fourth another fort for a second point. The result will be the same no matter which passes his opponent enters with this strategy (if there were a difference as there is when other deployments are used, all scoring positions would simply be averaged to get the score for that strat-

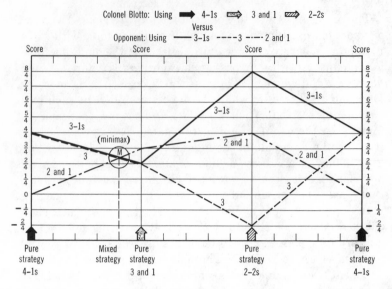

Colonel Blotto: Using ➡ 4–1s ▭▷ 3 and 1 ▨▷ 2–2s

Versus

Opponent: Using ──── 3–1s ╌╌╌ 3 ─·─·─ 2 and 1

FIGURE 1

egy). In this instance the score is two for Blotto and two for his opponent: or zero. No gain for either. This is indicated on the graph where pure-strategy "4-1's" meets pure-strategy "2 and 1."

The same simple arithmetic will show that when Blotto deploys his forces in the same way (singly) against his opponent's deployment of three ones (singly) or three together, the average result will be one point for Blotto (shown as four-fourths, since Blotto's vertical line is measured for convenience in fourths).

The second vertical line represents Blotto's pure strategy "3 and 1." Arithmetic will show that Blotto gains an average of one-half a point (two-fourths) in contact with his opponent's deployments of "3-1's" and "3"; and he will gain an average of three-fourths of a point in contact with his opponent's "2 and 1."

The third vertical line continues Blotto's score with pure-strategy two two's against his opponent's three deployments. The fourth vertical line is a repetition of the first. Of the three pure strategies available to Blotto, then, he will do best with "3 and

228 Game Theory and Related Approaches to Social Behavior

1," with a possible high score of three-fourths or a low of two-fourths or one-half. But can he do better?

The alternative, on von Neumann's principle, is to give up pure strategy for a mixed strategy. (The "mixture" could be made by rolling a five-sided die with one side marked "3 and 1" and the others marked "4-1's.") When lines are drawn between the average scoring points for each contact of strategies, all three lines intersect at the point "M." If then he mixes strategies to achieve this point, Blotto can win an average of more than two-fourths, no matter what strategy his opponent chooses. This in fact is also the best that he can do, assuming his opponent uses his best strategy. This is "minimax"—Blotto's highest minimum and lowest maximum.

An example of a similar problem in economics is the distribution (deployment) of spare parts. Thus, as Professor Tukey observes, "games of strategy . . . may have considerable practical value in diverse fields."

15

The crude analysis of strategic choice

DANIEL ELLSBERG

Ellsberg provides a simple example of a general broad application of a game theoretic approach to military strategy and international policy making. The model is not intended to be rigorous but does provide a useful conceptual scheme for analysis.

Many of the significant implications for U.S. military objectives of specific military choices—such as the introduction of a new weapons systems, a change in basing or deployment, new operational procedures or protective measures—depend upon their impact on the limited set of U.S. and Soviet "decision elements" shown in the following format:

U.S.	Soviet Union	
	Wait	Strike (p)
Wait	u_{11}, v_{11}	u_{12}, v_{21}
Strike (q)	u_{21}, v_{12}	—

Reprinted from the *American Economic Review*, **LI,** May 1961, No. 2,

We shall not try to define a "game" corresponding to this schema, though the format might suggest that interpretation; rather, it depicts some major, interrelated elements in two concurrent U.S. and Soviet decision problems: whether or not to launch an all-out nuclear attack upon the opponent. "Strike" denotes such an attack; the "Wait" strategy may be interpreted either as a "representative" or as a "best" alternative to Strike. The inclusion of a U.S. Strike strategy does not imply active consideration of such an alternative at any given moment; as a possibility, it is relevant particularly to Soviet calculations, for reasons indicated below.

The u's and v's are, respectively, U.S. and Soviet "von Neumann-Morgenstern utilities"[1] for certain (highly aggregated) consequences of their actions; p and q are, respectively, the U.S. and Soviet subjective probabilities (expectations, estimates of likelihood) that a choice of Wait will encounter an opponent's choice of Strike during a certain time period. Though all of these are subjective variables, they clearly depend upon estimates of objective outcomes under specified circumstances, based upon some form of explicit or tacit "systems analysis." For purposes of this discussion, the v's may be regarded as U.S. estimates of Soviet utilities—estimates which are not held with perfect confidence.

Symbols u_{21} and v_{21} are thus, respectively, U.S. and Soviet utility payoffs for "strike first" outcomes: the consequences of a surprise nuclear attack upon the opponent. Symbols u_{12} and v_{12} are "strike second" payoffs, reflecting the consequences of being struck first by the opponent. Symbols u_{11} and v_{11} are "no all-out

---

472–478, with permission of the author, RAND Corporation, and the American Economic Association.

[1] I.e., they indicate not merely order of preference among these outcomes but the decision-maker's preferences among "gambles": strategies which offer a set of possible outcomes with given subjective probabilities. It is assumed here that utility numbers can be assigned to outcomes so that the decision-maker's actual choices among strategies can be described as maximizing the "mathematical expectation of utility," the average of these utilities weighted by their respective subjective probabilities.

war" pay-offs, corresponding to situations in which neither opponent chooses Strike.[2]

The precise effects of a change in military "posture," hardware, policy, or plans upon these eight variables (including p and q) are, of course, hard to determine, uncertain, and subject to controversy; nevertheless, rough estimates are often made, and these are, in fact, the basis for most policy recommendations as to choices among military alternatives. Indeed, many such recommendations reflect estimates of effects only upon some subset (e.g., one) of these eight factors. The above schema has the advantage of directing attention at least to these eight, gross consequences of a military change. A typical, major military innovation will affect all of these variables, and in what may be opposing directions for a given or for different military objectives. Within a given set of strategic policy alternatives, "conflicts" may be inescapable; an improvement in terms of one dimension of choice (one military subgoal) may be unavoidably associated with losses with respect to another. Analyses which ignore several of these dimensions are thus likely to be inadequate. Isolated suboptimizing processes which overlook conflicts and "spill-over effects" among related subgoals may end by lowering over-all military security rather than raising it.

While the above highly simplified and abstract schema can by no means be regarded as an adequate model for the comparison of U.S. military alternatives, it may represent a minimum framework which is an advance over that implicit in much current discussion. Assuming that it is possible to estimate the effects of a military innovation (e.g., an airborne alert, the introduction of IRBM's in Europe, a fallout shelter program) upon the factors in this schema,[3] the question arises: what effects, or complexes of

---

[2] The utility subscripts have been chosen to show corresponding elements in the concurrent, related but separate U.S. and Soviet decision problems; if a "game" formulation were being followed, the subscripts for the v's would be transposed.

[3] However these estimates are derived and whether or not they are "reliable," the schema can be helpful in deriving their policy implications, in order to test the "consistency" of given policy recommendations with corresponding estimates and objectives.

effects, are "good"? For practical purposes the over-all goal of enhancing military security—reducing the likelihood of major losses from the threat or use of enemy military force—must be broken down into military subgoals, a list of specific strategic objectives. Some of these correspond directly to elements in our schema. Thus it is a major U.S. objective to lower p: roughly, to "improve the reliability of deterrence." Likewise, there is the goal of raising u_{12}: improving the strike-second outcome if deterrence should fail. Possible conflicts between these two subgoals are well known. However, by guaranteeing retaliation (lowering v_{21}) it may be possible to lower p greatly, more than compensating for the lower u_{12} which is associated with the low v_{21}. But what is the effect upon p of improving u_{12}, by planning counterforce tactics, or introducing civil defense? To answer this sort of question we must look at the impact not only upon u_{12} but upon all the elements in this framework, for p depends upon the whole configuration of factors in rather a complex way.

To the extent that a Soviet Strike represents a deliberate decision, it must reflect the fact that in Soviet calculations of pay-offs and likelihoods at some moment Strike appeared preferable to its best alternative. The goal of the U.S. "deterrence" policy is to ensure that this never arises: that at all times Strike appears inferior in Soviet calculations to some alternative ("Wait"). In our schema this condition appears equivalently as:

(1) $V(\text{Wait}) > V(\text{Strike})$, where V is the Soviet utility function; or

(2) $(1 - q)v_{11} + q \cdot v_{12} - v_{21} > 0$; or

(3) $(v_{11} - v_{21}) - q(v_{11} - v_{12}) > 0$.

Even though U.S. estimates may indicate that this condition holds at a given moment, p may not be 0; some U.S. uncertainty ($p > 0$) may remain, reflecting: (a) the possibility that U.S. estimates are critically mistaken; (b) the possibility that factors affecting Soviet calculations may change critically within the relevant period; (c) the possibility that Soviet behavior may be non-calculated, impulsive, or erratic, imperfectly co-ordinated, or subject to "unauthorized actions" by subordinates.

Each of these likelihoods is likely to be smaller, the larger the interval, $V(\text{Wait}) - V(\text{Strike})$.[4] Other things being equal, the "worse" Strike appears relative to its best alternative, then the more likely that the Soviets are "deterred," the more likely that they will stay deterred as pay-offs undergo exogenous shifts, and the more care that Soviet decision-makers will take to avoid accidents, false alarms, hasty decisions, unauthorized actions, or unco-ordinated, unmonitored policies. The size of this interval, then, provides a subcriterion among military choices on the path towards lower p. It is, in effect, an index of the sensitivity of the Soviet decision to "counter-deterrent" shifts in pay-offs (if q is given) such as: (a) a drop in the "no all-out war" outcome v_{11} (due to Soviet losses or expectation of losses in a limited war, shifts in prestige, influence or alliances, cold war failures, domestic setbacks or uprisings, political rivalries with third parties); (b) a drop in the Soviet "strike second" outcome v_{12} (due to increased U.S. force size or ability to exploit weaknesses in Soviet warning systems or defenses, or prospect of U.S. "annihilation tactics" in a U.S. first strike); a rise in the Soviet "strike first" outcome v_{21} (a reduction in U.S. "strike second" or retaliatory capability, due to changes either in U.S. or in Soviet posture, procedures, tactics). The larger the interval, $V(\text{Wait}) - V(\text{Strike})$, the larger (in utility terms) the pay-off disturbances required to make Strike appear preferable to Wait. This might be regarded as one index of the reliability of deterrence.

Another important index of this reliability is the sensitivity of the Soviet decision to shifts in q, the Soviet expectation of a U.S. first strike.

To understand why q is relevant at all to the Soviet choice, let us recall the earlier condition of deterrence:

$$V(\text{Wait}) - V(\text{Strike}) = (v_{11} - v_{21}) - q(v_{11} - v_{12}) > 0$$

Since typically $v_{11} > v_{12}$, it follows that a necessary condition for deterrence is:

$$(v_{11} - v_{21}) > 0 \quad \text{or} \quad v_{11} > v_{21}$$

---

[4] A unit interval having been established by the arbitrary assignment, say, of values 0 and 100 to two specified outcomes.

It cannot be taken for granted that this condition will hold; it does not follow automatically from the existence on both sides of nuclear weapons.[5] But in any case, this condition is not sufficient. Perhaps the most significant aspect of the current strategic balance is that, under typical conditions of technology and posture:[6]

$$v_{21} > v_{12}$$

It follows that deterrence can fail $[(v_{11} - v_{21}) - q(v_{11} - v_{12}) < 0]$ even though $(v_{11} - v_{21})$ is positive and large: if q, the Soviet expectation of a U.S. Strike, is sufficiently great.

An important question is: How high would q have to be to make Strike appear preferable to the Soviets?   A threshold value $\tilde{q}$, below which the Soviets would be deterred and above which they would prefer Strike, is given by:

$$(v_{11} - v_{21}) - \tilde{q}(v_{11} - v_{12}) = 0, \text{ or } \tilde{q} = \frac{v_{11} - v_{21}}{v_{11} - v_{12}}$$

We will refer to $\tilde{q}$, that probability of a U.S. Strike which would, with given Soviet pay-offs, make the Soviets indifferent between Strike and Wait, as the "critical risk" of a U.S. Strike. This threshold expectation, defined as a function of Soviet pay-offs, seems a highly significant property of the pay-off structure. Among the most important consequences of military choices is their impact upon this parameter, which serves as an index of the sensitivity of the Soviet decision to their expectation of being struck.

Extreme vulnerability of the U.S. retaliatory force will imply a low Soviet critical risk.   It leads to an extreme advantage of the

---

[5] As Albert Wohlstetter has pointed out, U.S. retaliatory power could be so vulnerable to a Soviet "no warning" attack as to promise less destruction than the Russians have suffered historically, whereas the "no war" outcome could, under abnormal conditions, appear very bad indeed.   ("The Delicate Balance of Terror," *Foreign Affairs*, Jan., 1959, p. 222.)

[6] Many of the implications of this relationship between the "strike first" and "strike second" outcomes are exposed in Wohlstetter's brilliant and authoritative article, *op. cit.*   In part, the present approach is an attempt to formalize some of the propositions in Wohlstetter's discussion.

"strike first" over the "strike second" outcome with $(v_{11} - v_{12})$ much greater than $(v_{11} - v_{21})$. With the resulting low $\tilde{q}$, the Soviets would find Strike preferable if they attached even moderate likelihood to a future U.S. Strike. This is clearly an undesirable state of affairs; a Soviet Strike could appear a rational response even to highly ambiguous indications of a U.S. attack, of the sort generated periodically by any warning system. Under the general objective of improving the "reliability of deterrence" it seems desirable to reduce the sensitivity of the Soviet decision to fluctuations in q; thus, it becomes a subgoal to increase the critical risk, $\tilde{q}$.

The principal method of achieving high $\tilde{q}$—implying that the Soviets will not prefer Strike to Wait unless they are very sure of a U.S. Strike—is to reduce the vulnerability of the U.S. retaliatory force by measures which do not improve markedly the U.S. "strike first" capability; e.g., the replacing of highly vulnerable weapons by Polaris submarines, airborne alert, hardened or land mobile missiles. As v_{21} is lowered relative to v_{12}, a situation is approached in which the Soviets would prefer Wait even if they were certain that the U.S. would attack $(\tilde{q} = 1$, corresponding to $v_{21} = v_{12})$.[7]

A further subgoal, towards improving the reliability of deterrence and lowering p, is to lower q, the Soviet expectation of a U.S. Strike. Most military choices operate directly upon payoffs, U.S. and Soviet, with indirect effects on expectations. Changes in U.S. pay-offs will influence q by affecting the Soviet image of the U.S. rational incentives to Strike. Just as p corresponds to the U.S. estimate of the reliability of U.S. deterrence, q is essentially the Soviet estimate of the reliability of Soviet deterrence. A way to lower q is to increase, in Soviet eyes, indices of the reliability of Soviet deterrence which are analogous to

---

[7] Conceivably, this result might be nailed home by making v_{21} appear worse than v_{12}; suppose that the Soviets were led to fear U.S. "annihilation tactics" with a large retaliatory force in case of a Soviet first strike, but were also made aware that the U.S. was preparing for a strictly countermilitary campaign, avoiding cities and aiming at quick cessation, if war should arise under any other circumstances. See Herman Kahn, *On Thermonuclear War* (Princeton, 1960), pp. 162–89.

indices of U.S. deterrence: to increase $U(\text{Wait}) - U(\text{Strike})$ in U.S. calculations; to increase $\tilde{p} = \dfrac{u_{11} - u_{21}}{u_{11} - u_{12}}$, the U.S. "critical risk"; to lower p.[8] This adds two new criteria of choice (lowering p being already included) to our list of military subgoals.

Having presented some apparatus of analysis at this length, there is little space in which to apply it here. Let us consider one example, by now rather familiar. Suppose that, as is frequently done, lowering the Soviet "strike first" outcome v_{21} were taken as the only significant subgoal under the objective of improving the reliability of deterrence; and suppose it were proposed to achieve this by emplacing "soft," fixed, slow-reaction IRBM's in Europe. Like any increase in our inventory of offensive weapons, this move would tend to decrease v_{21}. But only a little; fixed IRBM's are subject to no-warning attack by large numbers of accurate, high-yield Soviet medium-range missiles and bombers, and their existence would have a small or negligible effect on the expected outcome of a well-planned Soviet Strike. Even so, if other effects were ignored, as they often are, the move could seem desirable on the basis of this one criterion.

However, if we ask the impact of this move upon the other factors in our schema, conflicts with other criteria are likely to emerge. The most marked effects of the innovation would probably be: (a) a sharp decrease in v_{12}, the Soviet "strike second" outcome; (b) a sharp increase in u_{21}, the U.S. "strike first" outcome. Neither of these effects, at first glance, might seem undesirable in themselves, to count as "costs." Yet the drop in v_{12} relative to v_{21} would imply a lower Soviet critical risk $\tilde{q}$; it would take less assurance than before of a U.S. Strike to make a Soviet Strike seem preferable. And meanwhile, the actual Soviet expectation q might be increased; for the rise in u_{21} relative to u_{12} (which would change negligibly) would mean lower U.S. critical

***

[8] An interdependence between p and q emerges here; it has been ably explored under the heading, "The Reciprocal Fear of Surprise Attack," by Thomas Schelling, in *The Strategy of Conflict* (Harvard, 1960), pp. 207–29. I would suggest, without developing the point here, that this interaction is most significant when $\tilde{p}$ and $\tilde{q}$, the U.S. and Soviet critical risks, are both low.

risk $\tilde{p}$, and, for given p, a reduced interval $U(\text{Wait}) - U(\text{Strike})$, so that Soviet deterrence would appear less reliable than before.[9] Thus, the several criteria we have considered for the reliability of U.S. deterrence would indicate that this move might be associated with higher p than before.[10] Furthermore, Soviet recognitions of this effect could lead, via Schelling's "reciprocal fear of surprise attack," to higher q and a further upward pressure on p.

These results are to be contrasted to those of the measures mentioned earlier for reducing the vulnerability of the retaliatory force (raising $\tilde{q}$ by reducing v_{21} relative to v_{12}); moreover, a complex of such measures may be designed to raise u_{12} much more sharply than u_{21}, thus providing "second strike insurance" against the failure of deterrence while at the same time raising $\tilde{p}$, increasing the reliability of Soviet deterrence and lowering Soviet fears of attack.

Other specific arms control, civil defense, and active defense measures may be examined in terms of our schema; their implications for the various criteria will depend upon their differential effects upon all of the factors discussed.   The discovery, in a particular case, that the implications in terms of several of the criteria (subgoals) conflict is not a failure of the approach; on the contrary, it is a signal of the need for closer analysis in that case, for the weighing of criteria, or for the invention of new alternatives which avoid or alleviate the conflict.

It is clear that this simple framework cannot capture all the complexities of strategic choices.   It is in no sense a machine for providing answers; at most, it is a machine for asking useful questions and for preliminary testing of alleged answers.   As such, it

---

[9] Herman Kahn has emphasized that such an improvement in u_{21} may significantly improve u_{11}, by deterring the Soviets from such acts short of all-out Strike as might "provoke" a U.S. first strike if the U.S. first strike outcome were sufficiently high.   See Kahn, *op. cit.*, pp. 136–44 and *passim*. The objections, which I share, to such a policy of "Type II Deterrence" are too lengthy to discuss here.   At any rate, note that this subgoal, if accepted, would in this case conflict with the various criteria of the deterrence of a Soviet Strike (Kahn's "Type I Deterrence").

[10] This argument follows Wohlstetter, *op. cit.*, pp. 222–30, particularly p. 229.

can be helpful; simple as it is, it is far more flexible and complex than single-variable models implicit in much "literary" discussion.   Unfortunately, there has been a historical tendency on the part of policy-makers to reject the aid of abstract frameworks of the present sort on the grounds that they are "too simplistic," and then to make practical decisions on the basis of much cruder, implicit models.

16

Almost strictly competitive games

ROBERT J. AUMANN

Only the nonmathematical portions of Aumann's paper are reproduced here. Both the social and mathematical implications of his observation are of interest. He notes that the condition of strict competition or pure opposition of interests that exists in the zero-sum game is closely related to a condition of "almost strict competition" in certain nonzero sum games in which individual action to improve one's own gain or to damage one's competitor are equivalent.

Strictly competitive games (i.e., games equivalent to 2-person 0-sum games) can always be solved; it is always clear what each player should do, and the outcome is strictly determined. As is well known, this ceases to be true when we drop the assumption of strict competition. However, there are certain two-person games which still retain this (somewhat vague) property, although they are not strictly competitive. Examples are games that are

Reprinted from *The Journal of the Society for Industrial and Applied Mathematics*, vol. 9, No. 4, December 1961, with permission of the author and SIAM.

obtained from strictly competitive games by the addition of strictly dominated strategies (e.g., the prisoner's dilemma), and certain games of perfect information, which we can "solve" by working our way backward from the final move. We wish to give a characterization of such games.

The definition of strict competition is that for each player, helping himself and hurting his opponent are equivalent. Our basic idea is to "weaken" this condition while retaining its spirit.

Recall the definition of an *equilibrium point;* it is a pair of strategies at which neither player can increase his payoff by a unilateral change in strategy. Let us now define a *twisted equilibrium point* to be a pair of strategies at which neither player can decrease the other player's payoff by a unilateral change in strategy. Twisted equilibrium points are the same as equilibrium points, except that now the object of each player is to hurt his opponent, rather than to help himself. We will call a game *almost strictly competitive* if (i) these two notions are equivalent from the point of view of their outcomes, i.e., if the set of payoff vectors to equilibrium points is equal to the set of payoff vectors to twisted equilibrium points; and (ii) if the set of equilibrium points and the set of twisted equilibrium points intersect.

The prisoner's dilemma

4, 4	0, 5
5, 0	1, 1

is an example of an a. s. c. game.

Although the theory of a. s. c. games is basically noncooperative in its viewpoint, it has some applications to bargaining models for two-person cooperative games. The chief work in this area is that of Nash and Raiffa. We will not attempt here to summarize it, but merely recall some of the terminology. Given a two-person game C to be treated cooperatively, Nash breaks it up into a *threat game* and a *demand game.*

Our first remark is that the threat game is always a. s. c., no matter which demand scheme is used.

Our second remark is of a completely different nature. Optimal behavior in the threat game usually depends strongly on the demand scheme being used. It is of great interest to know under what conditions this optimal behavior will be independent of the demand scheme, since cooperative games must often be played without a clear and fixed formal notion of which demand scheme is being used. A sufficient condition is that the original game C be a. s. c. This condition is not necessary; the necessary and sufficient condition is that our condition (ii) be satisfied, i.e., that the set of ordinary and the set of twisted equilibrium points meet. This is equivalent to the existence of a saddle-point. The reader should note, however, that this only assures invariance of the optimal strategies, not of the payoffs.

17

Negotiation: a device for modifying utilities

F. C. IKLÈ IN COLLABORATION WITH N. LEITES

Iklé in collaboration with Leites takes steps toward developing a dynamic model of bargaining and negotiation procedures.   There is little doubt that this development must be pursued if our understanding of negotiation processes is to be furthered.   The relationship between dynamic and static models of political and social processes is not well understood.   One of the basic difficulties with the case of the theory of games hinges upon the relationship between the more dynamic or "extensive form" description of a game and the static or "normalized form" of a game.   For many human processes it is reasonable to question the legitimacy of treating these two representations as though they were equivalent.   This article stresses the dynamic aspects of negotiation, stressing the possibility of changes in utility evaluation as the negotiations proceed.

A variety of bargaining processes in real life can be understood by means of theoretical models.   Price theory and (in a more

---

Reprinted from "Political Negotiation as a Process of Modifying Utilities," *Conflict Resolution*, **VI**, No. 1, 19–28, with permission of the authors and RAND Corporation.

general way) the theory of "games of strategy" are helpful for our understanding of important real situations. But when we wish to study political negotiations, these theoretical tools seem to be of but limited use for the complex reality. They may at best give us some broad generalizations rather removed from the interesting details. We must first come to grips with the reality of political negotiations in a more systematic fashion before we can relate current bargaining theory to it.

This paper constitutes the initial output of a continuing study on political negotiations. The aim of the larger study is to develop a theory of negotiations; the aim of this paper is to present a formalization that can be used towards the construction of such a theory.

We shall put our formalization to the test by applying it to propositions from the literature on actual negotiation behavior or on "good" negotiating techniques. If successful, the reformulation of these propositions will make them more precise and will help to determine in what situations and to what extent they are valid.

Our formalization might be useful also for developing *new* propositions on the basis of data from actual negotiations. Later on, some elements of the formalization might be amenable to mathematical solutions.

The Formalization

UNSTABLE AND LARGELY UNKNOWN PREFERENCES (OR "UTILITIES")

The theory of games of strategy is concerned with situations that resemble certain aspects of political negotiations. We might therefore start to explain our formalization by discussing how it differs from traditional game theory. Game theory usually assumes the existence of a real utility for each player which is *stable throughout the game*. In addition, it is assumed that each player knows his own utility and often that of all the other players. (If the utility functions of the other players are not known, they are at least stable.)

The essence of our formalization is that it recognizes neither known nor stable utilities. For the time being, we shall leave aside the question as to whether there are no stable utilities in political negotiations, whether they exist but are unknown, or whether our formalization simply does not make use of stable utilities. (It may be possible later to reformulate a utility concept that takes account of this instability.) In order to avoid confusion with established concepts from game theory or economics, we shall resort to our own definitions and terminology where our concepts seem to differ. To a large extent, our concepts are of a psychological nature.

Traditionally, "utility" is experimentally determined (and hence operationally defined) by an *act of preference:* if a subject chooses alternative A in preference to alternative B, A is said to have a greater "utility" for this subject than B. More precisely, it should be recognized that the "utility" is associated with those characteristics and/or consequences of the alternatives (and the probabilities of their occurrence) that the subject *expects and considers* when making the choice. In the political realm, where the consequences of choices are so complex and intuition plays such a large role, it is clear that utility thus defined is unlikely to remain stable during the course of negotiations.

The "Disposition" to Prefer

To understand political negotiations, therefore, we need a concept that takes account of the changes in preferences, in distinction to the *act of preference* which occurs at the time a choice is made and which can be used operationally to define "utility" only at that time. We may define for each negotiator[1] and for a given time in the course of negotiations a "disposition to prefer" as the negotiator's estimate that he will prefer one alternative over another if

---

[1] Governments that negotiate with each other do not, of course, have a unitary interest. Each government is a collection of individuals and subgroups with somewhat conflicting interests, and has to work out a common position towards other governments. This complication will be considered later. For an interesting account of the negotiations within a government as part of the process of negotiations with other governments see Pruitt.

and when he has to make the choice. The most important choice is, of course, that between agreement at given terms and no agreement. Theoretically, we can ask each negotiator at any time during the negotiations what the least favorable terms are at which he would prefer agreement to no agreement. We call these terms—which are often quite vague—the negotiator's *Minimum Disposition* (at time t).

To construct a model of negotiations between two countries (or between two opposing alliances) we initially make the following simplifying assumption: the negotiations deal with an agreement where the two sides have a conflict of interest in only one set of mutually exclusive alternatives, $A, B, C, \ldots N$; and one side always prefers A to B, B to C, $\ldots (N-1)$ to N, while the preferences of the other side are in reverse order. (Note that this constant ordering of preferences does not imply constant utilities!) An example of such negotiations would be a disarmament agreement for which only the number of inspections is at issue, with Red always preferring a smaller number of inspections to a larger one, and conversely for Blue.

In Figure 1 Blue's Minimum Disposition covers alternatives 12 or 13, i.e., Blue estimates that it would prefer no agreement to an agreement that allows fewer than 13 or 12. (Blue is not sure whether its minimum lies at 12 or at 13.) Blue furthermore estimates that Red's Minimum Disposition lies somewhere between alternatives 18 through 21. Thus Blue's *Estimated Bargaining Range* extends from 12 through 21. This, however,.need not keep Blue from asking for more. If Blue asked for 23 it would pretend that it thought 23 was still within the bargaining range; we might call such a demand a *Sham Bargaining Position.*

We can now define concessions. Hitherto discussions of negotiations usually failed to distinguish between a negotiator who makes a "concession" by dropping a demand he never expected the other side to accept, and one who thinks his concession increases the attractiveness of a proposal that the other side might have accepted prior to the concession. Based on our model, we may call a negotiator's change in bargaining positions from one he prefers more to one he prefers less a *Sham Concession* if these two positions lie in his Sham Bargaining Range, and a

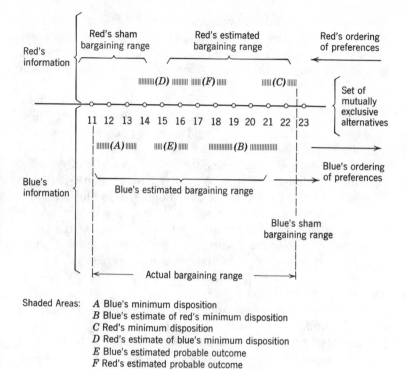

Shaded Areas:
 A Blue's minimum disposition
 B Blue's estimate of red's minimum disposition
 C Red's minimum disposition
 D Red's estimate of blue's minimum disposition
 E Blue's estimated probable outcome
 F Red's estimated probable outcome

FIGURE 1

Genuine Concession if they fall within his Genuine Bargaining Range.[2] While this particular terminology is unimportant, we know of no other satisfactory model for defining a "concession."

Actually, governments often enter negotiations without being conscious of their Minimum Disposition and without making an effort to estimate the opponent's Minimum Disposition. Political negotiators frequently seem to be somewhat reluctant to estimate the bargaining range. They may feel that such estimates might reduce flexibility and the capacity to put pressure on the

---

[2] A concession moving from the "sham" into the "genuine range," would combine both a "sham" and a "genuine" part.

opponent. The tendency not to estimate a bargaining range is also fostered by the fact that real negotiations are immensely more complex than our model, since most agreements involve a great many bargaining ranges which must be combined into an over-all bargain.

Instead of estimating the bargaining range, a negotiator may estimate a *Probable Outcome*, i.e., the approximate terms at which he expects agreement. The negotiator, might, of course, estimate both the Genuine Bargaining Range and the Probable Outcome and thereby—in the game-theoretical sense—imply a solution for the division of the payoff. In political negotiations, especially at the beginning, such a double estimate is seldom made. In a more complex situation, which, as was just said, is likely to prevail, the negotiator may form an image of the anticipated treaty whose terms represent the Probable Outcome on all of the disputed issues [e.g., a disarmament agreement with 15 or 16 inspections (Figure 1), such and such a budget, certain administrative arrangements, etc.].

Frequently, some conspicuous feature will dominate the negotiator's estimate of the Probable Outcome. Thus, geographic features may suggest to negotiators the Probable Outcome of a dispute on the division of a certain territory.[3] These prominent or "focal" outcomes may dominate the calculations of a negotiator so much that they begin to determine his estimates of the bargaining range (if he makes such an estimate): the negotiator begins to group his Minimum Disposition and his estimate of the opponent's Minimum Disposition around his estimate of the Probable Outcome. For example, once the negotiator estimates that a certain river will form the demarcation of a disputed territory, any major departures to the left or the right of that river may appear unacceptable to himself (i.e., beyond his Minimum Disposition) or to his opponent, respectively.

We must now consider the changes over time in the negotiators' own Minimum Disposition and estimated Probable Outcome, and in their estimates of the opponent's Minimum Disposition and

---

[3] Schelling pointed out the importance of such prominent, conspicuous, or focal points.

estimated Probable Outcome.   This change is not a perturbation or a "nuisance factor" that one might want to randomize or hold constant in a study of negotiations; it is the very essence of the negotiating process.   Sometimes, a negotiator may anticipate a change in the Minimum Disposition of his opponent.   For example, at the beginning of a conference Red may estimate both Blue's initial Minimum Disposition and Blue's terminal Minimum Disposition, and conceive of his bargaining task as the effort required to make Blue change from the former to the latter.

Modification of Dispositions and of Estimated Outcomes

As long as both sides try to get an agreement, they will seek to improve the terms for themselves through the modification of Dispositions and estimated Probable Outcomes.   If I am the negotiator, I will attempt to modify:

(A) My opponent's Minimum Disposition; i.e., make him believe or feel that he would prefer an agreement to no agreement on terms more favorable to me than he originally thought;

(B) My opponent's estimate of my Minimum Disposition; i.e., make him believe that the terms at which I would prefer no agreement are, in fact, less favorable to him than he had first thought.[4]

If my opponent pays more attention to his estimate of the Probable Outcome than to his estimate of the bargaining range, my efforts will also have to be directed to the former.   I might try to convince my opponent that his estimated Probable Outcome lies outside the bargaining range and hence is improbable, or that it would imply an "unfair" division of the bargaining range.   For example, in an earlier stage of the Berlin crisis many people in the West seemed to consider the *status quo* as a Probable Outcome if the West remained firm.   Khrushchev succeeded in convincing important segments of Western opinion that the *status quo* was beyond his Minimum Disposition.   According to the people so convinced, the West, if it asked for the *status quo*, either could not

---

[4] A further extension of this chain of "his estimate of my estimate of his estimate" etc. can be avoided in a mathematical formulation by using a normalization as a function of the preceding preferences (dispositions).

expect an agreement or would be putting forward a Sham Bargaining Position.

As a negotiator, I can try to modify the Minimum Dispositions or the estimated probable outcome in various ways. (A) I may modify my opponent's Minimum Disposition: (1) By altering the actual situation on which his Minimum Disposition is based. Particularly important are facts that make an agreement seem more urgent to my opponent than he first thought so that he will be willing to settle for less. The strengthening of forces or military advances during armistice negotiations belong in this category, as do threats (and actions to make threats credible) as to what would happen to the opponent if no agreement was reached. These actions represent bargaining moves in a broader sense and can, of course, be far more important in determining the terms of agreement than the negotiations proper.[5] (2) By pointing out the advantages and minimizing the disadvantages of my proposed terms to my opponent. (For example, the proponents of European integration explained to their nationalist opponents that the Common Market agreement could not really lead to the loss in national sovereignty that the opponents feared.) (3) By conveying to my opponent my (actual or faked) estimate of his Minimum Disposition. (This can easily be illustrated for economic negotiations: I convey to my opponent that I "know" that he can still make a profit if he sells to me for as little as . . . .) This may change my opponent's estimated Probable Outcome in my favor. (4) By portraying to my opponent a certain intrinsic development of the negotiations and convincing him that the *Negotiation Mores* require that he follow this development.[6] For

---

[5] Here we are concerned only with the effect of these bargaining moves on Minimum Dispositions. A more general study of negotiation will have to deal extensively with extranegotiatory actions in support of negotiations.

[6] By *Negotiation Mores* we mean the conceptions as to the "proper" conduct in negotiations, that are held by negotiators, their government, their domestic public, etc. Those who hold these conceptions generally believe that it is advantageous to conform to the "proper" conduct. Examples of such conceptions generally held in the West are: that a sequence of concessions by the opponent should be answered with some counterconcession, that one should adhere to an agreed agenda, that agreed solutions of

instance, I might demonstrate to my opponent that I made many concessions and convince him that he should reciprocate with a concession. If my opponent reciprocates to the extent of revising his Minimum Disposition, consideration of the Negotiation Mores must have led him to prefer agreement at terms which he originally found unacceptable. Thus, the Negotiation Mores become part of the negotiator's utility: violating them may cause political damage at home, make the negotiator feel badly, or aggravate relations with the opponent and thus spoil future negotiations.

(B) I may modify my opponent's estimate of my Minimum Disposition: (1) By altering the actual situation on which my opponent's estimate of my Minimum Disposition is based. Most important here are commitments, or "burning bridges." If a decision-maker convincingly commits his prestige to a prediction that he will obtain certain terms in negotiations, his opponent may be led to estimate that these terms, or something close to it, constitute the Minimum Disposition. (2) By convincing my opponent that it would be disastrous or impossible for me to agree to less than my proposed terms. I may use legal arguments, thus essentially say to my opponent: "You know that I am constrained by legal norms and I am explaining to you that it would be illegal for me to agree to your proposed terms; hence, I cannot do it." In disarmament negotiations the West is prone to use scientific justifications in an attempt to convince the Soviet Union that the West must insist on certain minimum terms. (3) By exhibiting attitudes consistent with a Minimum Disposition more favorable than my opponent's estimate. I may portray coolness towards the negotiations, suggesting that I am about to walk out unless the opponent's proposals become much more favorable for me.

---

components of a larger disputed area (e.g., agreed treaty articles) are to be preserved unless compelling reasons intervene. Among friendly countries the mores of negotiation are, of course, more important than among hostile governments; adherence to a larger set of rules is found both necessary and expedient. The reason for this lies in the continued relationship between friendly governments and the expectation (supported by past experience) of reciprocity in future negotiations. In the context of game theory, *Negotiation Mores* might be described as optional rules of a super-game whose violation carries with it a certain expectation of a penalty in the current or in future subgames with the same partner.

I may show total disinterest towards any proposals that are below my actual or fake Minimum Disposition by refusing to discuss them and reacting with scorn.

A number of studies on bargaining have dealt with various aspects of the process described here in terms of modifications of Minimum Dispositions. Corresponding to our above categories A(1) and B(1), changes in payoffs have been analyzed, particularly threats to affect the opponent's payoffs and commitments to affect one's own payoff. What seems to have received less attention are changes in the negotiators' expectations and estimates that are not due to factual changes in payoffs but nonetheless play an important role in the negotiatory process.

According to our model, the principal objective of a negotiator is to modify the opponent's estimate of the Probable Outcome and Minimum Disposition. In this effort, bargaining positions play an important role in the form of initial demands and offers, counterdemands and counteroffers, or positions regarding subsidiary details. In many negotiations, we may clearly distinguish between an offensive and a defensive side. The offensive side, wanting to change the *status quo*, often starts out with a *Prominent Demand*, which is combined with a clear threat, supported by elaborate justifications, and usually maintained during a large part of the negotiations if not to the end. Examples are the new status for West Berlin demanded by Khrushchev, a package of a wage increase plus welfare measures demanded by a labor union, or the extension of the limit for foreign fishing vessels successfully demanded by Iceland a few years ago.

In most labor-management negotiations, management does not view an increase in wages as an unacceptable outcome, although it will attempt to stay close to the *status quo*. In other words, the Minimum Disposition of management, right from the outset, is a change in wages to its disadvantage. In political negotiations, however, the initial Minimum Disposition of a *status quo* power is normally the *status quo* and nothing less.[7] Therefore, a *status quo*

---

[7] For the offensive side, the Prominent Demand may initially represent its "level of aspiration." But for the defensive side the initial "level of aspiration" is the *status quo* (i.e., its Minimum Disposition and level of

power is at a disadvantage if it enters negotiations defensively when faced with a Prominent Demand: its initial bargaining position is identical with its Minimum Disposition. It can make concessions only by revising its view as to what it initially considered to be the terms at which it would prefer no agreement. If it is concerned about reaching agreement, it will contribute to the erosion of its own Minimum Disposition, and third parties may hasten this erosion further. With the passage of time, the Minimum Disposition of the *status quo* power will be remembered more and more as an initial bargaining position (which, indeed it was, too); and according to the Negotiation Mores, such a position ought to be followed by revised, later bargaining positions. Third parties may mistake the difference between the Prominent Demand of the offensive side and the initial position of the defensive side as the actual bargaining range, i.e., the range within which both sides would prefer agreement to no agreement.[8] These third parties will then estimate that the Probable Outcome

---

aspiration coincide). It is our impression, however, that the concept "level of aspiration" is based on an operational definition that makes it largely inapplicable (or not very meaningful) to political negotiations. We might get ourselves into insoluble questions about estimates of feelings associated with a hypothetical event, if we tried to ask a negotiator (or a government!) whether he would be "satisfied" or "dissatisfied" with particular terms of an agreement (i.e., whether these terms would be above or below his "level of aspiration" as distinct from the question whether the negotiator presently thinks that he would accept or reject an agreement at those terms (our Minimum Disposition). Yet, many of the bargaining experiments concerned with "levels of aspiration" are highly relevant for the political bargaining process that we have in mind. Thus, Siegel and Fouraker show that if Blue makes many offers below Red's Minimum Disposition (which is constant in their experiments), Blue may decidedly shift Red's estimate of the Probable Outcome (and hence Red's counteroffers) to Blue's advantage. For instance, in the experiment reported on p. 77 in the Siegel and Fouraker book, the seller who made 14 unacceptable bids as against only 7 by the buyer won a much larger share of the payoff. (We are indebted to Daniel Ellsberg for pointing out this interesting relation.)

[8] However, there is no "actual bargaining range" (in terms of our model) in this postulated situation, since the defensive side prefers no agreement to any deterioration of the *status quo*, and the offensive side prefers no agreement to an agreement that would merely confirm the *status quo*.

lies somewhere between these two "extremes," and that a "fair"
outcome should be about in the middle.

Some Additional Problems

Our formalization obviously has to be developed further in order
to take account of the important aspects of political negotiation.
Let us just mention a few of these required developments.

As said before, political negotiation normally involves many
bargaining ranges, i.e., many more or less independent sets of disputed alternatives. Hence, our one-dimensional model described
in Figure 1 must be made multidimensional. In reality, negotiators combine outcomes (or estimated Probable Outcomes) on
several bargaining ranges into one over-all agreement, thereby
making comparisons between different utility scales. (Are three
additional inspections worth thirty per cent fewer of my nationals
on the inspection teams? Does the desirable agreement on an
under-secretary make up for the undesirable voting formula on
the budget?) These comparisons are themselves unstable, much
as the utilities underlying them. The negotiators will attempt
to modify the comparisons of their opponent, similar to their
effort to modify the opponent's Minimum Disposition. The
importance of the agenda is partly due to the fact that it provides
an ordering for these comparisons.

Another problem of which our formalization ought to take
account is the effect of the passage of time on negotiating positions. The prolongation of a status of no agreement may cost
one side more than the other, so that dilatory negotiation tactics
have an asymmetrical effect.

Reformulation of Propositions

FIRST EXAMPLE: SHOULD ONE MAKE
UNACCEPTABLE DEMANDS?

Henry Kissinger discussed the argument heard in the West that
one should not make "unacceptable" proposals. He objects to
this argument, in part because its consequence would be to con-

fine the debate between East and West to issues of embarrassment to the West.

According to our formalization, making "unacceptable" demands means to put forward a Sham Bargaining Position. What are the pros and cons of doing this? Sham Bargaining Positions may *improve* the chances of a favorable agreement because: (1) Our estimate of the opponent's minimum disposition is often very uncertain. We cannot find out whether we were wrong to our disadvantage unless we put forward what we think is a Sham Bargaining Position. In other words, if we try, we might discover that our opponent accepts more than we thought he would. (2) We may modify our opponent's Minimum Disposition to our advantage precisely by putting forward Sham Bargaining Positions.[9] (3) Given the fact that we are to some extent constrained by Negotiation Mores according to which it is bad to stand pat and concessions ought to be met by concessions, Sham Bargaining Positions permit us to show "flexibility" or to make "concessions" without seriously jeopardizing our Minimum Disposition. (4) Sham Bargaining Positions make it more difficult for our opponent to estimate our Minimum Disposition. (Our opponent has an advantage over us if he knows our Minimum Disposition and we remain ignorant about his.)

Sham Bargaining positions, however, can also be disadvantageous because: (1) It may be difficult to marshal public support for such positions. (2) Sham Bargaining Positions may cause my opponent to think either that there is no room for agreement or that I am simply unwilling to come to an agreement.[10] He may react to this by breaking off further negotiations. (3) Sham Bargaining Positions may delay agreement. (4) The sequel to Sham Bargaining Positions has to be (sham) conces-

---

[9] This is the mechanism described above on p. 250 as technique A (3). See also end of footnote 7.

[10] The former means that the opponent thinks there is no positive actual bargaining range. In the latter case he thinks that I am unwilling to conclude an agreement at this time, although there might be a positive actual bargaining range if I wanted an agreement. Sham Bargaining Positions may be used when no agreement is desired, but there is an interest in *pretending* that efforts are being made to reach an agreement.

sions (if my estimate of my opponent's Minimum Disposition was approximately right). This may set an unfavorable precedent for other negotiations because it indicates that my initial positions are not firmly held.

SECOND EXAMPLE: HOW TO AFFECT THE SOVIET
ESTIMATE OF A WESTERN MINIMUM DISPOSITION

Philip Mosely wrote that in negotiations with Soviet representatives "it is important to adopt in the beginning a single clear position, one which can be upheld logically and politically during the discussions. The Soviet delegation will not report this position as the final and strongly held one until they have had a chance to attack it from all sides. Indefinite repetition of arguments must be accepted as an inevitable preparation to negotiate.

In situations where this requirement prevails, Sham Bargaining Positions may be disadvantageous, since Western negotiators might find it difficult to uphold them "logically and politically." In such a situation, it would be better for Western negotiators to put forward a single position, perhaps one comfortably better than the Western Minimum Disposition, but—if possible—short of the Western estimate of the Soviet Minimum Disposition. Then the Western negotiators should defend this position as forcefully as if it were their Minimum Disposition.

THIRD EXAMPLE: NEGOTIATION MORES WORK TO
ONE'S DISADVANTAGE UNLESS OBSERVED BY
BOTH SIDES

Admiral Joy reported from the Korean armistice negotiations: "We Americans tend strongly to a line of action that we call 'being reasonable.' This means that each party to a dispute should be prepared to modify his position somewhat in an effort to achieve an agreeable solution. Yet, such an attitude is based on the implicit assumption that each party to the dispute sincerely believes his position is the correct one. We do not compromise with a man who insists that 2 plus 2 equal 6. . . . The point is that the relative reasonableness of initial positions taken must be considered before we decide that both parties in a dispute should give a little.

This passage reflects an interesting partial emancipation from the Negotiation Mores. The rule that concession ought to be met by concession, Joy argues correctly, can only be followed if doing so does not lead to a position one finds unacceptable. We cannot make a concession to the point of agreeing to what we think means 2 plus 2 equal 5. However, Joy proposes to make our adherence to the Negotiation Mores depend on the intrinsic "correctness" of the opponent's position, rather than on reciprocal concessions by both sides as long as both ask for more than their Minimum Dispositions. Politics is not like arithmetic, what is 2 plus 2 equal 5 to one side may mean 2 plus 2 equal 4 to the other. In politics we often do compromise with a man who initially seems to insist to us that 2 plus 2 equal 6, because under the impact of the negotiations we revise our Minimum Disposition and learn to accept that 2 plus 2 equal 5. Joy's own account of the armistice negotiations contains examples of this process.

part 5

GAMING (PSYCHOLOGICAL,
SOCIOLOGICAL, AND POLITICAL)

18

Some observations on
political gaming[1]

H. GOLDHAMER AND H. SPEIER

This provides an excellent over-all view of political gaming and stresses "free" or open gaming as contrasted with highly formalized games where all rules are specified and known in advance. One of the major differences between the problems analyzed by classical game theory and the problems dealt with in political gaming is that in the former, the rules are always assumed to be known; in the latter, this is rarely the case. In order to take into account the hunt for the appropriate rules, in political gaming, experts are often used as referees to judge whether moves or other actions are feasible or plausible in the diplomatic or political situation being simulated. The reader is recommended to see Thomas' and Deemer's excellent historical review of war gaming[1] and to consider and contrast this article with that of Guetzkow. In this, the stress is on operational gaming; in the other, on gaming for educational purposes.

Excerpts from "Some Observations on Political Gaming" *World Politics* **XII** (1959), 71–83 with permission of the authors, publisher and RAND.

---

[1] "The Role of Operational Gaming in Operations Research" *Journal of the Operations Research Society of America*, **5**, No. 1, February 1957, 1–27.

Political gaming has antecedents both outside and within RAND. Prior to World War II, political gaming was applied to questions of foreign policy in Germany and Japan, although we were not aware of this at the time that we started our own experimentation.

Before Hitler assumed power in 1933, the leaders of the German Reichswehr were much concerned about Polish military strength and political designs. The German armed forces were then restricted to 100,000 men in strength. In 1929, a young staff officer, the later General Erich von Manstein, charged with the responsibility for the organization of a war game involving German defense against a Polish attack on East Prussia or Upper Silesia, realized that the outbreak of war would be preceded by mounting political conflict. In that conflict, he thought, Germany would have to avoid giving France and Czechoslovakia cause for entering the war as Poland's allies and the League of Nations a pretext for not declaring Poland the aggressor. Manstein proposed that the strictly military exercise be introduced by a political game in order to let political and military leaders learn from each other. High-ranking members of the Foreign Office played the roles of the president of the League of Nations Council and of the Polish and German Foreign Ministers. In his recently published memoirs, Manstein writes that the inventiveness of the player representing Poland in alleging German provocations left his German counterpart "completely speechless" and that the skillfully simulated procrastination of the League was grimly appreciated by all participants. "We had the impression also," Manstein reports, "that the gentlemen from the Foreign Office, to whom such a playing-through of possible conflicts seemed to be completely novel, were thoroughly convinced of the value of the game."

According to exhibits offered in evidence at the Tokyo War Crimes Trials, the Japanese Total War Research Institute, established in 1940, engaged in games of aggression that involved having teams of high-ranking specialists in the Japanese government play the political and military roles of leading powers in the Pacific area. In these exercises Japan was represented not by one team, but by several—Army, Navy, Cabinet—and the views of these teams had to be co-ordinated before Japan as a whole could act. Some of the moves in this game anticipated actual measures taken by the Japanese government after Pearl Harbor.

RAND's interest in political gaming grew out of work in political analysis and previous experimentation with the use of gaming techniques for other purposes. For several years RAND has worked extensively with various sorts of highly formalized war games. At one point an attempt was made to devise a "cold war game" in which a few political and economic factors were assigned numerical values so that the relative worth of alternative strategies could be assessed quantitatively. Players were allowed only a limited choice of specified moves. This experiment was abandoned when it became clear that the simplification imposed in order to permit quantification made the game of doubtful value for the assessment of political strategies and tactics in the real world.

The first proposal for a political game of the type with which we have been working was made by Herbert Goldhamer in 1954. He suggested a procedure that avoided schematic simplifications of the international political situation and attempted to simulate as faithfully as possible much of its complexity. The government of each country was to be represented by a separate player or group of players. (In practice, of course, all countries never were represented, but only those regarded as most significant for the geographical or problem area around which the game was centered.)

In addition, "Nature" was to be represented by an individual or a team, and there was to be a team of referees. The role of "Nature" was to provide for events of the type that happen in the real world but are not under the control of any government: certain technological developments, the death of important people, non-governmental political action, famines, popular disturbances, etc.

Participants in the game were to be area specialists who could draw on their knowledge and accumulated area experience. With the exception of the American Team, all government teams were to act as they judged "their" governments would in the circumstances prevailing at any given time of the game ("predicted strategy"). The American Team was less restricted; it was permitted to pursue any strategy which it judged to be optimal; in particular, the United States Team was not required to follow the foreign policy line of any administration or to have special regard for the constraints placed upon American foreign policy in reality by domestic considerations. The game was thus designed to permit tests of a wide range of United States strategies.

The referees had the task of ruling on the feasibility of each move; that is, they were to disallow any move that they did not regard as within the constitutional or physical power of the government proposing it. For three reasons the referees also played the role of "Nature." This arrangement saved manpower; it restricted the number of arbitrary moves which might have been made had full-time players represented "Nature"; and it permitted the referees to make certain nongovernmental moves which constituted indirect, partial evaluations of the state of affairs that had been reached at any chosen point of the game. For example, the referees could introduce such evaluations in the form of press roundups, trade union resolutions, intelligence reports, speeches made in the United Nations, etc. (The governmental players were permitted, however, to challenge the plausibility of such moves.)

In the course of 1955 and early 1956, four political games were played, starting with the rules suggested by Goldhamer and gradually developing additional refinements. The first two games extended over only a few days. The third game lasted four weeks in the summer of 1955, and a dozen RAND staff members devoted approximately half time to it. The fourth was conducted during the month of April 1956. Three senior Foreign Service Officers from the Department of State participated in the fourth political game, along with specialists from RAND's Social Science, Economics, and Physics Divisions. In the fourth game, unlike previous plays, all thirteen team members devoted practically full time to the exercise, one of them spending part of it on liaison functions. In addition, a number of consultants were called upon whenever the development of the game required competence in fields of which the full-time players did not have special knowledge. The players were assisted by a sizable secretarial staff.   Prior to the start of gaming, considerable time was spent on the preparation of a "scenario" and "strategy papers."

Since the fourth game is by far the most exhaustive test we have given this technique thus far, the following observations refer primarily to it.   One reference to the earlier games will, however, be useful in order to explain what is meant by the "scenario."   In our first attempts at political gaming, we started with the historical present as a backdrop.   From then on, game events moved into the future under their own momentum.   It sometimes proved difficult to prevent the initial action in the game from being overtaken by or becoming entwined with developments reported in the daily newspaper.   The fourth game, therefore, was projected further in the future, with the opening moves to be made as of January 1, 1957.   The "scenario," written in March 1956, represented an effort to describe how the world of January 1, 1957, would look.   It provided the players with a common state of affairs from which to begin.   The scenario rid them of the intrusion of current news into the game and served to focus it on problems of special analytical interest.

In this game, as in the third, all moves by national teams were made in written form and submitted to the referees for clearance prior to distribution.   The government teams were generally required to state (to the referees) the motives of their moves and the expectations on which they were based.   The referees could challenge not only the feasibility of the moves but also their plausibility or the reasoning behind them; and if the government teams so desired, the referees could be asked to state their objections in writing.

Some moves were "open" and available to all teams; others were "game classified."   The referees determined the distribution of each paper and, as controllers of information, could "leak" the contents of "game classified" papers, in whole or in part, sooner or later, accurately or in distorted form; thus the referees served as surrogates for the intelligence function in the political process or for actual "leaks" of classified information in the free press. They did not act for the Communist press, since it is government-controlled.

Prior to the April 1956 session, the government teams drew up strategy papers.   These were "game classified" and were distributed only to the referees.   Also certain parts of the scenario were "game classified"—e.g., sections containing descriptions of certain weapons developments.

During the three weeks of actual play, 150 papers were written by the participants.   Many of these consisted of moves by government teams; moves were dated in "game time" and numbered sequentially with reference both to the action of each team and to the game as a whole.   "Game classified" background papers served to give the referees a basis for judging the motivation of any given move, and to provide a written record of the analytical thought relating the move to the strategy paper of the actual team.

The fourth game was focused on the activities of the United States and the Soviet Union with respect to each other and to Western Europe.   In the first week some major activity did develop involving the Middle East and some minor activity involving North Africa and Asia.   But on the whole these areas received secondary attention because of limitations in time and a determined effort to keep the game focused (and not because of an *a priori* judgment about the political importance of these areas).

Events of the game carried well into the summer of 1957 (game time).   After three weeks of play, the complete set of records was thrown open to all participants, including the strategy papers and all other "game classified" documents.   Time was allowed for the study of these papers, and then a few days were devoted to meetings of all participants to assess and evaluate the game.

In short, the game was so designed as to meet six main requirements:

1. *Minimal formalization:* The government teams were not limited to any prescribed set of moves, as is the case in a game like chess and in some war games; nor did the game contain any pre-established prescriptions automatically entailing certain consequences from particular types of moves.[2]   Such formalization would beg many questions that we regarded as the proper subject of discussion and inquiry within the exercise itself or as resolvable only by research outside the game.   Rather than work from

---

[2] In war games, these prescriptions are called "planning factors."

highly simplified and schematic assumptions up to a richer and more complex game world, we followed the opposite approach.

2. *Simulation of incomplete and incorrect information:* In foreign affairs, state secrets, which all governments keep with varying degrees of success, are important obstacles in the process of decision-making. In our game the introduction of "game classified" moves and their unpredictable handling by the referees tried to take account of this factor.

3. *Simulation of contingent factors:* In political life many events are beyond the control of the most powerful actors, a fact designated in political theories by such terms as *fortuna*, "chance," "God's will," "changes in the natural environment," etc. We tried to simulate this fact by moves of "Nature."

4. *Plausibility of game events:* We vested insurance against implausible game events not only in the political judgment of the referees but also in that of the participants responsible for governmental moves. We found no tendency for politically knowledgeable and responsible players to invent "wild" moves in order to relieve the tedium of the often slow and deliberate maneuvering of the governments involved in the game. Indeed, we found that some players in their desire to behave responsibly were at times unnecessarily cautious in their moves. We believe that continuing participation in political games resolves this difficulty.

5. *Clarification of issues:* Our aim was not to move on rapidly from point to point of the game but to clarify by discussion the issues raised in the course of the play. Such discussions took place during the game within each team before a move was proposed or on occasion between a government team and the referees, and after the game among all participants. Furthermore, we directed effort toward the clarification of intellectual issues by providing a focus of the game in the scenario and the strategy papers, by restricting the number of teams participating full time, and by selecting highly qualified specialists as players.

6. *Exploration of novel strategies:* We tried to stimulate efforts to meet this requirement by prescribing "predicted" and "optimal" strategies respectively to various teams in advance of the play.

The Social Science Division has carried on several discussions to assess whether the game procedure is worth the substantial investment of time and energy that it requires. The immediate stimulus to the Social Science Division's venture in this field was the difficulty of deriving from the results of research and from general political and military knowledge a sense of the probable trend of future international affairs and the most likely consequences ensuing from policies and military postures that might be adopted by the United States or other countries.

Evidently the principal difficulties here are those inherent in scientific and applied scientific work, especially in the social sciences. Any basic improvement in our ability to forecast the consequences of an actual or hypothecated change in the political-military world will surely depend on advances in our theoretical and empirical knowledge. Granted this, there still remains the problem of making the most effective use of any given level of empirical knowledge and theory. In this connection the political game was primarily envisaged as a means for securing a more effective collaboration of the specialized skills involved in political-military analysis. The political game provided an easily and sharply defined division of labor for the participants, and it gave them a more systematic means of adjudicating the conflicting claims of different lines of argument. It also demanded of them extensive and explicit statements of the political and military assumptions from which they argued. In these ways it helped the participants to achieve a more effective co-ordination of the knowledge and intellectual talents at their disposal. In addition the game provided, through its sequence of moves and countermoves, a "calculation" of consequences (anticipated and unanticipated). In this respect the political game is somewhat similar to the use of Monte Carlo methods, whereby machine simulation takes over the job of a purely mathematical derivation of results.

It should not be supposed, however, that the political game displaces customary forms of intellectual collaboration such as the writing of political analyses, by individuals or jointly, and seminar-style discussions. On the contrary, we found that one of the most useful aspects of the political game was its provision of an orderly framework within which a great deal of written analysis and discussion took place. In describing our experience to others, we have continually emphasized that oral or written discussion of political problems that arise during the game is one of its most valuable features.

Making effective use of a given level of knowledge and theory does not, of course, preclude advancing knowledge and theory through gaming. While obviously such benefits will vary from player to player and from problem to problem, participants in our games did find opportunities to check their suppositions, both of a factual and of a more theoretical character, against the game events. It is not easy, however, to derive these benefits, and we suspect that they often get lost in the process of playing the game. A critical and self-conscious effort is needed to retain these benefits in a more lasting and transmissible form.

We did not expect and we have not so far found that the political game enables us to test strategies or to forecast political developments with any real degree of confidence. Unlike a written analysis, however, the game does provide some testing of a strategy prior to the test made by history itself (if that strategy is indeed followed in the real world). However, the political analyst working in his study "controls" not only the political maneuver he is analyzing but also the responses of hostile, neutral, and allied countries. In the political game, the analyst must contend with responses made by other players and not those which he assumes will follow from the line of action he is proposing. In a fairly comprehensive political game, there are numerous plausible alternative moves that governments may make, and the one line of many branching lines of development pursued in a single game cannot usually be accepted as an adequate test. To test strategies and to forecast political developments would require several replications of the gaming problem. This we have not yet attempted. On the other hand, our experience does show that even though an over-all strategy may not be tested (in terms of a clear payoff) by a single game, players do become aware during the game of pitfalls and problems that surround a strategy or some aspect of it.

The requirement of the political game that the participants make definite acts on behalf of their governments provided a very real stimulus to political inventiveness and a keen realization of possible contingencies that in analytical work might have seemed less important or less likely. On several occasions in our fourth game, certain developments in the game suggested the need for particular types of contingency planning in the real world or anticipated events that did occur later.

We hoped that the political-military questions arising in the game would indicate problems for further research and that gaming would thus help to shape our research program. This proved to be the case, but probably the major benefit lay in the fact that the game served to suggest research priorities for problems of which we were already aware and to define these problems in a manner that would make the research more applicable to policy and action requirements.

We believed when we began our work in gaming that the political game would prove to be a useful educational device. Our experience (and that of academic institutions with which we have collaborated) has increased our conviction in this regard.

First, the political game provides a lively setting in which students of politics, acting as observers or apprentice participants, can learn a good deal about the structure of the contemporary political world and about some of the reasons behind political decisions. Factual information takes on a new interest and importance when it is required for intelligent participation in the game, and political principles assume special significance when they are illustrated by political actions and situations with which the student is associated as a participant. Needless to say, these benefits are realized only if the students receive continuous criticism from politically knowledgeable persons or participate in a game with such persons.

Secondly, the political game performs an educational function also for individuals with considerable political training and knowledge. We found that the game provided excellent opportunities and incentives for such participants to acquire an overview of a political situation and to amass relevant information that the ordinary intellectual division of labor and specialization by area or discipline do not make available. Some players found that they were exploring new fields of knowledge, some of which they had not previously associated with the conduct of foreign policy, such as developments in weapons technology. Area specialists were not infrequently made more keenly aware of the specific ways in which the world outside their area of specialization affected the politics of countries within their area.

A third educational benefit of the political games we played was to give players a new insight into the pressures, the uncertainties, and the moral and intellectual difficulties under which foreign policy decisions are made. This, or course, is in part a tribute to the earnestness and sense of responsibility with which the participants played their roles, since otherwise these pressures and perplexities would not have made themselves felt.

In conclusion we are setting forth a few variants in the form and content of the game that any thorough exploration of this procedure ought to test.

1. *Time:* In our experiment the initial scenarios with which the games began still resembled reality rather closely. The effect of more extreme deviations from current political and military reality in the game remains to be tested. For example, the character of the game might be strongly modified by a scenario in which NATO had been dissolved, various national states in addition to the present three nuclear powers were in possession of nuclear weapons, and the political leaders of the major powers of the world were replaced by unknown persons. Such a game, removed from immediate political reality, could conceivably lead to the discovery of entirely new problems and to new insights and provide a greater emphasis on analytical results or generalizations. It might also be of interest to play games covering *past* history.

2. *Tempo:* While the groups involved in the exercise at MIT played the game in rapid-transit fashion, this procedure has not been tried out by senior players. The best "tempo" of the game remains to be determined.

3. *Replication and variant strategies:* Fast games would lend themselves especially well to replication, and without replication certain results of the game cannot be validated. Alternatively, it would be desirable to have two or more sets of teams play simultaneously a game with the same scenario, or else to begin a single game with sufficiently large teams so that they could be split to explore branching strategies when important alternative continuations develop at any stage of the game.

4. *Predicted vs. optimal strategies:* Our own experience has been

largely, though not exclusively, based on allowing the United States Team to pursue any strategy it deems optimal, but requiring other government teams to pursue the strategies to be expected of them ("predicted strategy") in the given circumstances of the game. More experimentation would permit games in which the United States plays expected strategies and other governments optimal strategies, or in which all governments play expected strategies or all governments play optimal strategies.

5. *Scope:* There are a number of variants to be explored in which the scope of the game is changed so as to encompass smaller or larger political-geographical areas or more or less specialized policy problems. It is possible that the value of the game to students increases when its scope is enlarged, while the inverse relation may exist regarding the value of the game to decision-makers. The latter, however, will want some assurance that specialization of the game problem does not obscure important side effects of the policies involved in the game.

6. *Political behavior:* The game offers opportunities for studying problems other than policy choices and their consequences. For example, by simulating international conferences within a given game (which we have tried on occasion), additional data can be developed for the study of negotiatory behavior. To be sure, special arrangements toward this end for observation and recording have to be made in advance. Similar opportunities exist with regard to the study of, and training in, specialized political and economic warfare problems, the drafting of diplomatic notes, the study of the effect of uncertainty and stress upon decision-making, and a host of other problems that arise in the conduct of foreign affairs.

7. *International participation:* It would be desirable to have a few foreign political analysts play the roles of their own governments so that close consideration of each nation's interest would be increased. (Teams representing Communist governments could be composed of both American and foreign specialists.) It is to be expected that such a game, if carefully prepared, would substantially enhance among all participants the understanding of national "bias," collective security, the nature and problems of coalitions, and the viewpoints of neutrals.

19

A use of simulation in the study of internation relations

H. GUETZKOW

This is a report on a large-scale project to utilize gaming in a simulated environment involving international affairs.   The gaming has been carried out with undergraduates and graduate students and has been of value as a teaching device.   The extensions of this type of game for research purposes are discussed.   In my estimation one of the most important uses to be obtained from the type of game described here is having students construct it prior to playing.   The construction of game models serves as an excellent device for clarifying concepts concerning the functioning of political or diplomatic systems.   The amount of paperwork and "choreography" required in a game of this size is often not appreciated by those who have not been involved in such an endeavor.   If this game is to be made larger, more complex, or subjected to much analysis, it will be absolutely necessary to have most of the game prepared for computer operation.

Events, as recorded in all their variety in historical and contemporary documents, are the usual basis for the development of

---

Reprinted selections from the article "A Use of Simulation in the Study of Internation Relations," *Behavioral Science,* **4,** July 1959, No. 3, 183–191 with permission of H. Guetzkow and the publisher.

theory about relations among nations. These international events our theory must explain, and these events we eventually hope to predict. Such theory building—consisting of the development of adequate concepts and the relations of these concepts to each other in propositions—must encompass the welter of facts from life situations. Our theories of international relations—be they implicit or explicit—are the stuff from which we compose our policies, and write our newspapers and textbooks. This essay describes an initial effort to utilize simulation techniques as complementary means both for the development of theory and for instructional purposes.

Simulation is an operating representation of central features of reality. Simulations may take the form of war games, of pilot chemical plants, of ship-and-harbor scale models, of computer-inventory systems. There are a multitude of such representations (Malcolm). Will a social simulation of inter-nation relations prove to be of value as a heuristic device for theory development in international relations research? May inter-nation simulation be arranged to allow live participants to play component units for training purposes? Three exploratory runs of an inter-nation simulation in the laboratory of the Program of Graduate Training and Research in International Relations at Northwestern University in 1957–58 suggest that simulation technique may be useful for purposes of both research and training.

Background for Simulation

The efforts in simulation at Northwestern were stimulated by two streams of intellectual endeavor, one represented in the war game and the other deriving from the social psychological group experiment.

The war game has been in existence for many centuries. During the 19th century it flowered in the "rigid" game, in which complicated problems were played by military decision-makers with outcomes determined by elaborate rule books. During the latter part of the 19th century, the "free" game was reinstated, in which the game "director," a battle-experienced military officer, determined the outcomes of plays on the basis of his judgment.

Participants in World War I and II employed the war games as a training device—and in World War II, the device was used extensively as a quasi-research tool, for prediction of the outcome of military efforts, such as the Battle of Midway and the invasion of the Ukraine. After World War II the development of the war game continued, returning to more rigid forms with the cumbersome rule book being replaced by the lightning-swift programmed computer. From the point of view of the student of international relations, the flowering of a RAND Corporation effort—the military-political game, COLD WAR, as developed by its Division of Mathematics and the POLITICAL EXERCISE, as initiated by Goldhamer and developed in its Division of Social Science (Goldsen)—is most useful.[1]

The immediate impetus for explorations in simulation came from the author's work in the social psychology of groups. Since the 1930s, experimental psychologists and sociologists have developed face-to-face groups in laboratories to test theories of group interaction (Cartwright and Zander; Hare, Borgatta, and Bales). This work with contrived face-to-face groups has been elaborated in the laboratory study of organizations with component parts at both the Graduate School of Industrial Administration at Carnegie Institute of Technology (Guetzkow and Bowes) and at Case Institute of Technology. An inter-nation simulation may be thought of as another step in the construction of social systems, the contriving of an inter-organizational system.

But the deeper source for this work is found in the developments in decision-making, as exemplified in the work of Simon and Snyder. Simon and his colleagues developed their interests in decision-making from the perspective of public and, later, private administration (Simon, Smithburg, and Thompson; March, & Simon, with Guetzkow). Snyder and his colleagues developed

---

[1] We are most grateful to RAND personnel for the many courtesies extended during our visits to Santa Monica and Washington. Drs. John Kennedy, Robert Chapman, Olaf Helmer, Lloyd Shapley, and Milton Weiner shared their experience in developing the COLD WAR game; Drs. Hans Speier and Joseph Goldsen allowed us many hours for discussion of their POLITICAL EXERCISE.

their ideas from the perspective of decision-making in foreign politics (Snyder, Bruck, and Sapin; Snyder).

Description of the Internation Simulation

Contrived face-to-face groups, even when they are created in the experimenter's laboratory, are more replications of reality than they are simulations. The component units—that is, the persons participating in the experiment—necessarily respond to their social environment as human beings even though the environment may be artificially simplified. In the war game, however, there is more role-playing, in which the actors need to imagine many features of the military situation and respond to each other's moves in terms of these self-imposed role conceptions. Usually there is time compression, so that, for example, a month's warfare may be enacted within a day. The mechanical and civil engineer often builds his simulation by reducing his phenomena in scale. The operations research analyst represents the flow of traffic in symbolic form, so that he may use digits in a computer as simulation of a distribution of vehicles. In making such an analogue, there often is simplification, as when traffic is allowed only to turn left or right, even though vehicles in reality can make U-turns. All these devices have been used in developing the internation simulation. We have attempted to represent social units—nations, in this case—in their inter-relations with each other. We have simplified and reduced the number of variables involved. We have used both analogies and replication in contriving the parts. *Our simulation is an operating representation in reduced and/or simplified form of relations among social units by means of symbolic and/or replicate component parts.*

When one builds literary and mathematical models, one makes choices as to which features of a system are to be represented (Guetzkow). When building social simulations, such choices also must be made. One is forced to specify units and interrelations which often may be left abstract and general in verbal models. The concreteness to be embodied in this description of the internation simulation must not be taken seriously. As the work proceeds, revisions necessarily will make the representation more adequate. Eventually, variations will be introduced in order to check effects of different forms of the simulation. The choice of variables and the representation of their interlocking is highly tentative.

FIVE NATIONS AND THEIR TWO DECISION-MAKERS

In the three initial, exploratory runs described in this paper, five "nations" were operated simultaneously. During the first run, the nations were manned by one, or two, or three decision-makers. Those three units operated by one participant tended to be outward oriented, with less attention given to internal considerations. The nation which was operated by three decision-makers became quite bogged down in its internal processes, so that it had little time left for inter-state interactions. The unit manned by two decision-makers seemed balanced in its orientations. In the second and third runs, each nation was manned by two participants, senior and graduate students concentrating in political science.

In each unit, then, an "internal decision-maker" (IDM) made the nation's final decisions with regard to overall policies of the nation as they related to both external and internal considerations. Another participant served as "external decision-maker" (EDM), conducting the relations of his unit with other nations. The EDM reported to the IDM and might have been replaced by the latter. Yet, some IDMs used their EDMs as collaborators in their decisions. The two positions attempt to represent decision-making as it encompasses the nation as a whole, especially as the government relates to its resources and society, and as the nation relates to an external environment, consisting of other nations.

OFFICE-HOLDING

Considerable effort was made to embed the external decisions in the internal environment. The decision makers were under pressure to maintain themselves in office. Office holding depended upon the extent to which the expectations of the nation's validators (e.g., citizens, elites, juntas, and other forces which maintain decision-makers in office) were met. The probability of being maintained in office depended upon calculations made by the researchers as to how well both external and internal goals were being achieved by the nation in question. At the end of three periods of decision-making, the retention or loss of office was ascertained in each nation on the basis of random determinations (with the probability set as the average of the probabilities obtained for each period). By averaging probabilities, the decision-makers were able to take long-range points of view in making decisions which might decrease their momentary chances for office holding. Such a situation typically occurs in electoral processes in which there is delayed response to official actions. When the probability of office holding, however, decreased to specified critical levels, an immediate determination was calculated, even though the routine determination was still some periods off. Such consequences simulated revolutions and coup d'etats.

NATION-GOALS

In the experiment each nation attempted to accomplish its goals, which then served as a basis for its decisions. In two of the runs, the goals were formulated by the decision-makers themselves; in the third simulation, goals were assigned to the IDMs by the researchers. Goals included objectives such as security, domination, cooperation, and internal growth.

RESOURCE DECISIONS

Each nation periodically received basic resources which it could allocate to its internal functioning or utilize in external affairs, either as aid or as strategic strength. Its internal use of these resources could be distributed to its validators for immediate gratification or for building up of basic resources during the coming periods. These decisions were recorded on a decision-form by the IDMs, so that they might serve as one of the bases for computation of the probability of office-holding.

Once each nation had its preliminary goals and had learned how to make its decisions with regard to its resources, the simulation was put into operation. Besides bi-lateral interaction, the EDMs arranged for conferences of some or all of the nations, with and without their IDMs. The EDMs made treaties, giving aid with or without restrictions. The strategic strength of the nation was used for various purposes, including intimidation of other nations. It was possible for one nation to declare war upon another, alone or within alliances. Some nations endeavoured to build permanent forms of international cooperation. As the interaction developed, the nations were allowed to reformulate their goals.

In the first exploratory run, there were direct communications among the EDMs in bi-lateral contacts and at conferences. However, to insure perspective on the total scene by the decision-makers, it was useful to create a communication system beyond the one established by the EDMs. During the second and third runs, an external communications system was devised by the researchers in which events were reported to all nations, so that there was more understanding by the decision-makers of what was happening within the interaction system. In this "world newspaper" reports were made by the researchers on the office losses as they occurred, how aid was extended, how treaties and alliances were developed. In addition, the EDMs were permitted to publish communiques and announcements for propaganda purposes.

Perhaps most exciting is the potential which simulation models hold for exploration of contemporary verbal theories about international relations. It is feasible to simulate such characteristics as variation in size of nation, representing small and great powers in the same interaction system. It is possible to so structure the simulation as to have nations with rapid growth and slow growth in interaction with each other. We have an impressive literature which can provide hypotheses for examination within the internation simulation.

For instance, we might study the proposition by Haas and Whiting that although "the majority of alliances are concluded for purposes of self-preservation, the dynamics of international relations often transform them into pacts of self-extension for at least one of the parties." By examining the messages of the EDMs, we may understand the arguments used in persuading other nations to join alliances. Then, once established, we can check the extent to which the alliance now is used for self-extension. Consider Kennan's hypothesis, that international "conflicts are to be effectively isolated and composed" the more accurate the perception of the given power relationships surrounding the conflict. By asking our decision-makers to record their perceptions of power among the units, we can check whether accuracy in such perceptions does lead to more adequate conflict management in the simulation. Because of the costly nature of simulation, it will be wise to explore a number of related hypotheses simultaneously. For example, while one is working Kennan's hypothesis, it would be feasible, by varying the number of nations, to check Kaplan's notion that "mistakes or failure in information can be tolerated more easily if the number of actors is greater."

Gradually tighter bodies of verbal theory are being developed. One might use simulation for exploring these verbal constructions. For example, the theory of political integration created by Van Wagenen and Deutsch and their colleagues at the Center for Research on World Political Institutions might be mirrored in simulation. Would their prediction of a pluralistic security-community among the nations be realized when conditions of mutual responsiveness to each other's needs are simulated? (Deutsch et al.) Or explore Guetzkow's hypothesis that "the more adequately the members of a group envision the techniques of intergroup collaboration as means to their ends, the greater the tendency to move toward collaboration." It would seem feasible to explore Kaplan's constructs of state systems, such as the hierarchical system, even though no exemplification of this phase exists at present in nature. Benson has utilized Quincy Wright's "propensity-to-act" notions in his all-computer simulation.

Once we settle upon a particular design for the inter-nation simulation, it will be feasible to represent the assembly of existent nations. First, one would need to characterize each of these nations on the present variables which are incorporated into the simulation. Using these characterizations as initial conditions, the simulation might be operated, generating consequences—that is, predictions of the evolution of the present international system.

It would seem, however, undesirable—in the present stage of underdevelopment of simulation—to attempt to have our participants role-play particular countries, such as Spain and Indonesia. Would not such encouragement toward role-playing tend to secure reactions in terms of the presuppositions each participant has as to the nature of a particular country's reactions in a foreign policy situation? Then, as was done in the RAND exercise, we would be embodying our participant's theories of how nations are supposed to react rather than exploring reactions produced by the interaction itself.

Use of Simulation for Training

An inter-nation simulation may prove useful for training purposes in a number of situations (Guetzkow, 1958b). It may be used as exercise material in the training of policymakers, and it may complement texts and lectures in the teaching of international relations to undergraduate and graduate students.

As the war game has been judged of practical value in providing decision-maker experience to military executives, so the manning of an inter-nation simulation may be helpful in the training of foreign policy makers. The business decision-game, developed by the American Management Association, is found useful for certain levels of management training, especially as it allows specialized executives to gain over-all perspectives.[2] It was just in this respect that the RAND political exercise was thought to have been most fruitful. Goldsen reports, "The game puts a premium on the mobilization and reordering of preexisting knowledge in relation to a special focus, a focus on political action, policy thinking . . . and the analytic assessments of the consequences of alternative courses of action. Seeing new inter-connections of earlier insights . . . seems to have been considerably fostered by the game. . . " The inter-nation simulation, used in conjunction with substantive training in foreign policy, could provide quasi-practical experiences in the exercise of policy judgment. By making explicit that which is often implicit, the simulation would encourage the use of more sophisticated decision-making procedures. Because the simulation could be arranged to provide a constant bombardment of decision-events, practice in decision-making under continuous pressure might be obtained

---

[2] We are grateful for the many courtesies of Mr. Virgil Kraft in allowing us full access to their simulation without cost.

from its use by policy officers preparing for heavy interaction situations. Perhaps the inter-nation simulation can be developed as an adjunct to the case materials being used in the career development programs for foreign service officers in our Foreign Service Institute.

Undergraduate senior students were involved along with graduate students in the three initial exploratory runs reported herein. Seniors with an international relations course background seemed to profit from the experience more than those without. They felt they were actually making use of their knowledge, as they came face-to-face with the quasi-realities of foreign policy decisions. This opportunity to behave as responsible decision-makers increased their enthusiasms for further understanding of the nature of international politics. They felt they were plumbing the depth and extent of their knowledge. One of the students reported, "The simulation really brought me down to earth. I finally faced the complexities of international relations. All nations wanted their own ways and it's hard to accomplish what you want." The simulation might be integrated as a series of laboratory exercises in international relations. As Alger suggests for an international organization course, the simulation might be designed to demonstrate progressive stages of international structure, going from bi-lateral relations to international conferences, to intermittent councils, to continuous session international bodies without and with secretariates (Alger).

The graduate students found their experiences in the simulation rewarding in many of the same ways as the undergraduates. But in addition, they were most intrigued with its potential as a research tool for building explicit theory.

20

Experimental games:
a review

A. RAPOPORT AND C. ORWANT

The article from which these selections have been made contains a comprehensive summary of published results on experimental games up to the middle of 1961.

Theoretical Considerations

Literature on game experiments is rapidly becoming voluminous, but it is still possible to cover it in a single review. There are many ways of organizing such a review, depending on what features of the experiments are of central interest. One might be interested in the personality aspects of the players which have a bearing on the ways games are played. Or one might be interested in the effects of the conditions under which a game is played, e.g., presence or absence of communication. Changes attributable to experience are certainly of interest. Indeed the game

Reprinted selections from the article "Experimental Games: A Review," *Behavioral Science*, vol. 7, No. 1, January 1962, with permission of the authors and *Behavioral Science*.

situation contains many features of fundamental relevance to different aspects of behavioral science. After considering various possibilities, we have decided to classify the studies under review by the kind of games around which the experimental situation was built. In some cases, this necessitated breaking up a study and reviewing different portions of it in different sections, since games of different types were sometimes included in a single paper. We did not think that this procedure violated the continuity of our presentation. On the contrary, there are advantages to this sort of organization in that different foci of interest emerge naturally in different types of games, as will appear from our descriptions of the types and of the problems associated with their study. The plan of our review therefore will follow this scheme:

1. Two-Person Zero-Sum Games
   (a) with saddle points
   (b) without saddle points
2. Two-Person Non-Zero-Sum Games
   (a) Prisoner's Dilemma and related types
   (b) co-ordination games and related types
3. n-Person Games (n ≤ 3)
   (a) nonnegotiable
   (b) negotiable
4. Game Situations with Imperfect Information about Payoff Matrices.

A fifth category, so-called simulation games, is sketched briefly.

In what follows, we have listed some of the research problems associated with each of the listed categories of games.

ZERO-SUM GAMES WITH SADDLE POINTS

A saddle point in the matrix of a 2-person zero-sum game is an entry which is at the same time a smallest entry (negative entries are the smaller the larger they are numerically) in its row and a largest in its column. The indefinite article indicates that there may be more than one such minimum (maximum) in a row (column). It can be shown that if a matrix has several such saddle points, the corresponding entries are all equal; and moreover, their co-ordinates are interchangeable. Thus if (x_1, y_1) and (x_2, y_2) are both saddle points, then (x_1, y_2) and (x_2, y_1) are also saddle points with equal entries: It follows that if the normative theory prescribes a strategy choice which contains a saddle point, it does not matter which strategy (containing any of the saddle points in the matrix) is chosen: the resulting payoffs to each of the players respectively will be the same.

The rationale of the theory of the zero-sum game which prescribes the choice of strategy corresponding to the row (column) with saddle point is so straightforward and compelling that given the utilities as entered in the payoff matrix and each player's knowledge of them, it seems the only possible rationale. Here the normative aspect of game theory is strongest. Therefore, an experiment on a game with saddle points will naturally be guided by a hypothesis that the saddle-point strategies will in fact be chosen by sufficiently intelligent players. If the results confirm the hypothesis, little remains to be asked further. If not, it seems natural to seek an explanation for this presumed departure from rationality.

It is to be expected that saddle-point strategies will be chosen most consistently in the simplest games of this sort, namely in 2×2 games. In larger games, the crucial role of the saddle point may not be immediately apparent to the players. One might therefore expect that even if saddle-point solutions are not chosen initially, they will be chosen with increasing frequency after several plays of the game. Therefore, three variables will be of interest: the complexity of the game, i.e., the number of strategies available; the sophistication of the players; and experience in playing the game.

ZERO-SUM GAMES WITHOUT SADDLE POINTS

Here the well-known normative prescription to each player is a mixed strategy, i.e., a probability distribution on the available strategies, which has the property that the resulting expected values of the gains to each player respectively have minimax properties. In other words, by playing the prescribed mixed strategy, each player can assure for himself *in the long run* as much gain (little loss) as the constraint of the game allows. The rationale is no less compelling than in the case of games with saddle points. In practice, however, one can no longer expect these results experimentally, even in 2 × 2 games, with nearly the confidence which is justified in 2 × 2 games with saddle points. There are two important reasons for this.

First, the concept of mixed strategy is a sophisticated one. Not only is the proof of the minimax theorem which underlies the mixed strategy rationale derived from profound mathematical ideas, but also, given the knowledge of the principle, the calculation of minimax strategy mixtures is a complex computational problem. Even in the 2 × 2 case, players ignorant of game theory cannot be expected to carry out the computation as a matter of course.

Second, the rationale, in contrast to the saddle point case, includes the concept of expected value, i.e., depends on an averaging process over the matrix entries. This average is invariant with respect to linear transformations of the entries, but not with respect to more general transformations. We recall that the saddle point is invariant with respect to any monotone (order-preserving) transformation of the entries. This means that the actual utilities of whatever the players are playing for must be determined to a greater degree of precision in the case of games without saddle points than in the case of games with saddle points. Specifically, in the latter case only an ordering preference among the outcomes needs to be determined—a relatively direct procedure. In the former case, some such procedure as is suggested by von Neumann and Morgenstern involving preferences between risky outcomes is required for determining utility on an interval scale.

It follows that in 2-person zero-sum games without saddle points, departures from solutions prescribed by the normative theory cannot be explained in as simple terms as in games with saddle points. These departures may now be due not only to nonrational behavior or to ignorance, but also to lack of calculating ability or to utility functions which, although monotone, are not linear in the payoff units.

Nor is it a simple matter to pin down the factors responsible for departures from minimax solutions by controlling for some of them. For instance, showing the players how to calculate such solutions may well be interpreted by them as instructions to adhere to them. Their utility functions (if such exist) may then become irrelevant to their choices and the hypothesis of "rational choice" may be tautologically self-predictive.

PRISONER'S DILEMMA AND RELATED TYPES

The Prisoner's Dilemma type of 2-person game is represented by the following payoff matrix (Scodel, Minas, Ratoosh, and Lipetz):

$$
\begin{array}{c@{}c}
 & \begin{array}{cc} B_1 & B_2 \end{array} \\
\begin{array}{c} A_1 \\ A_2 \end{array} &
\left[\begin{array}{cc}
(x_1,\, x_1) & (x_2,\, x_3) \\
(x_3,\, x_2) & (x_4,\, x_4)
\end{array} \right]
\end{array}
$$

subject to the following conditions:

$$\text{(i)} \quad 2x_1 > x_2 + x_3 > 2x_4$$

$$\text{(ii)} \quad x_3 > x_1$$

$$\text{(iii)} \quad x_3 > x_2$$

$$\text{(iv)} \quad x_4 > x_2$$

The principle feature of this type of game is that for both players, Strategy 2 dominates Strategy 1, i.e., A_2 dominates A_1 for the row player and B_2 dominates B_1 for the column player. However, the choice (A_2, B_2) results in a payoff (x_4) to each player smaller than x_1, associated with (A_1, B_1). We have already noted above that no nonambivalent normative prescription of strategy choice is possible in this case. Therefore, even consistent strategy choices cannot be explained by rationality or non-rationality of the players.

A convenient index of behavior (i.e., a dependent variable) in this sort of game is the relative frequency of choosing Strategy 1. This frequency can be calculated over a sequence of repeated plays of the same game by the same pair of players, or over several players in a "one-shot" experiment, or in a grand average over both plays and players. Obviously averages of this sort can be questioned on several grounds. Averages over repeated plays throw away information about the effects of experience; averages over players throw away individual propensities to "co-operate" (choose Strategy 1) or to "defect" (choose Strategy 2). The averaging procedure can be defended on the ground of focusing on some other *independent* variables than experience or individual propensity; for example, experimental conditions, payoff matrices of several games, gross differences between *populations* of players, and the like. Therefore subdivisions of these studies will be according to the principal independent variable of concern to the investigator.

Modifications of the Prisoner's Dilemma game are effected in a straightforward manner by dropping one or more of conditions i–iv above. In particular, the dominance of Strategy 1 by Strategy 2 can be dropped. Experiments on some such weaker forms of the Prisoner's Dilemma game have been reported (Scodel et al., Minas, Scodel, Marlowe, and Rawson, Lutzker).

Another modification can be effected by dropping the symmetry requirement, which in the Prisoner's Dilemma insures that the game "looks" exactly the same to both players. We were not able to find studies on asymmetric games of this type.

CO-ORDINATION GAMES

In a pure co-ordination game, the interests of the players coincide. The problem arises from the absence of the possibility of direct communication between them. This problem is not really directly related to the strategic problems with which game theory is typically concerned. Nevertheless, since situations of this sort can be formally depicted as games in normal form, i.e., in terms of ranges of strategy choices open to each player, they have sometimes been considered in the context of game-theoretical discussions, notably by Schelling. This author has also brought out the role of "prominence" as a guide to strategy choice in co-ordination games. When it is important for both players to "read each other's mind" in order for both to benefit, the prominence or distinctive character of certain choices plays, or ought to play, an important part. For example, if two people must independently of each other name a point within an area bounded by a circle, under the condition that both win if they name the same point, but lose otherwise, it seems obvious that the center will be named.

No other point is conceivable, if only because no other point even has a name. The center, then, being the only distinctive point within a circle, has the property of "prominence."

Considerations of this sort belong to the psychology of "tacit agreements" and, as already noted, have little to do with the principal concerns of game theory. Still, it has been maintained, perhaps with justification, that in real-life situations which have been cast by strategic analysts into game form, considerations of this sort do play an important part. Therefore any method drawing on game theory and purporting to deal with real-life problems or with experiments in behavior should include considerations derived from the existence of tacit agreements and "telepathic communications" of this sort. We shall report experiments dealing with these situations under this category of games. If the interests of the players do not entirely coincide, we get modifications of the "pure co-ordination" game (cf. Games 11, 12.)

NONNEGOTIABLE n-PERSON GAMES

These are games in which the players are not allowed to communicate and hence cannot negotiate. Therefore, no explicit coalitions with attending side deals can be made.[1]

The principal theoretical result on n-person nonnegotiable games is a generalization of the minimax solution which has been shown to exist for all n-person zero-sum games (Nash, 1950). Since any n-person game can be made a zero-sum game by the addition of a fictitious $(n + 1)$st player, who has no strategy choices but who shares in the payoffs (wins what the others collectively lose and vice versa), the condition "zero-sum" is not an essential restriction in this case.

As in the case of the 2-person non-zero-sum games, the so-called

---

[1] There is another class of situations in which side deals cannot be made. These are situations in which the units of payoff are not transferable; for example, if they are units of some intangible "satisfaction." This remains true even if communication and bargaining are allowed. For a far-reaching theoretical treatment of such a situation see Braithwaite. Some experiments of Flood deal with situations of presumably the same type. In our terminology, however, nonnegotiable games shall mean only those where explicit communication between the players is not allowed.

Nash equilibrium point (the analogue to the minimax) cannot be considered as a normatively prescribed solution, because if a tacit coalition could be achieved among two or more players, the members could, in general, improve all of their respective payoffs by departing jointly from the Nash equilibrium point. Therefore, the experimental treatment of this class of games leads essentially to the same sort of questions as the treatment of 2-person non-zero-sum games.

NEGOTIABLE GAMES

The formation of coalitions is the main feature of these games. A theory of the n-person game has been treated (von Neumann and Morgenstern) essentially in this context. Characteristically they assume that the payoffs are transferable, conservative, and infinitely divisible; in other words, that a coalition can apportion its winnings among the members in any way whatsoever, provided only that the sum of the individual payoffs remains constant.

Once a coalition is formed, the remaining players can do collectively no worse and generally can do better if they also form a coalition. The n-person zero-sum game then reduces to a 2-person zero-sum game, where the theory is complete. Thus the only new theoretical questions concern the process of coalition formation and the apportionment of the joint payoff (the "imputations") among the members.

Each possible coalition, being potentially one of the two players in a 2-person zero-sum game (against the other coalition), "commands" a certain payoff, the so-called "value" of the game to that coalition. The association of this commanded payoff to each possible coalition is called the characteristic function of the game. The domain of that function is all possible subsets of the n-players (who presumably can form coalitions). The range of the function is the set of payoffs commanded by these coalitions.

The principal theoretical result of von Neumann and Morgenstern on negotiable n-person games concerns the "solutions" of such games. The word "solution" in this context departs so far from its meaning in common usage that it becomes somewhat misleading. The von Neumann and Morgenstern solution of an n-person game is in no way a prescription to any player individually, or even to any set of players collectively, concerning what coalitions they should form and what the associated imputations should be. A solution is rather a *set* of imputations with the property that for every imputation outside the set there exists an imputation belonging to the set which dominates the former. Moreover, no imputation within the set defined by the solution dominates any other imputation within this set.

So defined, the concept of solution has practically no prescriptive or predictive value in an *n*-person negotiable game. At most, it may give an indication as to which imputations somehow "go together"; that is, if there are continual shifts in the coalition structure resulting in replacements of one imputation by another, the concept of solution indicates sets of imputations within which these shifts will tend to take place. Note that this indication sounds more like a predictive than a prescriptive one. Moreover, von Neumann and Morgenstern are led to conjecture that the question of *which* set of imputations (which solution) will form the range of outcomes of an *n*-person game will be determined by extra-game-theoretical considerations, e.g., "social norms" and the like. Thus the predominantly normative game theory is once again forced toward empirically determined points of departure.

Experimental verification of solutions or of the associated social norms would be extremely difficult, mainly because a solution usually embodies a vast (typically infinite) class of imputations, and the number of solutions of any game is, itself, generally vast (also typically infinite). For this and other reasons, game theoreticians were led to modify the assumptions underlying the *n*-person negotiable game. The modifications usually involve certain restrictions on the dynamics of coalition formation or on the definition of a solution. These restrictions delimit the range of prescribed (or predicted) coalitions and imputations. The theory then becomes more "falsifiable" and thus experimental verifications become more feasible.

In *n*-person game theory, various attempts have been made to specify further what coalitions will form and to narrow down the number of solutions to be considered. Vickrey defines a *strong* solution as one where the sequence (1) an imputation in the solution, (2) a change to a nonconforming imputation, and (3) a return to an imputation in the solution, *always* means that at least one of the players participating in the original deviation ultimately suffers a net loss. A strong solution thus has an inherent stability not possessed by other solutions, and is therefore more likely to occur than weaker solutions.

Luce and Raiffa define ψ-stability as an imputation and a given coalition structure which is stable when no admissible changes in the coalition structure are immediately profitable.

From any given coalition structure, every possible coalition is not admissible. This concept, however, does not answer the question of what coalitions form, only the stability of coalitions once formed. ψ-stable pairs, like solutions, are generally not unique; the problem of how to select just one still exists. Luce presents another definition of stability for n-person games, the concept of k-stability, which is defined explicitly in the glossary. Roughly, the concept states that a game is k-stable if there exists at least one k-stable pair (set of imputations and coalition structure). Otherwise, the game is k-unstable.

The characteristic function of a game is the assignment of the value of the game (guaranteed minimum payoff) to each subset of players forming a coalition, assuming that the complementary set of players will also form a coalition. Consequently, this assumption of exactly two coalitions sometimes gives an unrealistically conservative value of the characteristic function.

Some game experiments, mostly those proposed or conducted by game theoreticians, have been guided by the above-mentioned considerations. Other experiments designed largely by psychologists, sociologists, etc., indicate a more empirically oriented approach, revolving around attempts to answer the question of what a set of people would do if placed in the typically ambivalent (strategically speaking) situation of the n-person negotiable game.

The interest in such experiments is not primarily to test specific mathematical models (since the extant mathematical models make hardly any specific predictions). Rather, the interest is akin to that of the naturalist who is beginning to explore a new area. We shall give below two examples of this approach; one involving group preference decisions (Flood), another, a simulated competitive-co-ordinating problem (cf. Game 29). Both experiments are, properly speaking, beyond the scope of this review, because neither has been cast into a standard game-theoretic format (extensive form, normal form, or characteristic function form). We are including them only as examples of less formal and more "realistic" approaches to experimental games; a subject left to others to discuss.

GAME SITUATIONS WITH IMPERFECT INFORMATION ABOUT PAYOFF MATRICES

These situations offer an opportunity to test theoretical models of the learning process as it applies to a small group of two or more persons in the context of a game. Doubtless the design of such experiments was inspired by the theoretical richness and at times the good successes of mathematical (especially stochastic) models of learning. The complications introduced by the interdependent effects of choices by the players makes the theoretical framework of such models even richer. The mathematical treatment, although at times exceedingly difficult, especially in its statistical, evaluative, and parameter-estimating phase, nevertheless remains rigorous and straightforward, thus offering opportunities for systematic, "cumulative" theory construction. These theoretical considerations are treated elsewhere, e.g., by Flood, Bush and Mosteller, and Suppes and Atkinson.

Actually, learning can be said to be involved even in those situations in which the payoff matrices are completely known to the players. For one thing, as has been pointed out, even straightforward solutions, e.g., minimax mixed strategies, are not necessarily obvious to naive players; and so, it can be expected that such solutions will become more frequent only gradually, as experience accumulates. Secondly, normative prescriptions are lacking in non-zero-sum and other "higher" type games, so that any stabilization of behavior in the long run can be attributed to "learning," regardless of whether the behavior finally adopted is more or less advantageous to the players than initial behavior. For example, in repeated plays of the Prisoner's Dilemma, the players may well "learn" not to trust each other, and so concentrate on the defecting choice, even though this choice is to their joint disadvantage. It is possible to construct learning models leading to just this result, even assuming complete knowledge of the payoff matrix by the players.

Thus "game-learning theory" encompasses even situations in which knowledge of the payoff matrix is initially available. Under the present category, however, we shall treat only studies in which such knowledge is not available. For example, one experiment (Suppes and Atkinson) in which the game matrix is known even though "learning" takes place will be subsumed under the preceding category (2-person, zero-sum), while those experiments in which the matrix is not known will be described under the present category.

Experimental Results and Comments

In what follows, we shall present the matrix of each game on which an experimental study has been reported with a reference to the study; next the purpose of the experiment, i.e., the questions asked and answered in the study, as revealed by the experimental results, and the author's comments and conclusions; next our own comments (so designated) including critical remarks and conjectures. Description of experimental procedures will be kept to a minimum and confined to those aspects which seem to us essential to the results obtained. This does not mean, of course, that other, perhaps unsuspected aspects of the procedure may not be equally or even more essential to the results, but this is for future experimenters to discover. For detailed descriptions of the procedures, the reader can, of course, consult the original papers.

Extensive literature exists on experiments in decision-making which can be classed as 1-person games, or games against nature, but these situations are not properly included under experimental games with more than one player.

TWO-PERSON ZERO-SUM GAMES

Game 1 (Lieberman)

$$
\begin{array}{c@{\quad}ccc}
 & B_1 & B_2 & B_3 \\
A_1 & \begin{bmatrix} 15 & 0 & -2 \\ A_2 & 0 & -15 & -1 \\ A_3 & 1 & 2 & 0 \end{bmatrix} & & \text{payoff to player } A.
\end{array}
$$

TYPE.   3 × 3 2-person zero-sum game with saddle point.

PURPOSE.   To see whether the minimax strategy pair (A_3, B_3) is predominantly chosen.

PROCEDURE.   15 pairs of subjects, 200 plays each.   Payoffs 1¢ per point.

RESULTS.   About half the subjects conformed to minimax predictions.   These choices increased during the game to more than 90 per cent on the final 10 trials.   The more often one player chose Strategy 3, the more often the other did the same.   Nonoptimal choices were made primarily to alleviate boredom.   The payoffs of −1¢ and −2¢ seemed approximately of zero utility for some subjects, while the positive payoffs had an inordinately high utility.   The certainty of the zero payoff apparently reduced its utility.

COMMENTS.   Except for deviations largely due to the boredom of repeated identical choices, the choice of minimax strategies in a 2-person 3 × 3 game (by college students) seems fairly well corroborated.

Game 8 (Deutsch)

$$
\begin{array}{cc}
 & A & B \\
X & \begin{bmatrix} (9, 9) & (-10, 10) \\ (10, -10) & (-9, -9) \end{bmatrix}
\end{array}
$$

TYPE.   Prisoner's Dilemma.

PURPOSE.   To examine the extent to which co-operation can be achieved in this game under various conditions of communication, and to study the influence of the orientation induced in the players.   (Deutsch [1960a] reports further results from the same experiment.)

PROCEDURE.   Thirty to 78 players, *one* play each.   Payoffs were in imaginary money; however, each matrix entry is assumed to be valued in dollars for purposes of the experiment.   The plays were conducted under four different conditions:

1. No communication allowed
2. Communication allowed
3. Nonsimultaneous choices
4. Reversible choices

In the first two conditions, strategy choices were made simultaneously and in secret, except that negotiation was allowed in Condition 2. A fifth category was run later in which choices were nonsimultaneous in Condition 2. In Condition 3, one player made his choice first; this choice then was made known to the other player. Condition 4 was the same as Condition 1, except that after both players had made their choices and they were announced, each could change his choice, and keep changing it, until neither player desired to change during a 30-second interval.

Experiments were also conducted under three different sets of instructions to the players.

(a) Co-operative. Each subject was led to feel that the welfare of his opponent as well as his own welfare was of concern to him.

(b) Individualistic. Only the self's welfare was to be taken into account.

(c) Competitive. Each player was to try to do as well as he could for himself and also better than the other.

In each case, each player was given to understand that the other felt the same way as he.

RESULTS. The data are summarized in Table 1.

As is apparent from Table 1, the opportunity to communicate resulted in an increased tendency for co-operative choices; the increase is greatest for individualistically oriented subjects. The competitive group neither engaged in nor expected trustworthy communication. Subjects given the co-operative orientation predominantly chose co-operatively.

A 10-trial game was run where subjects always chose simultaneously and in secret. Results were similar to the no-communication, simultaneous choice 1-trial game. The likelihood of co-operative behavior did not increase significantly over the extended

TABLE 1   EFFECT OF COMMUNICATION ON CO-OPERATION FOR GAME 8

Condition	N	Individuals Choosing Co-operatively	Pairs in Which Both Chose Co-operatively
No communication			
Simultaneous choice			
Co-operative	46	89.1	82.6
Individualistic	78	35.9	12.8
Competitive	32	12.5	6.3
Communication			
Simultaneous choice			
Co-operative	32	96.9	93.8
Individualistic	34	70.6	58.8
Competitive	48	29.2	16.7
Reversibility			
Co-operative	74	94.6	94.6
Individualistic	70	77.1	77.1
Competitive	62	36.1	36.1
No communication			
Nonsimultaneous choice			
Co-operative	46	78.3	73.9
Individualistic	48	20.8	4.2
Competitive	30	16.7	6.7
Communication			
Nonsimultaneous choice			
Co-operative	32	84.4	81.3
Individualistic	42	52.4	38.1
Competitive	44	34.1	27.3

series of trials.   "Choice behavior" over the ten trials was a relatively ineffective form of tacit communication.

COMMENTS.   Results from this experiment indicate a strong connection between motivation given to the subjects and their corresponding choice behavior, particularly in the co-operative and competitive choice conditions.   For the most part, these subjects

Experimental Games: A Review   297

behaved just as they were instructed to behave; statistical variations due to the other constraints of the experiment are apparent in the table.

Perhaps more interesting is the behavior of individualistically oriented subjects. Results are largely a function of the specific constraints imposed. Essentially, an individualistic orientation leaves the subject to his own devices, and he behaves according to the dictates of his personality. Thus, we return to the situation of the Prisoner's Dilemma: for those who co-operate, we can ask what price defection; for those who compete, how much reward in cell (1, 1) or punishment in (2, 2) is required for them to co-operate.

In another study using the same game matrix, Deutsch gave the subjects no motivational orientation. Each subject played the game twice, choosing first in the first position and supposedly having his choices announced to the second player (who was fictitious). In the second position, the subject was informed that the other player (still fictitious) had made the trusting choice, row 1.

RESULTS. Subjects who were trusting when they chose first tended to be trustworthy when they chose second; they expected the same behavior of the other player. Subjects who were suspicious and untrustworthy expected to be exploited by the other player; these subjects responded to a trusting choice by taking advantage of it.

The subjects used in this experiment had been tested on the F scale several weeks prior to the experiment. Their behavior in the game correlated highly with their scores on the F scale: almost all subjects making trusting and trustworthy choices had relatively low scores on the F scale; almost all with high scores on the F scale made suspicious and untrustworthy choices.

COMMENTS. It is empirically well verified that behavior on the Prisoner's Dilemma type game is a function of personality factors, whether induced by giving the subjects motivational orientations, or giving them none, in which case they supply their own, as in this experiment. It seems that in this type of game where "rationality" prescribes no precise strategy, the individual's motivation, whether inherent or induced, determines his strategy.

Game 9 (Loomis)

$$
\begin{array}{c}
\quad\overset{\text{II}}{} \\[-2pt]
\quad\overset{A\qquad\qquad B}{} \\[-2pt]
\text{I}\quad
\begin{array}{c}
X \\
Y
\end{array}
\left[
\begin{array}{cc}
(10,\quad 10) & (-20,\quad 20) \\
(20,\ -20) & (-10,\ -10)
\end{array}
\right]
\end{array}
$$

TYPE. Prisoner's Dilemma

PURPOSE. To investigate the effect of communication on the development of trust, and to see if a higher level of communication between subjects would result in more co-operative behavior.

PROCEDURE. 198 college students each played 5 trials. Player II was always a stooge, though Player I was not aware of this. The subjects were individualistically oriented and communicated by written note. Ten experimental groups were run, half note senders and half receivers. An eleventh group was run without communication, as a control. The notes were standardized forms expressing expectation ("I would like you to choose *A*"); intention ("I will choose *X*"); retaliation ("If you do not choose as I want you to choose, then on the next trial, I will choose *Y*"); and absolution ("If you do choose as I should like you to choose after first not doing so, then I will choose *X* on the next trial"). These statements were combined to achieve five levels of communication, ranging from expectation alone to all the above elements.   The stooge's responses were always optimally co-operative, incorporating all the above criteria.

RESULTS. The note was effective in establishing perceived mutual trust at all communication levels; perceived trust was an increasing function of the communication level. Of the subjects perceiving trust, 78 per cent were trustworthy; in general, behavior was consistent with perception. Of the inconsistent subjects, most of the risk-takers were senders and most of the double-crossers were receivers. Of the control group, only 10 per cent perceived trust, compared with 66.6 per cent of the communicating subjects.

COMMENTS. Other empirical evidence (Deutsch) has shown the increased co-operation resulting from communication in *individ-*

ualistically oriented subjects. Notable in this experiment is the increasing frequency of co-operation (perceived trust) obtained as communication became more definitive of the sender's wishes, intentions, etc.

Game 13 (Willis & Joseph)

$$
\begin{bmatrix}
(10, 20) & (0, 0) \\
(0, 0) & (20, 10)
\end{bmatrix}
$$
(a)

$$
\begin{bmatrix}
(10, 30) & (0, 0) & (0, 0) \\
(0, 0) & (20, 20) & (0, 0) \\
(0, 0) & (0, 0) & (30, 10)
\end{bmatrix}
$$
(b)

$$
\begin{bmatrix}
(10, 40) & (0, 0) & (0, 0) & (0, 0) \\
(0, 0) & (20, 30) & (0, 0) & (0, 0) \\
(0, 0) & (0, 0) & (30, 20) & (0, 0) \\
(0, 0) & (0, 0) & (0, 0) & (40, 10)
\end{bmatrix}
$$
(c)

TYPE.   Two-person non-zero-sum co-ordination game.

PURPOSE.   To investigate the effects of motivation on co-ordinating strategies.

PROCEDURE.   Subjects were eighty male undergraduates, instructed according to one of the conditions below:

1. *Self-interest.* Each subject was instructed to maximize his total payoff without regard for his opponent.
2. *Co-operative.* Each subject was instructed to do as well as possible for himself but advised that co-operating with his opponent would allow each to do better.
3. *Competitive.* Each subject was instructed to do better than his opponent, i.e., to maximize his relative total payoff.

In addition, some of the situations were identified as games, the others as bargaining situations. In all cases subjects had to agree on a trial for each to get a positive payoff; differing responses resulted in a zero payoff to both. There was no communication. Each pair of subjects played 50 trials of each of two games; half the pairs played the 2-response and then the 3-response game, and the other half played the 3-response, then the 4-response game. Subjects were rewarded in points and paid nominally. Additional pairs were run on Conditions 1 and 2, and paid 1¢ per 10 points. The average winning was $1.22.

RESULTS. It was expected in the 3-response game that choice 2 would predominate; it did not. When the 3-response game was played first, choice 2 ranked second in frequency; it ranked last when this game was played second. In the 3-response and 4-response games, agreement usually occurred in the end categories. There seemed to be no correlation between frequency of agreement and total payoff split over the 50 trials. Pairs of subjects playing the 2-response, then 3-response games agreed significantly more often than the other group. Self-interest and co-operative groups showed no significant differences with respect to total payoffs or frequency of agreements. The competitive group agreed significantly less often.

An interesting question is why solution (2, 2) in the 3-response situation did not predominate, although it was structurally prominent. Possibly this was because the several trials used meant that there was no longer strictly tacit bargaining due to intertrial feedback. The resulting partial communication may have obscured the logical choice. Instructions were not explicit about the structure of the payoff matrix; subjects knew only whether the game was 2, 3, or 4 responses. Points were indicated to subjects separately after each trial. Clear-cut learning trends were found in the self-interest and co-operative groups, but not in the competitive group. Apparently, there was no difference in point reward or money reward.

COMMENTS. Initially the subjects did not know the specific payoffs, but the actual amounts involved were indicated after each trial and subjects had a written record of them; therefore, we do not include this game in the "imperfect information" category, although it could be considered in it.

We would expect solution (2, 2) to occur in the 3-response game, on the early trials at least, for all groups, and selection of (2, 2) by the co-operative group to continue. Perhaps attempts made by one subject to collaborate on (2, 2) often resulted in a zero payoff, so that the subject preferred the smaller payoff of 10 to risking a zero payoff.

If another experiment was run explicitly showing the payoff matrices to the subjects at the outset, we would expect quite different results. In this situation, however, showing the payoffs initially would probably make the solutions too obvious to the subjects.

Game 16. Kalisch, Milnor, Nash, and Nering report the results of six *n*-person negotiable games presented in characteristic function form. Payoffs for the possible coalitions forming in the six games are given in Table 3.

PURPOSE. To discover what coalitions formed and how the payoffs were divided among coalition members, and to present, if possible, a theory of coalition formation based on the data from these experiments.

PROCEDURE. Eight subjects played four 4-person games eight times, a 5-person game three times, and a 7-person game twice. The games were co-operative and allowed side payments. Payoffs were in chips which were redeemed after the experiment. Before each game, players had a 10-minute bargaining period and were instructed that their objective was to form final coalition agreements which determined both a set of players and the distribution of any gains and losses accruing to the coalitions.

RESULTS. Members of a coalition tended to split the winnings evenly, particularly among the nucleus of the coalition. Once the coalition had formed, it tried to extract larger shares from subsequent members. Subjects tended to consider only the coalitions with large positive payoffs worth forming; initial coalitions usually consisted of only two players, who generally split winnings evenly.

TABLE 3 PAYOFFS TO COALITIONS FOR GAME 16

	Game			
	16a	16b	16c	16d
Coalition A	0	−40	−20	−20
B	0	10	−20	−40
C	0	0	−20	−40
D	0	−50	−20	−20
AB	60	10	0	30
AC	40	0	0	0
AD	20	−50	0	−10
BC	60	50	0	10
BD	40	0	0	0
CD	20	−10	0	−30
ABC	80	50	20	20
ABD	80	0	20	40
ACD	80	−10	20	40
BCD	80	40	20	20

Game 16e

Coalition A	−60	ABC	40
B	−30	ABD	10
C	−20	ABE	20
D	−50	ACD	20
E	−40	ACE	30
AB	10	ADE	0
AC	20	BCD	0
AD	−10	BCE	10
AE	0	BDE	−20
BC	0	CDE	−10
BD	−30	ABCD	40
BE	−20	ABCE	50
CD	−20	ABDE	20
CE	−10	ACDE	30
DE	−40	BCDE	60

Game 16f

Number of players in coalition	Payoff to coalition
1	−40
2	0
3	−20
4	20
5	0
6	40

The geometric arrangements of seating the players seemed to be influential in determining the coalitions formed in the 5-person and 7-person games; there were no apparent position effects in the 4-person games.

Although players were instructed to act selfishly and competitively, they frequently adopted a co-operative attitude.

There seemed to be a reasonably good fit between the observed data and the Shapley value, though the actual outcomes were more extreme. Milnor defines several bounds for the amounts which Player i or set S should get in any play of an n-person game. These "reasonable outcomes" are usually compatible with the data, especially in the 4-person games. Contrary to expectations, strategically equivalent games (Game 16a and 16d; 16b and 16c) do not show very close agreement. There is not sufficient data to test adequately the von Neumann–Morgenstern concept of solution.

Game 21 (Lieberman)

CHARACTERISTIC FUNCTIONS:
    Game a: If coalition (1, 2) forms, 1 gets 4¢, 2 gets 2¢.
           If coalition (1, 3) forms, 1 gets 4¢, 3 gets 2¢.
           If coalition (2, 3) forms, 2 and 3 each get 3¢.
    Game b: Coalition (1, 2) gets 10¢; (1, 3) gets 8¢; and (2, 3) gets 6¢.

TYPE.   Three-person zero-sum negotiable games.

PURPOSE.   To study coalition formation in 3-person games where Game 21a has a specific solution, but Game 21b has no precise prescription for each subject or each play.

PROCEDURE.   Each player, designated 1, 2, 3, chooses the number of one of the other two players. If two players choose each other, a coalition is formed which wins an amount of money from the third player. Game 21b required the subjects to decide by written communication how to divide the winnings obtained. Both games allowed written communication between moves.

Subjects were 48 Harvard undergraduates. Each player in

Game 21*a* received \$2.50 to use in the game; those in Game 21*b* received \$3.00. The game ran for 40 trials.

RESULTS. In Game 21*a*, the von Neumann–Morgenstern solution is for Players 2 and 3 to form a coalition to take 3¢ each from Player 1. For Game 21*b*, von Neumann–Morgenstern offer the solution: if coalition (1, 2) forms, 1 gets 6¢, 2 gets 4¢; for coalition (1, 3), 1 gets 6¢, 3 gets 2¢; for coalition (2, 3), 2 gets 4¢, 3 gets 2¢. This solution is nondiscriminatory although many other sets of imputations are possible. The Shapley value for Game 21*b* is 2¢ for Player 1, 0¢ for Player 2, and −2¢ for Player 3.

The von Neumann–Morgenstern solution for Game 21*a*, the formation of coalition (2, 3), occurred 70 per cent of the time over all 40 trials. Results from the second game showed unstable coalitions forming. As was expected, coalition (2, 3), yielding the smallest possible payoff to the winners, occurred most often. However, a large minority in the first game did not play the von Neumann–Morgenstern solution, and players in the second game employed an intuitive notion of trust, realizing that an advantage lay in entering a stable coalition with a player they trusted. In all, the von Neumann–Morgenstern solution has some modest predictive merit in Game 21*a*. The Shapley value had neither descriptive nor predictive merit. Apparently, behavior in the second game can best be described by the notion that the winnings should be divided evenly.

COMMENTS. From the results of these games, we can see some of the reasons for the difficulties in building adequate theories of coalition formation. Many empirical results have showed that subjects are inclined to divide proceeds evenly; Flood's split-the-difference principle applies. Though this may not be an optimal mode of play, it is more stable than many strategies offering larger shares of the winnings to individual players. Luce's theory of ψ-stability of coalitions generally fits data very well in situations of this nature. Solutions which predict an equilibrium point, i.e., the Nash solution, are perhaps a little too conservative, particularly in games replicated for many trials. Players invariably depart from this strategy, since they see that they can better their own winnings without jeopardizing those of their opponents.

A middle-of-the-road strategy occurs in most cases, not accounted for by theory, but decidedly prevalent in practice.

In contrast to the n-person game subjects who attempt to form stable coalitions with evenly distributed wealth, we also find situations where players are primarily competitive. This, however, is seen to occur more often in 2-person than in n-person games. Competition for its own sake is sometimes induced by the presence of third parties who may be integral to the game or stooges of the experimenter, or by motivating the subject to be competitive, or by giving the subject no pregame orientation and letting him follow his own impulses.

The amount of money available to be won is, of course, a strong determiner of competition or co-operation. Practically all the experiments reviewed here deal with small amounts of money, points, nominal rewards, or prizes to the outstanding subjects. None of the experiments pays really large amounts of money, for obvious reasons. However, it is plausible to think that subjects would act quite differently, both from a competition-co-operation viewpoint and also from the point of view of logically reasoning through the game situation, if several dollars were at stake rather than several cents. This leads to the question of utility which is a nonlinear function of money. We have already mentioned the difficulties encountered with the utility concept.

Not only are the experimental games nonrealistic concerning money, they are frequently nonrealistic as situations, and thought of as just "games." Subjects rarely are involved in these situations as they would be in a real-life problem of conflict.

In spite of all the negative criticism, these few experiments in n-person game theory have provided a beginning toward answering questions of conflict. Whether either the theory or the empirical verification of it can progress very much without the other is doubtful at this point. Certainly the experimental results have given an intuitive notion of what often happens in situations where coalitions must be formed, even if these results do not generalize to theory. The theory, on the other hand, has given us several ways to look at the experimental results, using different rationales which people might use. The interesting point here is not which theory or theories to discard on the basis of the data, but of the many different strategies which can apply in these situations and still be considered rational, since enough people have had reasons for using them.

GAMES WITH IMPERFECT INFORMATION
ABOUT THE PAYOFF MATRICES

Game 28 (Shubik)

$$
\text{I} \quad
\begin{array}{c}
\text{II} \\
\begin{bmatrix} (\ 6, 3)(\ 6, 7) \\ (10, 3)(10, 7) \end{bmatrix}
\begin{bmatrix} (1, 3)(2, 3) \\ (1, 1)(2, 1) \end{bmatrix} \\
\quad (a) \qquad\qquad (b)
\end{array}
$$

$$
\begin{bmatrix} (\ \ 2, \ \ 1)(-1, \ -1) \\ (-1, \ -1)(\ \ 1, \ \ \ 2) \end{bmatrix} \\
(c)
$$

$$
\begin{bmatrix} (\ \ 3, \ \ \ 3)(-1, \ -1) \\ (-1, \ -1)(\ \ 2, \ \ \ 2) \end{bmatrix} \\
(d)
$$

$$
\begin{bmatrix} (3, \ \ \ 3)(-2, \ \ \ 7) \\ (7, \ -2)(-1, \ -1) \end{bmatrix} \\
(e)
$$

$$
\begin{bmatrix} (5, 2)(-10, \ -13) \\ (4, 1)(-20, \ -23) \end{bmatrix} \\
(f)
$$

TYPE. Two-person non-zero-sum nonco-operative games with imperfect information about the payoff matrices.

PURPOSE. To investigate the descriptive merit of four game-theoretical solution concepts.

PROCEDURE. Five subject-pairs played each of the six games. No money was involved. Subjects knew only their own payoff matrices. Communication was not allowed except through a monitor who transmitted only the information about the choice of each player after every trial. Trial lengths were pre-selected and told to the players two or three trials before termination; games varied from ten to 22 trials. Subjects were told to maximize their individual scores.

RESULTS. Theoretical solutions (1) maximizing the sum of the payoffs, (2) the Nash equilibrium point, (3) minimax, and (4) maximization of difference in gain between the two players were used for comparison with the data. Predictions of optimal strategies for each game, corresponding to the above four criteria, are presented in Table 4. (Exact mathematical definitions are given in the glossary.) In Game 28a, we see that the players are strategically independent. This is an inessential game, i.e., there is nothing to be gained by negotiation or collusion.

TABLE 4   PREDICTED SOLUTIONS

Criterion Game	1	2	3	4
28a	(2, 2)	(2, 2)	(2, 2)	(2, 2)
b	(1, 2)	all	all	(2, 1)
c	(1, 1) or (2, 2)	(1, 1) or (2, 2)	($\frac{2}{5}$ row 1; $\frac{3}{5}$ col. 1)*	(1, 2)
d	(1, 1)	(1, 1) or (2, 2)	($\frac{3}{7}$ row 1; $\frac{3}{7}$ col. 1)	all
e	(1, 1)	(2, 2)	(2, 2)	(2, 2)
f	(1, 1)	(1, 1)	(1, 1)	all

* Mixed minimax strategies where the probability, p_i, is of playing row 1. $1 - p_i$ is the probability of playing row 2; similar definitions apply for column.

The last five trials were used to test the hypothesis that the nonco-operative solution theory (Nash equilibrium point) is the best predictor.

In Game 28a, all four solution theories predict the same strategy pair and are in accord with the data. In Game 28b, Solutions 1 and 4 must be rejected; Solutions 2 and 3 have no power of resolution. Subjects seemed to prefer Solution (2, 2) giving Player I a payoff of 2 and Player II a payoff of 1. Solutions 1 or 2 account for all the data in Game 28c; Solutions 3 and 4 must be rejected. In Game 28d, Solutions 1 and 2 are consistent with the data of four of the five pairs. Solution 3 must be rejected; Solution 4 has no resolution power. Solutions 2, 3, and 4 are acceptable for Game 28e; Solution 1 must be rejected. In Game 28f, Solutions 1, 2, and 3 agree with the data; Solution 4 has no power of resolution.

The Nash equilibrium point (Solution 2) was never at odds with the data, although it did not always have power of resolution.

COMMENTS. It is interesting to note in Game 28b that the strategy settled on gave a maximum payoff to I and a minimum payoff to II. This could occur simply from lack of co-ordination; it could also occur if I was attempting to do the best possible for himself and better than his opponent. It is still difficult, however, to rationalize these results on any grounds.

Game 28e was a Prisoner's Dilemma game. At least half the subjects were able to locate their opponent's maximum and minimum matrix entries (according to a written questionnaire given after the experiment). In addition to learning occurring, apparently many subject pairs tried tacit signalling, closely connected with threat strategies.

Although initially players in these games lacked information about their opponent's payoff matrices, an umpire announced the choices of both players after each trial; subjects were permitted to record this information. After a few trials, subjects should have been in a fairly good position to determine what strategy was preferred, even if they could not make accurate guesses about the opponent's payoff matrix. Directly following the experiment, subjects were asked to estimate what they thought their opponents' matrices were; these estimates were accurate for Games 28a and 28f, where optimal strategies coincided; misperceptions were more frequent for the other games.

At any rate we would expect a learning situation to occur in these games, as it did. It would be most interesting to apply the several behavioral hypotheses of Suppes and Atkinson to these games. Though it was hypothesized that the Nash solution would best fit the data, as perhaps it did, the predictions based on it did not have outstanding merit. The other solution concepts contribute to the evidence that game theory is not descriptive and will not predict human behavior, especially in games with imperfect information about the payoff matrices.

21

Experimental games and bargaining theory

THOMAS C. SCHELLING

Schelling presents a cogent argument for the use of gaming in the study of international affairs, touching on its value for experimentation and as a teaching device as well. These excerpts do not include the specific rules and description of the gaming exercise utilized by Schelling. Possibly one of the most important of the didactic uses of gaming is the construction of games. The constructing of a playable interesting game to study a bargaining situation or to serve as a background for some process of interest is an excellent way to learn about model building in general.

Games have been used in the study of international politics; if they were not so demanding of time and energy, they would probably be used more. A Berlin crisis, or a busy day in the life of the United Nations, lends itself to this procedure. Participants usually represent "countries" and they may be encouraged to play the "role" of the country, acting as they believe the country would act, or they may be encouraged to behave in the game as

Reprinted from *World Politics*, **XIV**, October 1961, No. 1, 47–68, with the permission of the author and publisher.

they believe the country ought to behave in its own interest. The game may be organized for research, the participants being scholars and policy analysts; or it may be organized as training, to give students vicarious experience in the complexities of international politics.

And *complexities* are precisely what the game usually generates. Games organized for the benefit of students are invariably reported as having opened their eyes, in an unprecedented way, to the varieties of choice that can confront nations, to the varieties of interpretation that can be put on a country's behavior, to the great cloak of detail that surrounds even the simplest international crisis, and to the limitations on formal theory as a guide to international conduct in the real world. These complexities motivate, too, the games organized to examine a problem rather than to raise the sophistication of a student; part of the rationale of game organization is that no straightforward analytical process will generate a "solution" to the problem, predict an outcome, or produce a comprehensive map of the alternative routes, processes, and outcomes that are latent in the problem.

Games do generate these complexities and, by most reports, do it in a fruitful and stimulating way. If an understanding of international politics requires familiarity with both theory and practice, busy games seem to provide an important touch of practice. But though they may be peculiarly suitable for bringing out the rich complexity of international processes, games are not limited in principle to that end of the scale. Frequent references to chess remind us that more austere games may be useful in the study of bilateral or multilateral conflict. The more abstract and stylized game can certainly not pretend to provide vicarious experience in the practice of international politics, but it may have a role in the theory.

A game may be useful in revealing the *structure* of conflicts rather than the details. A game may be useful in the articulation of a theoretical model if it is designed for that purpose, just as games richer in detail may help to fit theory into its institutional context. The purposes do not necessarily compete with each other, nor do the games. It is worthwhile to examine international politics in all its complexity, and worthwhile to examine the underlying structure by the use of an abstract model.   Similarly, games may be helpful at either end of the spectrum, or in between.

The methodology will be different, though.   One kind of game may be used to elucidate a theoretical model, the other to show its limitations.   One may be used to bring out the order, the rationality, and the coherence of the international structure; the other to illustrate the disorder, the irrationality, and the incoherence.   Depending on the purpose and what is to be emphasized, one not only designs the game differently but defines the purpose differently.   One can question whether an experimental game serves an essential purpose, or even any useful purpose, toward the end of the spectrum that can be encompassed by a theoretical model.   Toward the other end, where theory meets its limitations, some need to generate a "sample" of vicarious experience may seem to be compelling; but the haphazard quality of game playing, while helpful in supplementing theoretical models, might seem to be precisely what one wants to eliminate in examining the theory itself.

The question is a sound one, but it does admit an answer. Even the most austere and economical theoretical model is unlikely to be fully determinate.   It will be too complex to yield to any straightforward comprehensive analysis.   It is not usually a mathematical problem to be "solved," but a model that generates a variety of potential behavior even within the framework of a few variables and constraints.   Furthermore, among the processes that it leaves indeterminate will be some that inherently involve the interaction of two or more decision centers.

For this reason there is likely to be, even within the simplified model, some scope for "free activity," for bargaining, for the reaching of understandings and misunderstandings, for accommodation and co-operation, and for conjectures about each other's decision processes, value systems, and information.   The theoretical model is thus usually not a comprehensive specification of how the participants behave, but rather a specification of the framework within which they pursue certain objectives according to certain criteria.   What the model leads to in terms of *behavior* of the participants is usually beyond the reach of straightforward analysis.

Even if it is not, the game itself may be a fruitful way of developing a working acquaintance with a theoretical structure. Just designing the game, checking it for internal consistency and for whether it contains the essentials of the desired theoretical model, can be a useful exercise and sometimes a check on the consistency of the concepts in the model. The game furthermore provides an extensive definition of the terms of the theory, and may facilitate communication and comparison. One can point to phenomena that the game generates, and not be limited to abstract characterizations of what he has in mind.

But the game can go one step farther. A theoretical model often has the characteristic that it is not formally or mathematically determinate of behavior even for fully rational participants who understand the game. The reason is that, among the phenomena of international politics that a theory wants to elucidate, are the processes of understanding and misunderstanding. The theory may therefore want to leave scope for misunderstandings, as well as understandings; and a game designed to correspond to the theory will want to provide for behavior that can lead to understandings and misunderstandings. And there is no straightforward way, no formal analytical way, for ordinary "rational" analysis to anticipate the outcome. The reason is simple: it takes two to make a misunderstanding.

Consider an example. A theoretical model permits certain kinds of communication; correspondingly, a theoretically oriented game permits the transmittal of messages. How can we discover the various ways in which a message may be misinterpreted? Keep in mind that the misinterpretations that the sender of a message can perceive and anticipate, he can guard against; the ones that matter most are those he cannot perceive in advance. The question then becomes, how do we identify the possible interpretations of a message that did not occur to the person who sent it? Putting it more crudely, and more generally, how can an analyst draw up a list of the things that would never occur to him? If the essence of the game is that there are two or more separate participants, two or more centers of consciousness and of decision, we can generate understandings and misunderstandings. Thus the "game" formulation of the theory is a meaningful one; it can contain something essential to the theory. And to study it in relation to the theory—in a sufficiently abstract model to permit theoretical handling, and the isolation of critical variables—an austere, abstract, stylized, theoretical game may have a use.

A Game for the Study of Theory

This paper is about such a game, in a research project just being initiated. It is an experimental study of the bargaining process involved in limited war and other conflicts, a process in which bargaining is by maneuver as much as by words, in which communication is poor, legal enforcement is unavailable, and the participants make irreversible moves while they bargain, are uncertain about each other's values, and have some power to inflict gratuitous damage on each other. The research will utilize variants of an experimental game.

The game in its present form bears no particular resemblance to war. It does use a map, but so do a lot of children's games. It may remind one of the game that goes under the name of "Salvo" or "Battleship," in which each player places his ships on a set of squares and takes turns firing at the other's ships whose whereabouts he can learn only when the other reports a hit. But there is a difference between the game proposed here and the familiar two-person parlor games.

The difference is that two-person parlor games are always "zero-sum" games—games of pure conflict in which one's gain is the other's loss. Mutual gain and mutual loss are out of the question; and bargains, threats, and co-operation—even grudging co-operation—cannot occur if both players understand the game and play to win. In the game proposed here that is not so. Some outcomes are better for both players than others and the player is to be motivated to get the highest *absolute* score for himself, not to impose a low score on an opponent, and *not* to concern himself with his *relative* score.

The fundamental idea is that war—whether a "fighting" war or a process of strategic maneuver—is not a zero-sum game. It requires at least some co-operation or accommodation between the two sides. It is a "bargaining situation," in which the conflict and the interdependence are inseparable. While secrecy may play a role, it is usually necessary to reveal preferences to reach efficient trades and compromises, to make threats credible, and to demonstrate inability to comply with proposals and threats. It is important to impress on the opponent (partner) some truth about one's own mode of behavior. Communicating one's intentions and what one expects of the other is important to successful play, and is necessarily a preoccupation of the players. The players are both partners and adversaries, as concerned to avoid severe mutual damage as to gain at the expense of each other.

This kind of situation does not arise in the traditional parlor games.[1] This is why a game like chess has only a limited relevance as a "war game." If one wants to study an actual parlor-type game—an abstract, formalized game—to get insight into the strategy of limited war or the strategy of threats, reprisals, deterrence, and bargaining, there are no ready-made games available. It has been necessary to invent a game.

The game used in this research has been designed to require co-ordination of strategies and to make co-ordination difficult. It has been designed to make it difficult to identify an obviously "fair" or symmetrical outcome. It has been designed to require no significant technical skill that has to be acquired through repeated plays. The skill involved is intended to be more akin to bargaining skills, strategic ingenuity, skill in coercing an opponent, rather than skill in the mechanics of the game itself.

The game differs from traditional war games in two respects. First, virtually all war games have been either explicitly or implicitly "zero-sum" games. They have involved no scope for collaboration between the adversaries; any motivation toward "winning" has been toward winning over the opponent, outdoing the opponent, winning relative to the opponent (except to the extent that, as in tennis, one may be interested in displaying style as well as in winning). Second, this game is not designed to look much like war; it is designed for minimum technical complexity. It is

---

[1] The reason probably is that non-zero-sum games are no fun unless actual rewards are provided—i.e., unless the partners (competitors, rivals) can jointly beat the "house."

designed for research rather than training. (It does appear, though, to have some important value in the communication of ideas.) It is designed to have a simple enough structure, and few enough variables and parameters, to permit measurement, classification, manipulation, and analysis, in accordance with a theoretical framework. It is also designed to be economical in the interest of repeated plays, and to be capable of reproduction without access to unique materials.

It should be emphasized that in this game players are supposed to play to win. While in some variants there will be a scenario and other details suggestive of some "real" situation, it is not intended that subjects play any such version of it in a "role-playing" sense. The players are not to imitate decision-makers in some real situation that the game is trying to mimic. For the purpose of this game, in contrast to certain very different-looking and less stylized war games and, especially, "political games," one is playing to maximize his score and not for any other purpose.

This poses a problem. Players have to interest themselves in their absolute scores, not just in how well they beat an adversary. While competitive spirit is precisely what one wants in studying a zero-sum game, like most parlor games, and can usually be relied on to make people value precisely the kind of score they are supposed to be maximizing, it cannot be relied on to make people interested in their *absolute* scores in a two-person game. Money rewards are therefore used, both to appeal to profit motives and to dramatize the payoff structure of the game and to attach symbolic value to it.

Theory and Methodology

The basic notion underlying the use of an experimental game in an empirical study of the "bargaining process" is that formal theory—game theory, for example—is inadequate by itself, and necessarily so, in the study of bargaining games. Games of this sort necessarily contain an element of indeterminacy; the constraints imposed by the quantitative structure of the game are insufficient to determine a solution, even for "rational," internally consistent, strategies of behavior by the participants. In any game of this sort there is some need for the concerting of action, for reaching understandings, for communicating and inferring intentions, for arriving at consistent expectations of each other, and for the development of norms, traditions, or other constraints analogous to the limits in limited war. How the participants can interact to teach a shared expectation, how they can invent means of signaling their intentions, what kinds of rules and traditions they can perceive and recognize jointly cannot be arrived at by *a priori* reasoning, even by ideally rational players. There is an essential element of empirical study involved.

This is not, it should be emphasized, simply a matter of players' behaving in practice in a manner different from what a theory of rational behavior would suggest. Rather it is that players are capable, at least in some circumstances, of doing a good deal better than a purely formal theory of rational behavior could account for. How it is that they can do better is a question that, though amenable to theoretical analysis, ultimately requires empirical confirmation.

The possible relevance of experimental work seems demonstrated by some experiments with questionnaires than can be considered "one-move" non-zero-sum games. The research initiated with this new game can be viewed as an attempt to do for bargaining extended over time what the questionnaire did for one-shot games.

An important question is whether the conclusions reached, or the phenomena observed, can be generalized to cover actual conflict situations, actual bargaining processes, of which limited war may be the most vivid example. Here it should first be said that a game of this sort is not intended to reproduce all the significant characteristics of a real conflict; it is not intended to epitomize real, live conflict or to constitute a "well-balanced" model in which all elements receive proper emphasis. It is intended rather to single out aspects of the problem that provide a coherent subject for analysis and are susceptible of experimental simulation in the laboratory. A game of this sort focuses mainly on the perceptual and cognitive processes of the participants, rather than on emotional behavior or individual value systems. (So far as possible the player's value system is provided him by the game itself;

and while emotional involvement is undoubtedly present, even if we try to keep it out, it is on a different scale from the duress, tension, preoccupation, and panic that might occur in a real, live conflict situation.)

The game furthermore is limited in its relevance to the behavior of individuals (or perhaps very small groups) and to those aspects of organizational behavior, bureaucratic behavior, group political behavior, and other collective decision processes that most depend on, or are limited by, the capabilities and characteristics of individuals, or at least in which the capabilities and characteristics of individual decision processes can be isolated in analysis.

What makes a game of this sort, limited as it is, attractive as a means of coming to grips with some aspects of limited war and similar conflicts is that we are poor in alternative ways of studying the phenomena empirically. We are generally limited to intensive studies of a few particular cases. The knowledge we can get from experimenting with a game may not be comprehensive or terribly reliable, but, compared with what we have or can get in any other way, it looks good.

There is another reason for supposing that even a quite artificial game can produce results of real significance. A great many propositions about limited war, industrial disputes, etc., are phrased in such general terms, and based on reasoning or evidence of such simplicity and generality, that they would have to apply to a situation as simple and artificial as the kind of game described above. In other words, even if we are skeptical about the propositions that can be proved by the evidence of a game of this sort, a good deal of the existing theory, or lore, is susceptible of being disproved.

Consider, for example, propositions about the advantage or disadvantage of communication between adversaries in limited war, or propositions about the tendency for certain bargaining processes to display outcomes that have some property of "equality" or "symmetry." Many of these seem to be based on very general observation and introspection, expressed in phrases like "It stands to reason that . . ." or "No one would ever. . . ." A game of the sort described *can* demonstrate, with respect to a proposition, that its truth does not follow from any simple universal observation or intuitive hunch. The proposition may, of course, still be true; but if the reasoning and the evidence can be discredited, it must be abandoned unless new grounds for it can be found.

Take specifically the following question: if in a game like the one described here, which involves a great deal of ignorance on the part of each player about the other's value system, or even in one that involves (as the specific form of the game described above does not) ignorance about some of the moves available to the other player or the moves he has already made, a proposal is made to improve the players' knowledge about each other's value systems, moves available, positions reached, etc., what do we anticipate about the advantages and disadvantages to the two players? A proposition frequently expressed is "It stands to reason that the player to whom we give the greater knowledge about his opponent receives the advantage." Of course, in a game of this sort, both players can be advantaged or disadvantaged simultaneously, it being a non-zero-sum game; this pointed out, the proposition may be rephrased to the effect that the greater gain, or the relative advantage, is bound to go (other things being equal) to the one who gets the greater information. This proposition is based on faulty reasoning, but it seems compatible with intelligence and sophistication. If it is false, as is conjectured here, its falsity can be demonstrated by a game as simple and artificial as the one proposed. Those who hold to a proposition of this sort are likely to hold it on the basis of very general considerations—considerations so general as to be contradicted if the proposition proved to be strikingly false in regard to a simple little game that, simple as it is, is as complex as the theoretical model that was implicitly in mind when the proposition was voiced.

This example illustrates another aspect of the methodology involved in a game like this one. When a game simple enough to be analyzable produces a result contrary to expectation, it is likely to produce it for reasons that become apparent once the phenomenon is observed, particularly when it is observed in relation to the structure of the game or to alternative structures of the game. Thus a conclusion that is reached is not necessarily supported solely by statistical evidence from repeated play of a game whose relevance to the world is in question. Rather the conclusion, once it has been suggested by the experimental results, can often be rationalized in theoretical terms. The game is thus a tangible representation of a theoretical model, a model whose moving parts can be better understood if they can be articulated experimentally.

This point can be expressed in another way. Experimental games can be used to discover, and demonstrate, important *possibilities* that might have been missed without it. The significance and relevance of these possibilities may still depend on reasoning and on evidence obtained elsewhere; but the existence of the possibilities, and some notion of how they relate to the structure of the game, can be discovered by the artificial game. This would, for example, be true of the proposition that the advantage may well go not to the player who enjoys the increased knowledge and information but to the other player, and that it may even be an absolute disadvantage to one of the players to obtain new information if he cannot conceal the fact that he has it. (This point about information is not being emphasized here as the main one to be investigated, but as a readily comprehensible illustration of an hypothesis to which the experimental game would be relevant.)

On the whole, it is expected that conclusions reached by this kind of experimental research will not depend much on refined statistical analysis. We shall be looking for rather striking results. Since the intent is to relate the observed phenomena to some theory that closely parallels the game itself, as well as to demonstrate the potential significance (rather than the actual significance in a particular context) of the variables to be manipulated and observed, a main effort will be to learn how to manipulate the parameters and structural features of the game in order deliberately to generate particular results and phenomena. The intent is not, therefore, to pursue to the end a prearranged schedule for varying the parameters, and subsequently to analyze the results statistically. Instead there will be fairly continual feedback between the results observed and the further design of the experiments. The results of the questionnaire experiments referred to above illustrate, on a simple scale, this methodology.

There is a secondary purpose of this experimentation that

relates to the development of theory. It has to do with the value of the sheer construction of the game and analysis of its structure and manipulation of its parameters. To build a game of this sort, and especially to build into the game particular features that one wishes to represent, requires that one define his concepts operationally. A game of this sort imposes discipline on theoretical model-building; it can be a test of whether concepts and propositions are meaningful, and a means of demonstrating so when they are. In the actual construction of the game, and in discussion of the game's features with persons who have played it or observed it played, it has frequently been the case that certain plausible concepts had to be abandoned when an effort to identify them (or to incorporate them) in the game revealed that they were meaningless or innocuous, or that they rested on inessential distinctions.

Closely related is the use of the game as a means of theoretical communication. If one wishes to define carefully, and to illustrate, a particular distinction or proposition about the strategy of conflict, the game often provides a tangible and unambiguous representation of the concepts involved—a way of pointing to what one means and avoiding reliance on ambiguous verbal description.

Two examples may help. One has to do with the notion of equality or symmetry in the outcome of a game. As mentioned above, the policy-oriented literature on limited war frequently uses words like "equality" and "symmetry" and "reciprocity" in describing the kinds of rules and limits or outcomes that may be acceptable to the parties involved; the theoretical literature on bargaining and game strategy does the same. And with an exceedingly unambiguous model or "game" in mind, with perfect information about value systems and the moves and strategies available, concepts like "equality" and "symmetry" can at least be meaningfully defined. Suppose, however, that one enriches the game, even to the limited extent of the game described—or suppose that one goes farther still to add contextual detail which, though inessential to the logical structure of the game, contains some power of suggestion, or moral, casuistic, or legalistic significance, or which entails some precedent, tradition, or analogy. Then such concepts as "equality" and "symmetry"—in the strategies employed, in the rules and constraints that the players generate and observe, or in the outcome of the game—are embarrassed by the sheer lack of an obviously meaningful definition. The empirical contents of the original proposition therefore disappear. One cannot define "equality" in terms of the acceptability of an outcome or a rule to both players, and simultaneously preserve any empirical content in the proposition that rules or outcomes will be acceptable only if they meet the condition of "equality."

The second example concerns the structure of conflict that is built into the game. It is interesting to argue whether the game described, or a variant of it, captures the spirit of the conflict involved in war, race relations, industrial disputes, interagency disputes, bureaucratic rivalry, or competition in traffic for the right of way. If one doubts whether a particular game embodies the essentials of a particular dispute, it is interesting to see whether the game can be made to represent that dispute by varying the scoring system, the information structure, or the timing and nature of the moves; if it cannot, it is interesting then to see whether radical changes in, or additions to, the moves and scoring system can reproduce the essentials of the dispute in question. In the trial plays held so far, it has frequently been the case that during *post mortem* a player denied the analogy between the game and the kind of conflict involved in international disputes; a revision in the scoring system was attempted to reflect someone's notion of what was essential to an international dispute. It is interesting that in many cases the revision that would satisfy a particular analyst could be demonstrated to be a non-essential change—a change only in certain parameters, and not in the structure of the game. In other cases it became clear that certain types of dispute were inherently incapable of being represented. But clarity and agreement could be reached much more quickly on these theoretical points by working with the actual game than if no tangible model had been present.

22

Studies of interpersonal bargaining[1]

MORTON DEUTSCH AND ROBERT M. KRAUSS

These excerpts give the first of a series of experiments run by Deutsch and Krauss, together with the discussion of the results from the series. It should be noted that in the gaming experiments described in these selections, there is a considerable difference in communication conditions. In the first experiment of Deutsch and Krauss, there was no face-to-face communication and no verbal information. In the second, headsets were provided and bilateral or unilateral verbal communication were permitted. In the third experiment, bilateral verbal communication was required. In the work of Bixenstine and Wilson, communication is only numerical. In the game So Long Sucker, there is almost no structure to the actual game and all communication is face-to-face, verbal, and with few, if any, rules of debate. Most of the games reported by Rapoport depend on numerical information without face-to-face communication. Guetzkow's game has an intermix of numerical and verbal information and communication together with varying

---

[1] This paper was awarded the 1961 Meritorious Essay Prize in Socio-Psychological Inquiry by the American Association for the Advancement of Science. Parts of it have appeared previously in Deutsch and Krauss.

Reprinted from *Conflict Resolution*, **VI**, No. 1, March 1962, 52–76. With permission of the authors and publisher.

conditions of interpersonal contact. Schelling's game is without direct communication between the players.

Introduction

A *bargain* is defined in Webster's Unabridged Dictionary as "an agreement between parties settling what each shall give and receive in a transaction between them"; it is further specified that a bargain is "an agreement or compact viewed as advantageous or the reverse." When the term "agreement" is broadened to include tacit, informal agreements as well as explicit agreements, it is evident that bargains and the processes involved in arriving at bargains ("bargaining") are pervasive characteristics of social life.

The definition of "bargain" fits under sociological definitions of the term "social norm." In this light, it may be seen that the experimental study of the bargaining process and of bargaining outcomes provides a means for the laboratory study of the development of certain types of social norms. It is well to recognize, however, that bargaining situations have certain distinctive features which, unlike many other types of social situations, make it relevant to consider the conditions which determine whether or not a social norm will develop as well as to consider the conditions which determine the nature of the social norm if it develops. Bargaining situations highlight for the investigator the need to be sensitive to the possibility that, even where cooperation would be mutually advantageous, shared purposes may not develop, agreement may not be reached, interaction may be regulated antagonistically rather than normatively.

The essential features of a bargaining situation exist when

1. both parties perceive that there is the possibility of reaching an agreement in which each party would be better off, or no worse off, than if no agreement is reached;
2. both parties perceive that there is more than one such agreement which could be reached; and
3. both parties perceive each other to have conflicting preferences or opposed interests with regard to the different agreements which might be reached.

Everyday examples of a bargaining situation include such situations as: the buyer-seller relationship when the price is not fixed; the husband and wife who want to spend an evening out together but have conflicting preferences about where to go; union-management negotiations; drivers who meet at an intersection when there is no clear right of way; disarmament negotiations.

From our description of the essential features of a bargaining situation it can be seen that, in terms of our prior conceptualization of cooperation and competition it is a situation in which the participants have mixed motives toward one another: on the one hand, each has interest in cooperating so that they reach an agreement; on the other hand, they have competitive interests with regard to the nature of the agreement they reach. In effect, to reach agreement the cooperative interest of the bargainers must be strong enough to overcome their competitive interests. However, agreement is not only contingent upon the *motivational* balances of cooperative to competitive interests but also upon the situational and *cognitive* factors which would facilitate or hinder the recognition or invention of a bargaining agreement that reduces the opposition of interest and enhances the mutuality of interest.

The discussion of the preceding paragraph leads to the formulation of two general, closely related propositions about the likelihood that a bargaining agreement will be reached.

1. Bargainers are more likely to reach an agreement, the stronger are their cooperative interests in comparison with their competitive interests in relationship to each other.
2. Bargainers are more likely to reach an agreement, the more resources they have available for the recognition or invention of potential bargaining agreements and the more resources they have for communication to one another once a potential agreement has been recognized or invented.

From these two basic propositions and additional hypotheses concerning the conditions which determine the strengths of the cooperative and competitive interests and the amount of available resources, we believe it is possible to explain the ease or difficulty of arriving at a bargaining agreement. We shall not present a full statement of these hypotheses here but shall instead turn to a description of a series of experiments that relate to Proposition 1.

EXPERIMENT I

The first experiment to be reported here was concerned with the effect of the availability of threat upon bargaining in a two-person experimental bargaining game we have devised. Threat is defined as the expression of an intention to do something which is detrimental to the interests of another. Our experiment was guided by two assumptions about threat:

1. If there is a conflict of interest and a means of threatening the other person exists, there will be a tendency to use the threat in an attempt to force the other person to yield. This tendency will be stronger, the more irreconcilable the conflict is perceived to be.
2. If threat is used in an attempt to intimidate another, the threatened person (if he considers himself to be of equal or superior status) will feel hostility toward the threatener and will tend to respond with counterthreat and/or increased resistance to yielding. We qualify this assumption by stating that the tendency to resist will be greater, the greater the perceived probability and magnitude of detriment to the other and the lesser the perceived probability and magnitude of detriment to the potential resistor from the anticipated resistance to yielding.

The second assumption is based upon the view that to allow oneself to be intimidated, particularly by someone who does not have the right to expect deferential behavior, is (when resistance is not seen to be suicidal or useless) to suffer a loss of social face and, hence, of self-esteem; and that the culturally defined way of maintaining self-esteem in the face of attempted intimidation is to engage in a contest for supremacy *vis-à-vis* the power to intimidate or, minimally, to resist intimidation. Thus, in effect, it can be seen that the use of threat (and if it is available to be used, there will be a tendency to use it) should strengthen the competitive interests of the bargainers in relationship to one another by introducing or enhancing the competitive struggle for self-esteem.

Hence, from Proposition 1, it follows that the availability of a means of threat should make it more difficult for the bargainers to reach agreement (providing that the threatened person has some means of resisting the threat). The preceding statement is relevant to the comparison of both of our experimental conditions (described below) of threat, *bilateral* and *unilateral*, with our experimental condition of *nonthreat*. We are hypothesizing that a bargaining agreement is more likely to be achieved when neither party can threaten the other, than when one or both parties can threaten the other.

It is relevant now to compare the situations of bilateral threat and unilateral threat. For several reasons, it seems likely that a situation of bilateral threat is less conducive to agreement than is a condition of unilateral threat. First, the sheer likelihood that a threat will be made is greater when two people rather than one have the means of making the threat. Secondly, once a threat is made in the bilateral case, it is likely to evoke counterthreat. Withdrawal of threat in the face of counterthreat probably involves more loss of face (for reasons analogous to those discussed above in relation to yielding to intimidation) than does withdrawal of threat in the face of resistance to threat. Finally, in the unilateral case, although the person without the threat potential can resist and not yield to the threat, his position *vis-à-vis* the other is not so strong as the position of the threatened person in the bilateral case. In the unilateral case, the threatened person may have a worse outcome than the other whether he resists or yields; while in the bilateral case, the threatened person is sure to have a worse outcome if he yields but he may insure that he does not have a worse outcome if he does not yield.

METHOD

Subjects (*Ss*) were asked to imagine that they were in charge of a trucking company, carrying merchandise over a road to a destination. For each trip they completed they made \$.60, minus their operating expenses. Operating expenses were calculated at the rate of one cent per second. So, for example, if it took thirty-seven seconds to complete a particular trip, the player's profit would be \$.60 − \$.37 or a net profit of \$.23 for that particular trip.

Each subject was assigned a name, Acme or Bolt. As the "road map" (see Figure 1) indicates, both players start from separate points and go to separate destinations. At one point their paths coincide. This is the section of road labeled "one-lane road." This section of road is only one lane wide; this means that two trucks, heading in opposite directions, could not pass each other. If one backs up the other can go forward, or both can back up, or both can sit there head-on without moving.

There is another way for each subject to reach the destination on the map and this is labeled the "alternate route." The two players' paths do not cross on this route, but the alternate is 56 per cent longer than the main route. Subjects were told that they could expect to lose at least $.10 each time they used the alternate route.

At either end of the one-lane section there is a gate which is under the control of the player to whose starting point it is closest. By closing the gate, one player can prevent the other from travel-

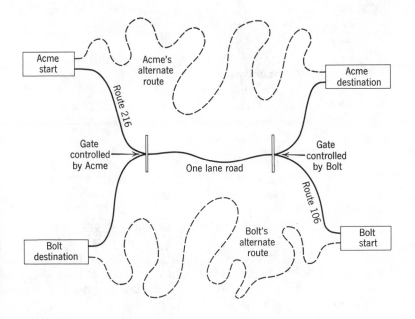

FIGURE 1. Subject's road map.

ing over that section of the main route. It is the use of the gate which we will call the threat potential in this game. In the bilateral threat potential condition (*Two Gates*) both players had gates under their control. In a second condition of unilateral threat (*One Gate*) Acme had control of a gate but Bolt did not. In a third condition (*No Gates*) neither player controlled a gate.

The only time one player definitely knew the other player's position was when they had met head-on on the one-way section of road. This was indicated by a traffic light mounted on the panel. When this light was on, neither player could move forward unless the other moved back. The gates were controlled by toggle switches; panel-mounted indicator lights showed, for both subjects, whether each gate was open or closed.

The following "rules of the game" were stated to the *Ss*:

1. A player who started out on one route and wished to switch to the other route could do so only after first reversing and going back to the start position. Direct transfer from one route to the other was not permitted except at the start position.

2. In the conditions where *Ss* had gates, they were permitted to close the gates only when they were traveling on the main route. (That is, they were not permitted to close the gate while on the alternate route or after having reached their destinations.) However, *Ss* were permitted to open their gates at any point in the game.

Ss were taken through a number of practice exercises to familiarize them with the game. In the first trial they were made to meet head-on on the one-lane path; Acme was then told to back up until she was just off the one-lane path and Bolt was told to go forward. After Bolt had gone through the one-lane path, Acme was told to go forward. Each continued going forward until each arrived at her destination. The second practice trial was the same as the first except that Bolt rather than Acme backed up after meeting head-on. In the next practice trial, one of the players was made to wait just before the one-way path while the other traversed it and then was allowed to continue. In the next practice trial, one player was made to take the alter-

nate route and the other was made to take the main route.
Finally, in the Bilateral and Unilateral Threat conditions the use
of the gate was illustrated (by having the player get on the main
route, close the gate, and then go back and take the alternate
route). The Ss were told explicitly with emphasis that they did
not have to use the gate. Before each trial in the game the gate
or gates were in the open position.

The instructions stressed an individualistic motivational orientation. Ss were told to try to earn as much money for themselves as possible and to have no interest in whether the other
player made money or lost money. They were given $4.00 in
poker chips to represent their working capital and told that after
each trial they would be given "money" if they made a profit or
that "money" would be taken from them if they lost (i.e., took
more than 60 seconds to complete their trip). The profit or loss
of each S was announced so that both Ss could hear the announce-
ment after each trial. Each pair of subjects played a total of
twenty trials; on all trials, they started off together. In other
words, each trial presented a repetition of the same bargaining
problem. In cases where subjects lost their working capital
before the twenty trials were completed, additional chips were
given them. Subjects were aware that their monetary winnings
and losses were to be imaginary and that no money would change
hands as a result of the experiment.

Sixteen pairs of subjects were used in each of the three experimental conditions. The Ss were female clerical and supervisory
personnel of the New Jersey Bell Telephone Company who vol-
unteered to participate during their working day. Their ages
ranged from 20 to 39, with a mean of 26.2. All were naive to the
purpose of the experiment. By staggering the arrival times and
choosing girls from different locations, we were able to insure that
our subjects did not know with whom they were playing.

RESULTS

The best single measure of the difficulty experienced by the bargainers in reaching an agreement is the sum of each pair's profits
(or losses) on a given trial. The higher the sum of the payoffs to
the two players on a given trial, the less time it took them to

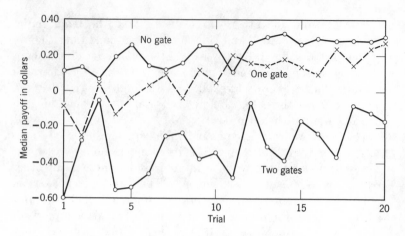

FIGURE 2. *Median joint payoff (Acme & Bolt) over trials.*

arrive at a procedure for sharing the one-lane path of the main route. (It was, of course, possible for one or both of the players to decide to take the alternate route so as to avoid a protracted stalemate during the process of bargaining. This, however, always resulted in at least a $.20 smaller joint payoff if only one player took the alternate route, than an optimally arrived at agreement concerning the use of the one-way path.) Figure 2 presents the medians of the summed payoffs (i.e., Acme's plus Bolt's) for all pairs in each of the three experimental conditions over the twenty trials. These results indicate that agreement was least difficult to arrive at in the No Threat condition, was more difficult to arrive at in the Unilateral Threat condition, and exceedingly difficult or impossible to arrive at in the Bilateral Threat condition.[2]

DISCUSSION

In the introduction, we presented our view of bargaining as a situation in which both cooperative and competitive tendencies

---

[2] Two further experiments on the effects of communication were run, which are discussed here although no details are given. The reader is referred to the original paper for their description.

are present and acting upon the individual. From this point of view, it is relevant to inquire as to the conditions under which a stable agreement of any form will develop. However, implicit in most models of bargaining (e.g., Zeuthen, Stone, Cervin, Suppes and Carlsmith) is the assumption that the cooperative interests of the bargainers will be sufficiently strong to insure that some form of mutually satisfactory agreement will be reached. For this reason, such models have focused upon the form of the agreement reached by the bargainers. Siegel and Fouraker report a series of bargaining experiments quite different in structure from ours in which only one of many pairs of subjects was unable to reach agreement. Siegel and Fouraker explain this rather startling statistic as follows:

Apparently the disruptive forces which lead to the rupture of some negotiations were at least partially controlled in our sessions. . . .

Some negotiations collapse when one party becomes incensed at the other, and henceforth strives to maximize his opponent's displeasure rather than his own satisfaction. . . . Since it is difficult to transmit insults by means of quantitative bids, such disequilibrating behavior was not induced in the present studies. If subjects were allowed more latitude in their communications and interactions, the possibility of an affront–offense–punitive behavior sequence might be increased.

In our experimental bargaining situation, the availability of threat clearly made it more difficult for bargainers to reach a mutually profitable agreement. Indeed, Bilateral Threat presents a situation so conflict-fraught that no amount of communication seems to have an ameliorating effect. These tendencies we believe are not confined to our experimental situation. The "affront–offense–punitive behavior sequence" to which Siegel and Fouraker refer, and which we have observed in our experiment, are common attributes of everyday interpersonal conflict. The processes which underlie them have long been of interest to social scientists and an imposing set of theoretical constructs have been employed to explain them.

Dollard et al. have cited a variety of evidence to support the view that aggression (i.e., the use of threat) is a common reaction to a person who is seen as the agent of frustration. There seems to be little reason to doubt that the use of threat is a frequent reaction to interpersonal impasses. However, everyday observation indicates that threat does not inevitably occur when there is an interpersonal impasse. We would speculate that it is most likely to occur when the threatener has no positive interest in the other person's welfare (he is either egocentrically or competitively related to the other); when the threatener believes that the other has no positive interest in his welfare; and when the threatener anticipates either that his threat will be effective or, if ineffective, will not worsen his situation because he expects the worst to happen if he does not use his threat. We suggest that these conditions were operative in our experiment; the subjects were either egocentrically or competitively oriented to one another[3] and they felt that they would not be worse off by the use of threat.

Everyday observation suggests that the tendency to respond with counterthreat or increased resistance to attempts at intimidation is also a common occurrence. It is our belief that the introduction of threat into a bargaining situation affects the meaning of yielding. Although we have no data to support this directly, we will attempt to justify it on the basis of some additional assumptions.

Goffman has pointed out the pervasive significance of "face" in the maintenance of the social order. In this view, self-esteem is a socially validated system which grows out of the acceptance by others of the claim for deference, prestige and recognition which one presents in one's behavior toward others. Thus, the rejection of such a claim would be perceived (by the recipient) as directed against his self-esteem and one which, in order to maintain the integrity of his self-esteem system, he must react against rather than accept.

One may view the behavior of our subjects as an attempt to make claims upon the other; an attempt to develop a set of shared expectations as to what each was entitled to. Why then did the subjects' reactions differ so markedly as a function of the availa-

[3] A post-experimental questionnaire indicated that, in all three experimental conditions, the Ss were most strongly motivated to win money, next most strongly motivated to do better than the other player, next most motivated to "have fun," and were very little or not at all motivated to help the other player.

bility of threat? The explanation for this lies, we believe, in the cultural interpretation of yielding (to a peer or subordinate) under duress, as compared to giving in without duress. The former, we believe, is perceived as a negatively valued form of behavior, with negative implications for the self-image of the individual who so behaves. At least partly, this is so because the locus of causality is perceived to be outside the voluntary control of the individual. No such evaluation, however, need be placed on the behavior of one who "gives in" in a situation where no threat or duress is a factor. Rather, we should expect the culturally defined evaluation of such an individual's behavior to be one of "reasonableness" or "maturity." Again, this may be because the cause of the individual's behavior is perceived to lie within the individual.

One special feature of our experimental game is worthy of note: the passage of time, without coming to an agreement, is costly to the players. There are, of course, bargaining situations in which the lack of agreement may simply preserve the *status quo* without any worsening of the bargainers' respective positions. This is the case in the typical bilateral monopoly case, where the buyer and seller are unable to agree upon a price (e.g., see Siegel and Fouraker; Cervin). In other sorts of bargaining situations, however (e.g., labor-management negotiations during a strike; inter-nation negotiations during an expensive cold war), the passage of time may play an important role. In our experiment, we received the impression that the meaning of time changed as time passed without the bargainers reaching an agreement. Initially, the passage of time seemed to pressure the players to come to an agreement before their costs mounted sufficiently to destroy their profit. With the continued passage of time, however, their mounting losses strengthened their resolution not to yield to the other player. They comment: "I've lost so much, I'll be damned if I give in now. At least I'll have the satisfaction of doing better than she does." The mounting losses and continued deadlock seemed to change the game from a mixed motive into a predominantly competitive situation.

The results of Experiments II and III justify, we believe, a reconsideration of the role of communication in the bargaining process. Typically, communication is perceived as a means whereby the bargainers coordinate effort (e.g., exchange bids, indicate positions, etc.). Usually, little emphasis is given to interaction of communication with motivational orientation. Certainly the coordination function of communication is important. However, as Siegel and Fouraker point out, free communication may also be used to convey information (e.g., threats, insults, etc.) which may intensify the competitive aspects of the situation.

It should be emphasized here that the "solution" of our bargaining problem (i.e., alternating first use of the one-lane section of the main route) is a simple and rather obvious one. Indeed, the sort of coordination of effort required by the game is sufficiently simple to be readily achievable without the aid of communication. (Note that Ss in the No Threat–No Communication conditions did as well as Ss in the two No Threat conditions with communication.) More important than this coordinating function, however, is the capacity of communication to expedite the development of agreements. In this context, agreements serve a function similar to that ascribed by Thibaut and Kelley to the social norm; that is, ". . . they serve as substitutes for the exercise of personal influence and produce more economically and efficiently certain consequences otherwise dependent upon personal influence processes" (Thibaut and Kelley). Effective communication, by this line of reasoning, would be aimed at the development of agreements or, to state it another way, at a resolution of the competitive orientation which produces conflict in the bargaining situation.

One must grant that our Ss were relatively unsophisticated in the techniques of developing agreements under the stress of competition. Possibly persons who deal regularly with problems of conflict resolution (e.g., marriage counselors, labor–management arbitrators, diplomats, etc.) would have little difficulty in reaching agreement, even under our Bilateral Threat condition.

Another barrier to effective communication lies in the reticence of our Ss. As we noted above, our Ss found talking to an unknown partner a strange and rather uncomfortable experience. This factor alone would limit the possibility of any communication, let alone communication which was effective.

The studies reported here are part of an ongoing program of research on the factors affecting interpersonal bargaining. In an experiment presently under way, we are attempting to develop communication procedures which will be effective in ameliorating conflict in the Bilateral Threat condition. Additionally, in projected studies we intend to investigate the effect of other structural factors on bargaining behavior.

It is, of course, hazardous to generalize from a set of laboratory experiments to the problems of the real world. But our experiment and the theoretical ideas which underlie them can perhaps serve to emphasize some notions which, otherwise, have some intrinsic plausibility. In brief, these are the following: (1) There is more safety in cooperative than in competitive coexistence. (2) The mere existence of channels of communication is no guarantee that communication will indeed take place; and the greater the competitive orientation of the parties *vis-à-vis* each other, the less likely will they be to use such channels as do exist. (3) Where barriers to communication exist, a situation in which the parties are compelled to communicate will be more effective than one in which the choice to talk or not is put on a voluntary basis. (4) If the bargainer's primary orientation is competitive, communication which is not directed at changing this orientation is unlikely to be effective. (5) It is dangerous for bargainers to have weapons at their disposal. (6) Possibly, it is more dangerous for a bargainer to have the capacity to retaliate in kind than for him not to have this capacity, when the other bargainer has a weapon. This last statement assumes that the one who yields has more of his values preserved by accepting the agreement preferred by the other than by extended conflict. Of course, in some bargaining situations in the real world the loss incurred by yielding may exceed the loss due to extended conflict.

23

Forms of social control
in two-person two-choice games

KELLOG V. WILSON AND V. EDWIN BIXENSTINE

It is well known in the literature of game theory that even in simple 2×2
*matrix games it is possible to select games with multiple equilibrium points,
with equilibria which are also jointly maximal, or which are jointly minimal and so forth. Wilson and Bixenstine offer an interpretation of these
different situations in terms of the power or amount of control a player
can exercise over his own and his opponent's gains and losses. This
analysis provides a valuable extension of the game theory concepts of
equilibrium.*

Conventional thinking about social relationships tends to classify them as either co-operative or competitive. Athletic contests and wars between nations are regarded as competitive while
marital relations are regarded as co-operative. Closer examination reveals, however, that nations at war commonly engage in

The preparation of this paper was supported in part by research grants
from the National Institute of Mental Health, Public Health Service and
from Nebraska Board of Control research funds. Reprinted from *Behavioral
Science*, **7**, No. 1, January 1962, 92–102, with permission of the authors and
publisher.

limited co-operative arrangements, married couples sometimes compete for the affections of their children, and athletic contests are co-operative in that they are played within the confines of a previously agreed-upon set of rules. The current cold war between the U.S. and the U.S.S.R. is another example of how co-operative and competitive elements can be mixed. Our foreign policies are very hotly competitive; yet we both seem to co-operate in a precarious abstention from mutual annihilation.

We feel that the rather negativistic description of games like the Prisoner's Dilemma as non-zero-sum, nonco-operative does little to illuminate why such games, and similar conflictual situations, are dilemmas. We feel a more profitable approach is to consider the forms of control that the participant in a game situation has over his own gains and the gains of the other person and the probable effects of these controls on the strategies of the participant. Our discussion is confined to the 2-person, 2-choice game and is somewhat speculative, although experimental evidence is introduced when it is available. We initially consider three elementary forms of control in 2-person games, then proceed to various combinations of these forms, and finally consider what personal values might be involved in decision-making in "mixed-motive" games.

Elementary Forms of Control in Two-Person, Two-Choice Games

Our emphasis on control over gains is by no means novel and is well known to practicing politicians and military strategists. Cartwright and his associates have given much attention to the effects of power in social situations, and Thibaut and Kelley have attempted to analyze group formation and functioning in terms of the control that the participants have over each other's gains and losses. While Cartwright and Thibaut and Kelley have emphasized power or control over others, we feel that control over personal gains should be examined as well. The necessity for considering both kinds of control is clearly indicated by the mixed-motive games (Tables 9 through 14) discussed in this paper. A similar emphasis may be found in Solomon's discussion of his experimental payoff matrices.

We are using the term *gain* to refer to the evaluation of the outcomes in a decision-making situation, and we will treat losses as negative gains. For the sake of simplicity, we will measure gains in monetary units, although some more inclusive form of measurement must be found eventually if our treatment is to have generality. Our concept of gain is very much like the concept of *utility* in game theory, and though there is some dispute on this point, we assume members of our culture have good "perceptual constancy" for money and that its utility is roughly proportional to its amount.

We chose not to use the term utility, since this concept has been operationally defined for situations where the participants make choices that affect themselves alone; e.g., choices between objects or sets of objects, or gambling games against "nature." As our later discussion indicates, the evaluation of personal outcomes in 2-person games very likely depends on the comparison of personal gains with those of the other participant. In the absence of evidence as to the way this evaluation interacts with utility to produce some resultant "subjective evaluation," we will confine ourselves to defining payoff matrices in terms of gains.

Another important feature of our subsequent discussion is that the payoff matrix of the game is assumed to be known to both participants. If these payoffs are not known to both, the player is not in a position to select a strategy which is "optimal" or to exercise his control except in an exploratory fashion. We will grant that many situations involve less than perfect knowledge of power positions and that acquisition of such knowledge is a problem of considerable importance.

ABSOLUTE CONTROL OVER PERSONAL
GAIN (AP CONTROL)

The player uses this form of control to choose his own gain (or loss), and his choices have no effect on the gains of the other player. An example of such a game which has this property for both players is given in Table 1.

Table 1 follows the conventional representation of payoff matrices. The Row player chooses between rows A and B and the

Column player chooses between columns A and B. The pairs of values in the cells represent the payoffs to the players—the first figure representing the payoff to Row and the second figure the payoff to Column. The units of measurement can be regarded as monetary. Thus, if both players choose A they both receive a payoff of five dollars or cents while if Row chooses A and Column chooses B, Row receives five and Column receives one. The same conventions will be followed in the other matrices in this paper.

An examination of Table 1 indicates that playing this game need involve little communication or negotiation. Each player simply receives five if he chooses A and one if he chooses B, and

TABLE 1 EXAMPLE OF ABSOLUTE CONTROL OVER PERSONAL GAIN (AP CONTROL)

| | | Column | |
		A	B
Row	A	5, 5	5, 1
	B	1, 5	1, 1

his choices have no effect on the gains of the other player. Obviously, there is good reason to believe that both players will settle on A as a choice once they understand the game. For the sake of brevity in subsequent discussion, we will use the label AP to refer to this form of control.

CONDITIONAL CONTROL OVER PERSONAL GAIN (CP CONTROL)

With this form of control, a player can choose his own gain only if he knows what the other player will choose. The game of Table 2 has this property for the Row player.

Table 2 indicates that Column's choices are a matter of personal indifference, since he will gain two for all four possible outcomes of the game. Knowledge of Column's choices are of considerable importance to Row, however, since he can always gain five if he matches Column's choice. Thus, "dependability" or "conventionality" of Column is important to Row, which gives Column a measure of control over Row. Column can sell advance information about his choices or some form of "dependability" to Row in return for a side-payment of some portion of Row's superior gains, which will, in effect, change the payoff matrix. (This point will be considered further under Conditional Control over Other's

TABLE 2   EXAMPLE OF CONDITIONAL CONTROL OVER PERSONAL GAIN (CP CONTROL)

		Column A	B
Row	A	5, 2	1, 2
	B	1, 2	5, 2

Gain.) We will use the abbreviation CP to refer to this form of control.

ABSOLUTE CONTROL OVER OTHER'S GAIN (AO CONTROL)

With this form of control, the choice of one player determines the gains of the other but has no effect on personal gains. The game of Table 3 has this property for both players.

Table 3 indicates that personal gain does not provide a basis for choosing between A and B. Personal gains are identical across choices A and B for both players. The choices made, however, uniquely determine the payoff of the other player, since the other player gains five if A is chosen and one if B is chosen. While neither player controls his own gains, he has absolute control over the gains of the person who determines his gains. This puts both players in an equally favorable position for preplay negotiations which will almost certainly result in an agreement for both to choose A. If either player does not live up to his agreement, the "injured" player can retaliate by choosing B on subsequent trials until the "offender" again chooses A. In view of this counter-control, we might expect most pairs of players to choose A predominantly, even without extra-game communication.[1] This would not necessarily happen, however, if maximizing the difference between personal gain and that of the other is rewarding. (See the discussion following Table 12.) We will use the abbreviation AO to refer to this form of control.

TABLE 3   EXAMPLE OF ABSOLUTE
CONTROL OVER OTHER'S GAIN (AO
CONTROL)

| | | Column | |
		A	B
Row	A	5, 5	1, 5
	B	5, 1	1, 1

Thibaut and Kelley refer to AO control as *fate control* and describe the conditions under which this type of control becomes converted to *behavior control*. For example, if this conversion occurred for the game of Table 3, Row would choose A as long as Column chose A and would switch to B only after Column had switched to B on a previous trial. Thus, Column's gains are made conditional on his past behavior. The similarity of this to many common forms of social control should be obvious.

CONDITIONAL CONTROL OVER OTHER'S GAIN

This form of control is an inevitable consequence of CP control, and so the game of Table 2 will serve as an example. In this game, Row can increase his own gains if he knows what Column's choice will be, and by the same token, Column can control Row's gains if he knows what Row's choice will be. As our discussion of Table 2 indicated, Column's dependability is advantageous to

---

[1] Luce and Raiffa describe a game similar to that of Table 3 and conclude that preplay communication would be advantageous.

Row, and if Row's maximum gains are superior to those of Column (as in Table 2), Column is in a good position to ask for a side payment if negotiation is permitted.   Column may be tempted to improve his position further once negotiation is concluded by being undependable, but it is easy to see that Row is in a good position to partially thwart excessive demands from Column by a random choice strategy.   Thus, we feel that most agreements concluded in games where CP control is present will tend to be stable but that some "temptations" to compete similar to those of mixed-motive games are present.

The "double-bind" dilemma described by Bateson, Jackson, Haly, and Weakland is a good example of how use of control analogous to CP can have serious consequences.   In discussing the familiar bases for schizophrenia, Bateson and his associates have concluded that as children, schizophrenics were frequently placed in "double-bind" situations where equivocal information was given by the parents so that the child was "damned if he did and damned if he didn't."   The postulated result was that, in effect, the child did not have the reliable cues needed for effective learning of the discriminations required in his socialization.   An approximate experimental analog of this would be a Column player who frequently lapses from dependable behavior after making an agreement with the Row player.   We can expect a rapid deterioration of communication of Row with Column; and that Column would have a great deal of difficulty in re-establishing any effective agreement with Row once Column had violated his agreement or attempted to use undependability as a means of improving on an agreed-upon side payment.

Combinations of Forms of Control[2]

In our preceding discussion of the elementary forms of control, the games associated with AP and AO control had a somewhat

---

[2] A system has been developed for analyzing and synthesizing payoff matrices for 2-person, 2-choice games in terms of the three basic forms of control described in this paper.   A payoff matrix is described by eight parameters including the level of AP, CP, and AO control for each participant (i.e., six parameters), the average gain in the payoff matrix, and the

"bland" character, while the games associated with CP control had some of the characteristics of problematic social situations. Paradoxically, we find that when CP control is enjoyed by both players we obtain a game with either predominantly co-operative or competitive features, while combinations of AP and AO control lead to the interesting mixture of competitive and co-operative features of the mixed-motive game.

COMBINATIONS OF CP CONTROLS

If CP controls are combined so that the gains of both players are increased by matching choices of the other, we obtain a game where both players will tend to co-operate in the sense that they can choose so that their own gains and the gains of the other will be simultaneously increased. An example of such a game is given in Table 4.

TABLE 4 EXAMPLE OF CO-OPERA-
TIVE (CO-ORDINATION GAME) COM-
BINATION OF CP CONTROLS

		Column	
		A	B
Row	A	5, 5	1, 1
	B	1, 1	5, 5

Since both players have conditional control over their own gains and the gains of the other, some sort of communication between the players to insure co-ordination of their choices would be called for. The amount of explicit communication or negotiation

average difference in gain between the two players. The system of synthesis and analysis is very similar to the Method of Orthogonal Comparisons sometimes used in connection with Analysis of Variance. The fact that a payoff matrix can be uniquely specified by eight parameters, six of which correspond to the forms of control of this paper, indicates that the descriptive system is exhaustive. A detailed description of the system may be obtained on request from the senior author (K.W.).

needed would seem fairly minimal, however, since neither player would be in a favorable position to sell "dependability" or "conventionality" like the Column player in Table 2. Both players in Table 4 could incur immediate losses from being "undependable," while Column player in Table 2 has an assured level of gain regardless of his choices. Schelling describes games like that of Table 4 as *co-ordination games* because of the convergent interests of the players, and emphasizes the importance of tacit "understandings" or conventions in social situations where the gains of the participants are analogous to those of Table 4 (e.g., finding your spouse in a department store where both gain only if you both come to the same place at the same time). The results

TABLE 5 EXAMPLE OF COMPETITIVE (ZERO-SUM) COMBINATION OF *CP* CONTROLS

| | | Column | |
		A	B
Row	A	+3, −3	−3, +3
	B	−3, +3	+3, −3

obtained by Azrin and Lindsley, Schelling and Sidowski, Wyckoff, and Tabary tend to confirm our prediction of co-ordination of choice even though their experimental conditions differ in some respects from those of Table 4.

If *CP* controls are combined so that Row gains when he matches Column's choice and Column gains when he mismatches Row's choice, we obtain a zero-sum game as in the example above.

Like Table 4, the presence of conditional control in Table 5 requires advance information or predictability on the other player's part before the control can be effectively utilized. Since the interests of the players are now strictly opposed, however, any effective and stable agreement or arrangement for side payments is nearly impossible. If the game of Table 5 is played repeatedly, the mixed (and minimax) strategy of randomly choosing *A* and *B* with probability one-half seems a likely result. If small amounts of money are involved, however, the players may try to "out-guess" each other or otherwise gain more than the zero expected value which the minimax strategy permits (Lieberman).[3]

COMBINATIONS OF AO CONTROLS

In discussing Table 3, we predicted that both players will soon settle on a joint co-operative (i.e., joint-return maximizing) strategy of choosing A, since each player is dependent on the other to increase his gains and each has equal retaliatory capabilities.   It seems plausible, however, that the introduction of marked asymmetries in the degree of AO control could well disrupt this hypothetical harmony.

TABLE 6   EXAMPLE OF ASYMMETRIC
COMBINATION OF AO CONTROLS

| | | Column | |
		A	B
Row	A	20, 3	1, 3
	B	20, 2	1, 2

As in Table 3, the choices of each player determine the gains of the other but have no effect on personal gains.   Row is in a more favorable position with regard to his maximum gain, but Column is very nearly free from Row's control and has a very great potential ability to reduce Row's gains.   In the absence of communication between the players, it seems likely that Column will not choose to increase Row's gains on all trials of a repeated game because of the resentment of Row's superior position regarding

---

[3] Deviation from minimax strategies would be justified in a zero-sum game only if the player was sure that the other player was behaving in a predictable manner.   Such deviations would not be very risky if the amounts of money are small.   Small amounts of money might also lead to deviations from optimal behavior due to inattention or boredom or, perhaps, to gain some idea of the other player's characteristic reactions.   Unfortunately, the latter comments would apply to most experimental games.

personal gain. If communication and negotiation for side payments is permitted, Column is in a very strong position to demand side payments from Row in return for Column's continued choice of A. The granting of side payments, however, will in effect modify the payoff matrix so that increasing the amount paid to Column will effectively weaken his position in making further demands, since these payments increase the amount of Row's control over him and decrease the amount of his control over Row. This game is analogous to the relations of an employer (Row) to an underpaid employee (Column). The employee is in an initially strong position to ask for a substantial wage increase, but once this increase is given the employer can more effectively reduce his gains by discharging him, and the reduction in the employer's net gains is less if the employee is discharged or quits.

COMBINATIONS OF AP AND AO CONTROLS

If we combine AP and AO controls so that increasing personal gain and the gain of the other player is simultaneously possible, we obtain results similar to those for analogous combinations of CP controls. In Table 7 we have so combined AP and AO controls for the Row player. Column player has no form of control. Since Column's choice has no effect, Row simply chooses whether he should simultaneously increase (A) or decrease (B) his and Column's gains. Unless he greatly dislikes Column, we can reasonably expect Row to choose A. In Table 8 we have given both

TABLE 7   EXAMPLE OF CO-OPERA-
TIVE COMBINATION OF AP AND AO
CONTROL FOR ROW, NO CONTROL
FOR COLUMN

| | | Column | |
		A	B
Row	A	3, 3	3, 3
	B	0, 0	0, 0

		Column	
		A	B
Row	A	+3, +3	0, 0
	B	0, 0	−3, −3

Row and Column the same forms of control as Row alone enjoyed
in Table 7. Here we obtain a co-ordination game similar to that
of Table 4, and again we would ordinarily expect that both players
will tend to choose A unless one severely dislikes the other.

In Tables 7 and 8 we predicted co-operative behavior, since the
interests of both players are allied and joint-return maximizing
behavior can therefore be expected. In Table 9 the operation of
AP control is opposed to the operation of AO control for Row,
and Column has no control of any sort. Here we have our first
example of a mixed-motive game. Row has the choice of increasing the joint return to both by making the co-operative choice of
A, or of increasing his own gains at the "expense" of Column by
choosing B. Column is in the position of a "sitting duck" since
he cannot retaliate should Row choose B. The only prediction

TABLE 9 EXAMPLE OF MIXED-
MOTIVE COMBINATION OF AP AND
AO CONTROL FOR ROW, NO CON-
TROL FOR COLUMN

		Column	
		A	B
Row	A	2, 2	2, 2
	B	3, 0	3, 0

we can make is that Row will tend to choose A if increasing the gains of Column is quite rewarding to him, but will choose B if he is more or less indifferent to Column's gains or dislikes Column to the point that decreasing Column's gains is rewarding. In Table 10 we have placed Row in the same power position as Column.

The game of Table 10 poses much the same kind of dilemma to the players as the Prisoner's Dilemma games described later in this paper. If either player chooses B he increases his own gains but decreases those of the other player, as was true for Row in Table 9. In addition, the other player now has a retaliatory power which can be exercised by choosing B. Since the joint B choice is obviously less satisfactory than a joint A choice, it seems reasonable to suppose that both players will settle on a joint A choice with repeated plays of the game. As our subsequent discussion of the experimentation with Prisoner's Dilemma games indicates, however, this tends not to occur in practice.

In Table 11 we have a game which potentially looks as if it would lead to a co-operative (i.e., joint-return maximizing) choice of A for single or repeated trials. The A strategy dominates B (i.e., choice of A insures a greater personal gain for both players) and also increases the gain of the other. Thus, there is no obvious potential temptation to choose B from the standpoint of personal gain, as is the case for Table 10 or the Prisoner's Dilemma game of Table 12. A B choice superficially would seem motivated only by an intense dislike of the other player or in retaliation for a B choice on a previous trial by the other player. In one experiment,

TABLE 10 EXAMPLE OF MIXED-MOTIVE COMBINATION OF AP AND AO CONTROL FOR ROW AND COLUMN

| | | Column | |
		A	B
Row	A	3, 3	1, 4
	B	4, 1	2, 2

TABLE 11   EXAMPLE OF PSEUDOCO-
OPERATIVE COMBINATION OF AP
AND AO CONTROLS

		Column	
		A	B
	A	4, 4	1, 3
Row	B	3, 1	0, 0

however, a 30-trial repetition of the game of Table 11 resulted in an average of only 47 per cent A choices by the individual subjects, and this proportion decreased from the first to the second 15-trial block (Minas et al., 1960). The authors attributed this seeming indifference to personal gain to a competitive tendency towards maximizing the difference between personal gain and the gain of the other, which reduces a "rational" tendency to increase personal gain.

COMBINATIONS OF AP, AO, AND CP CONTROLS

The only example of this form of combination which we will discuss is the Prisoner's Dilemma game. "The following interpretation [of this type of game], known as the prisoner's dilemma, is popular: Two suspects are taken into custody and separated. The district attorney is certain that they are guilty of a specific crime, but he does not have adequate evidence to convict them at a trial. He points out to each prisoner that each has two alternatives: to confess to the crime the police are sure they have done, or not to confess. If they both do not confess, then the district attorney states he will book them on some very minor trumped-up charge such as petty larceny and illegal possession of a weapon, and they will both receive minor punishment; if they both confess they will be prosecuted, but he will recommend less than the most severe sentence; but if one confesses and the other does not, then the confessor will receive lenient treatment for turning state's evidence whereas the latter will get 'the book' slapped at him. . . .

The problem for each prisoner is to decide whether to confess or not. The game the district attorney presents to the prisoners is of the nonco-operative variety." (Luce and Raiffa)

The Prisoner's Dilemma game was used in experimentation by Scodel et al. (1959). The payoff matrix of this game is given in Table 12.

This game places the players in an interesting conflict situation. Each player is quite naturally tempted to make the dominant B choice, thereby increasing personal gain (AP control) but decreasing the gains of the other (AO control). This would result in a joint outcome of one cent per trial, whereas they would gain three times as much by jointly making the co-operative A choice. If a player makes the A choice, he is implying trust of the other player not to choose B; and once this trust is violated, it is difficult not to also begin choosing B. Once a joint B strategy develops where there is no communication other than through the moves of the game, the only way a player can break the deadlock is to begin choosing A. Unfortunately, this has the effect of increasing the other player's temptation to continue choosing B and thus gain five. The "altruistic" player's willingness to continue choosing A is thereby decreased, since gaining zero while the other gains five is obviously not a pleasant experience.

The Prisoner's Dilemma type of game is somewhat like a good many situations in which maximizing short-term gain is opposed to long-term best interests. A person who deceives his friends or a businessman who misrepresents his product is in this position.

TABLE 12   EXAMPLE OF PRISONER'S
DILEMMA COMBINATION OF AP, AO,
AND CP CONTROLS

| | | Column | |
		A	B
Row	A	3, 3	0, 5
	B	5, 0	1, 1

Perhaps the admonition to "yield not to temptation" has its basis in this sort of situation. If the numbers in the payoff matrix above are suitably enlarged, we have a situation similar to the arms race between the U.S. and the U.S.S.R. We would obviously maximize our joint gains if both parties elected to disarm; but since we do not trust each other, the decision to disarm with no guarantee that the other will reciprocate is extremely risky, and we have both elected to take the safer but more wasteful course of continuing to arm.

Experimentation on Prisoner's Dilemma and Related Games

Solomon compared the effects of the power structure of four payoff matrices and the strategy of the (simulated) other player on the choices of the subjects and their anticipations of the other's choices. In his AP_1 matrix S (the subject) has a small amount of AP control and a larger amount of CP control, while O (the "other") has a large amount of AO control. Thus, it would be to S's advantage to vary his choices according to his anticipations of O's choice; and since O's gains are not affected by either S's or O's choices, S would most likely anticipate that O would choose to increase S's gains. In matrix AP_2, the power position of S is the same and O has the same AO control, but O also has a moderate amount of AP control which is opposed in direction to his AO control (as do both participants in Prisoner's Dilemma games). The effect of this difference in O's power position was to reduce the number of subjects choosing A on the first trial and anticipating an X choice from O (i.e., "trusting" behavior) from the 43 per cent obtained with AP_1 to the 22 per cent obtained with AP_2. A similar difference was also observed for the choices of the S's playing against six trials of the two co-operative strategies employed.

In Solomon's PP (Partial Power) matrix, O has the same amounts of AP and AO controls as in matrix AP_2, and S has the same amounts of AP and CP control as in matrix AP_2 but also a moderate amount of AO control which, unlike O's AO control, operates in the same direction as his AP control. Thus, matrix

TABLE 13 "ABSOLUTE POWER" MATRICES FROM SOLOMON EXPERIMENT (1960)

		AP$_1$ O				AP$_2$ O	
		X	Y			X	Y
S	A	+30, +30	−30, +30	S	A	+30, +30	−30, +40
	B	+20, +30	−10, +30		B	+20, +30	−10, +40

PP differs from AP_2 in that S can increase his own and O's gains simultaneously, but O can only increase his gains by decreasing S's gains. In the EP (Equal Power) matrix, both S and O are in the same power position, and S's AO control is now as large as that of O and opposed to his AP control. Unfortunately, the EP matrix also differs from the PP matrix in that both S and O have a substantial amount of CP control, which complicates the comparison of the effects of the PP and EP matrices. The EP game is quite clearly a Prisoner's Dilemma game, although CP control is somewhat more prominent than in Table 12. No differences in the obtained percentages of first-trial choices were observed between AP, PP, and EP, but PP did elicit more "trusting" choices than AP_2 when the simulated strategy of O was co-operative. The similarity of the effects of the EP and PP matrices is

TABLE 14 "PARTIAL POWER" AND "EQUAL POWER" MATRICES FROM SOLOMON (1960)

		PP (Partial Power) O				EP (Equal Power) O	
		X	Y			X	Y
S	A	+30, +30	+30, +40	S	A	+30, +30	+30, +40
	B	+20, +10	−10, +20		B	+40, −30	−20, −20

hard to interpret, since the particular combination of different forms of control may have induced effects which canceled each other.

Scodel et al. and Minas et al. report a series of experiments involving the Prisoner's Dilemma game of Table 12, the pseudoco-operative game of Table 11, and similar games. When the AP and AO controls operate in opposed directions, so that personal gain is increased by decreasing the other's gains as in Table 12, the result is that joint co-operative strategies occur on no more than 20 per cent of the trials. When AP and AO controls operate in the same direction, so that both players' gains may be simul-taneously increased (as in Table 11), the rate of joint co-operative choices is increased to only about 25 per cent. For both types of games, this percentage is often smaller in the second half than in the first half of the experiment.

The effect on first-trial choices and anticipations when AP and AO controls for the other player are opposed (in Solomon's AP_1 and AP_2 comparison) implies that the players in the experiments of Scodel and his associates may have played so unco-operatively because they did not trust each other. Deutsch found that vari-ous forms of communication between the subjects increased the degree of co-operativeness in Prisoner's Dilemma type games. Quite naturally, Deutsch and Solomon have emphasized the role of trust in the other person in decision-making situations and the effects of power structure and communication in eliciting trust. On the other hand, Scodel et al. found that free face-to-face com-munication between the subjects after 25 trials had no substantial effects on co-operation in the game of Table 12. Scodel and his associates have tended to regard game behavior as largely an attempt to maximize the difference between personal gains and gains of the other player even when this requires some reduction of personal gains (as in the game of Table 11).[4] It does not seem wise at this time to claim that these data or interpretations are

---

[4] In 3-person game experimentation by Rapoport, the potential personal advantage in "defecting" from a joint co-operative strategy was found to be inversely related to the obtained percentage of co-operative choices. The subjects in these experiments could communicate freely between games.

contradictory. There were major differences in procedure between the experiments of Deutsch and Solomon, who used large amounts of imaginary money, and the experiments of Scodel and his associates who used small amounts of real money and larger numbers of trials. Moreover, it is entirely possible that the effects of communication found by Deutsch might be effective mainly in the early trials before nonco-operation has been established, and that Scodel's attempt to use free communication to induce co-operation may have been too late to be effective.

Luce and Raiffa argue that a nonco-operative choice should be most common if a Prisoner's Dilemma game is played for a single trial, but that a joint co-operative strategy should be more common if there are repeated trials. While this is the wisest course of action if both parties are "rational" about maximizing their long-term gains, it seems to occur rarely in practice. We can argue that the unco-operative behavior of the subjects is "rational" if we assume that they are attempting to maximize the difference between their own and the other's gains in their favor, but we can well ask if there is any sense in which a value system of this sort is rational.

Value Systems of Game Participants

The importance of personal gain to the participant is obviously a major variable, and we have mentioned the importance of gain comparisons. A limited mathematical model constructed by one of us (K.W.) suggests that the importance of personal gain and of gaining more than the other act in opposition to the importance of increasing the other's gain. Thus, a person may wish to increase the gain of another but will tend not to do so if he has to make a considerable personal sacrifice, or if this results in the gains of the other being greater than his own.[5]

It is likely that the entire set of values which is operative is much more complex than those mentioned above. The extra-game relations of the players may be critical, since it seems plau-

---

[5] This model is not presented here because it has not yet been adequately tested.

sible that AO control may not be used to reduce the gains of the other if the player anticipates substantial future gains from a co-operative relationship. The reactions of the player to the power position within the game and his general advantage or disadvantage relative to the other player are of potential importance. Also, there are the player's reactions to influencing the gains of the other and having his gains influenced in return. Finally, it is probable that the conceptual system which the player uses to interpret the behavior of others so as to justify his own behavior plays an important role. An initially co-operative player may become unco-operative if he regards reduction of his own gains as an unjustified personal insult which demands extensive revenge.

Speculations of this sort could be continued indefinitely, but they seem fruitless in the absence of evidence. The experimental work of Deutsch, Lutzker, and Marlowe suggests that measurable personality variables can be used to predict game behavior, and this should be a promising area for future research. In general, personality theory has emphasized the role of personal motives and has neglected the role of the external situation, while formal game theory has emphasized situational determinants to the exclusion of others. A more balanced recognition of how both kinds of determinants interact would be of considerable benefit to both social psychology and to theories of personality and personality reorganization (i.e., psychotherapy).

Validity of Game Models of Social Interaction

Since the experimental games described above are somewhat limited in the range of choices permitted and the number of participants, are not an integral part of the participants' mode of living, and involve rather small gains, we may well ask if they are a valid representation of social interaction. This question is hard to answer, since the variables which influence "real-life" social interactions are commonly quite complex and subtle. If this were not so, the extreme simplification of laboratory experimentation would not be required.

It seems more appropriate not to raise the question of validity but to consider what variables present in social interactions are and are not present in 2-person, 2-choice games. The principal variables which are present are the power positions of the participants, whatever value systems are brought by the participants to the situation, and the past history of the other's choices. The principal variables which are not present are associated with communication. To be sure, the information about power positions and the past choices of the other are forms of communication, but they are not subject to the distortion which often occurs in real life. It is easy enough to permit communication and negotiation between the players, but such communication is bound to focus on explicit agreements and will probably lack many of the subtle and implicit elements sometimes found in social interaction. For example, it would be hard to approximate the equivocal communication of the mother who explicitly offers affection to her child but, when the child approaches, indicates dislike by her manner (Bateson et al.). Also, we expect that a power position which is assigned arbitrarily by the experimenter would be more resented by the subject in the inferior role than if that power position were earned in some legitimate competition, or assigned by some mutually accepted social tradition.

While important variables are unquestionably omitted, we feel that this is bound to be the case in any formal study of a complex phenomena. What is more important is that enough important variables *are* included to give the experimental work at least some validity.

24

"So long sucker"—
a four-person game

M. HAUSNER, J. NASH, L. SHAPLEY,
AND M. SHUBIK

This parlor game has little structure and depends almost completely on the bargaining ability and the persuasiveness of the players. In order to win, it is necessary to enter into a series of temporary unenforceable conditions. This, however, is usually not sufficient; at some point it may be to the advantage of a player to renege on his agreement. The four authors still occasionally talk to each other.

This game was invented in 1950 by Messrs. M. Hausner, J. Nash, L. Shapley, and M. Shubik. The aim was to produce an interesting, social game in which coalitions are both profitable and unstable. Technically, it is an essential four-person, no-side-payment game, in extensive form, with perfect information and no chance moves after the first. It has been played extensively in gatherings of different sorts, provoking a wide variety of reactions. The authors will welcome further reactions and comments.

Rules

1. A four-person game.[1]
2. Each player starts with 7 *chips*[1] (playing cards, or other

---

[1] For a longer game, more chips may be used. If the game is attempted

markers may be used instead), distinguishable by their color from the chips of any other player. As the game proceeds, players will gain possession of chips of other colors. The players must keep their holdings in view at all times.

3. The player to make the first move is decided by chance.
4. A *move* is made by playing a chip of any color out onto the playing area, or on top of any chip or pile of chips already in the playing area.
5. The *order of play*, except when a capture has just been made, or a player has just been defeated (Rules 6 and 9) is decided by the last player to have moved. He may give the move to any player (including himself) whose color is not represented in the pile just played on. But if all players are represented in that pile, then he must give the move to the player whose most-recently-played chip is furthest down in the pile.
6. A *capture* is accomplished by playing two chips of the same color consecutively on one pile. The player designated by that color must kill one chip, of his choice, out of the pile, and then take in the rest. He then gets the next move.
7. A *kill* of a chip is effected by placing it in the "dead box."
8. A *prisoner* is a chip of a color other than that of the player who holds it. A player may at any time during the game kill any prisoner in his possession, or *transfer* it to another player. Such transfers are unconditional, and cannot be retracted. A player may not transfer chips of his own color, nor kill them, except out of a captured pile (Rule 6).
9. *Defeat* of a player takes place when he is given the move, and is unable to play through having no chips in his possession. However his defeat is not final until every player holding prisoners has declared his refusal to come to the rescue by means of a transfer (Rule 8). Upon defeat, a player withdraws from the game, and the move *rebounds* to the player who gave him the move. (If the latter is thereby defeated, the move goes to the player who gave *him* the move, etc.)
10. The chips of a defeated player remain in play as prisoners, but

---

with more than four players, then the number of chips per player should be reduced.

are ignored in determining the order of play (Rule 5). If a pile is captured by the chips of a defeated player, the entire pile is killed, and the move rebounds as in Rule 9.

11. The *winner* is the player surviving after all others have been defeated. Note that a player can win even if he holds no chips and even if all chips of his color have been killed.

12. *Coalitions*, or agreements to cooperate, are permitted, and may take any form. However, the rules provide no penalty for failure to live up to an agreement. Open discussion is not restricted, but players are not allowed to confer away from the table during the game, or make agreements before the start of the game.

A bibliography with
some comments

This somewhat diffuse bibliography provides references to the applications of game theory, gaming, and related approaches to many areas. The comments given with some of the references are not intended to be reviews but merely serve to call to the attention of the reader features of the book or article which may be of interest.

Two informal classifications are given. The first is provided for all references to books or articles; they are categorized as being written primarily for social or behavioral scientists S; for those with a relatively high mathematical background M; or are intended as popularizations P. The second classification indicates the scope of the book or article. Psy. refers to psychology and social psychology; Soc. to sociology and to anthropology; Ec. to economics; Pol. to political and military science; S to behavioral science in general; and M to mathematics or statistics. For example, *Games and Decisions* by Luce and Raiffa is classified as S & M-S. This indicates that it is written primarily for behavioral scientists, although also for those with a relatively high mathematical background, and it is addressed to behavioral science in general. *Fights, Games and Debates* by Rapoport is classified as P & S-S, indicating that it can be read by the intelligent layman but is also of benefit to the behavioral scientist, and it is addressed to behavioral science in general. Braithwaite's *Theory of Games as a Tool for the Moral Philosopher* is classified as S & M, but further classification of this is left to the reader.

BIBLIOGRAPHIES

Brody, R. A.: "Deterrence Strategies: An Annotated Bibliography," *Conflict Resolution*, **IV**, No. 4, December 1960, 443–457.

Cragin, S. W., Jr., P. J. Fernald et al.: "Simulation: Management's Laboratory," Harvard University, April 1959.

Deacon, A. R. L., Jr.: "Selected References on Simulation and Games," (Processed) Saranac Lake: AMA Academy, April 1960.

Hellebrandt, E. T., and W. D. Fleishhacker, "General Business Management Simulation," (processed) Ohio University, 1959.

Malcolm, D. G.: "A Bibliography on the Use of Simulation in Management Analysis," Santa Monica: System Development Corporation, SDC, SP-126, November 10, 1959. Also published in *Operations Research*, 1960.

Minsky, M.: "A Selected Descriptor-Indexed Bibliography to the Literature on Artificial Intelligence," *IRE Transactions on Human Factors in Electronics*, 1961.

Pierce, A. M.: "A Concise Bibliography of the Literature on Artificial Intelligence," Bedford, Mass.: Air Force Cambridge Research Center, September 1959.

Riley, V. and J. R. Young: "Bibliography on War Gaming," Operations Research Office, Chevy Chase, Md. 1, April, 1957.

A valuable 94 page compendium with the first reference dating back to 1824. Comments and annotations are supplied for many of the modern war games.

Shubik, M.: "Bibliography on Simulation, Gaming, Artificial Intelligence and Allied Topics," *Journal of American Statistical Association*, **55** December 1960, 736–751.

BOOKS

Arrow, K. J.: *Social Choice and Individual Values*, John Wiley and Sons, 1951. S-Ec & S

Blackwell, D. and M. A. Girschik: *Theory of Games and Statistical Decisions*, John Wiley and Sons, 1954. M-M

Boulding, K. E.: *Conflict and Defense: A General Theory*, Harper, 1962. S-S

A provocative and broad discussion of many aspects of conflict is given. Boulding lays stress on the different manifestations of conflict in various organizations. He contrasts behavior of individuals, groups, formal and informal organizations; he discusses economic, industrial, and international conflict, as well as ideological and ethical conflict. The book is more valuable for general ideas than detailed analysis.

Braithwaite, R. B.: *Theory of Games as a Tool for the Moral Philosopher*, Cambridge University Press, 1955. S & M

Buchanan, J. M. and G. Tullock: *The Calculus of Consent*, University of Michigan Press, Ann Arbor, 1962. S-Pol

Chamberlain, N. W.: *A General Theory of Economic Process*, Harper, 1955. S-Ec

Dahl, R.: *A Preface to Democratic Theory*, University of Chicago Press, 1956. S-Pol

Douglas, A.: *Industrial International Peacemaking*, Columbia University Press, 1962, 670 pp. S-Ec

Hertz, J. H.: *International Politics in the Atomic Age*, Columbia University Press, 1959. S-Pol

Kahn, H.: *Thinking about the Unthinkable*, Horizon, 1962. P-S

This is a popularization of many of the ideas contained in *On Thermonuclear War*. Regardless of one's emotional reactions to the contents, Kahn presents an analysis and discusses "some strange aids to thought" which make a case for this approach to the study of political and military affairs.

Kaplan, M. A.: *System and Process in International Politics*, John Wiley and Sons, 1957. S-Pol

Kemeny, J. G.: J. L. Snell, and G. I. Thompson: *Introduction to Finite Mathematics*, Prentice-Hall, 1957.   S-S

An excellent elementary introduction to mathematical methods of use in the behavioral sciences.

Kuhn, J. W.: *Bargaining in Grievance Settlement*, Columbia University Press, 1961.   S-Ec

Kuhn, H. and A. W. Tucker (Eds.): *Contributions to the Theory of Games*, vol. I, Annals of Mathematics Studies, No. 24, Princeton University Press, 1950.   M-M

———, *Contributions to the Theory of Games*, vol. II, Annals of Mathematics Study, No. 28, Princeton University Press, 1953.   M-M

Leites, N.: *On the Game of Politics in France*, Stanford University Press, 1959.   S-Pol

Luce, R. D. and H. Raiffa: *Games and Decisions*, John Wiley and Sons, 1957, pp. 117–118.   S & M-S

This is a first-class exposition of many of the concepts of the theory of games in relation to the behavioral sciences. For serious work in the application of game theory, it is important to have mastered most of the contents of this book. To those not trained in mathematics, the writing may be somewhat austere, but it is certainly rewarding.

McDonald, J.: *Strategy in Poker, Business and War*, McGraw-Hill Book Company, 1953.   P-Pol & Ec

McKinsey, J. C. C.: *Introduction to the Theory of Games*, McGraw-Hill Book Company, 1953.   S & M-M & S

Morgenstern, O.: *The Question of National Defense*, Random House, 1959.   S-Pol

Phillips, Brig, Gen. T. R. (Ed.): *Roots of Strategy*, Military Service Publishing Company, Harrisburgh, Pa., 4th printing, March, 1955.   S-Pol

Rapoport, A.: *Fights, Games and Debates*, University of Michigan Press, 1960.   S & P-S

A stimulating and easy to read introduction into the construction of models of social processes. It contains an excellent exposition of the theory of games, as well as a discussion of war, arms races, and other epidemics, based heavily on the work of L. F. Richardson. In the third part, debates are contrasted with fights and games where changes in the value systems of the participants do not take place.

Richardson, L. F.: *Arms and Insecurity*, Quadrangle Books, Chicago, 1960a.   S & M-Pol

————, *Statistics of Deadly Quarrels*, Quadrangle Books, Chicago, 1960b   S & M-Pol

Riker, W. H.: *The Theory of Political Coalitions*, Yale University Press, 1962   S-Pol

This is a direct attempt at applying certain aspects n-person game theory to political behavior. The book is written definitely for the political scientist and not the game theorist. Much work of this type must be done by political scientists before satisfactory modifications can be made to game theory for their purposes. The mathematically inclined game theorist might argue that much liberty has been taken with the various concepts of solution employed here. It is evident that Riker's work calls for dynamic elements which are not yet sufficiently developed.

Schelling, T. C.: *The Strategy of Conflict*, Harvard University Press, 1960.   S-Pol & S

Shubik, M.: *Readings in Game Theory and Political Behavior*, Doubleday, 1954.   S-Pol & S

————, *Strategy and Market Structure*, John Wiley and Sons, 1959.   S & M-Ec

An application of game theory to the study of oligopoly. With, however, several chapters on the role of information and the construction of dynamic games which are of more general interest than to economic theory alone.

Siegel, S. and L. E. Fouraker: *Bargaining and Group Decision Making*, McGraw-Hill Book Company, 1960.   S-Psy & Ec

Simon, H. A.: *Models of Man: Social and Rational*, John Wiley and Sons, 1957, pp. 62–78.   S-S

Snyder, R. C., H. W. Bruck, and B. Sapin: *Foreign Policy Decision Making*, The Free Press, Glencoe, Ill., 1962.　　　　　　　　　　　　S-Pol

————, and J. A. Robinson: *National and International Decision-Making*, The Institute for International Order, New York, 1962.　　　S-Pol

This report is more or less an encyclopedia of projects for the development of knowledge in the behavioral sciences necessary to providing understanding about the major problems of war and peace. It also contains a very useful bibliography.

Thibaut, J. W. and H. H. Kelly: *The Social Psychology of Groups*, John Wiley and Sons, 1959.　　S-Psy

A discussion of the relationship between the approach of the authors and that of game theory to the study of dyads is given on pp. 24–30.

Thrall, R. M., C. H. Coombs, and R. L. Davis: *Decision Processes*, John Wiley and Sons, 1954.　　M & S-M & S

Tucker, A. W. and P. Wolfe (Eds.): *Contributions to the Theory of Games*, vol. III, Annals of Mathematics Studies, No. 39, Princeton University Press, 1957.　　　　　　　　　　　　　M-M

Ulmer, S. S.: *Introductory Readings in Political Behavior*, Rand McNally, 1961.　　　　　　　S-Pol

von Neumann, J. and O. Morgenstern: *Theory of Games and Economic Behavior*, Princeton University Press, 1944, 3rd. ed. 1953.　　　M-M & Ec

Williams, J. D.: *The Compleat Strategyst, Being a Primer to the Theory of Games*, McGraw-Hill Book Company, 1954.　　　　　　　　　　P-S

Zeuthen, F.: *Problems of Monopoly and Economic Warfare*, George Routledge and Sons, London, 1930.　　　　　　　　　　　　　　S-Ec

ARTICLES

Arrow, K. J.: "Alternative Approaches to the Theory of Choice in Risk-Taking Situations," *Econometrica*, **19**, 1951, 404–437.　　　S-Ec & S

Atkinson, R. C. and P. Suppes: "An Analysis of Two-

Person Game Situations in Terms of Statistical Learning Theory," *Journal of Experimental Psychology*, **55**, 1958, 369–378.　　　　　　S-Psy

Barth, F.: "Segmentary Opposition and The Theory of Games: A Study of Pathan Organization," *Journal of the Royal Anthropological Institute*, vol. 89, 1959.　　　　　　S-Soc

Barnard, J.: "The Theory of Games of Strategy as a Modern Sociology of Conflict," *American Journal of Sociology*, vol. LIX, March, 1954.　　　　　　S-Soc

————, "Where is the Modern Sociology of Conflict?" *American Journal of Sociology*, **61**, 1950, 11–16.　　　　　　S-Soc

Brody, R. A.: "Political Games for Model Construction in International Relations," Department of Political Science, Northwestern University, June 1961. (This contains a useful summary of several political gaming exercises and references to them.)　　　　　　S-Pol

Caplow, T. A.: "A Theory of Coalitions in the Triad," *American Social Review*, **21**, 1956, 489–493.　　　　　　S-Psy & Soc

Dahl, R. A.: "The Concept of Power," *Behavioral Science*, **2**, July 1957, 201–215.　　　　　　S-Pol

Deutsch, M.: "A Theory of Cooperations and Competition," *Human Relations*, **2**, 1949, 129–152.　　　　　　S-Psy

————, "Trust and Suspicion," *Journal of Conflict Resolution*, **2**, 1958, 267–279.　　　　　　S-Psy

———— and R. M. Krauss: "Studies of Interpersonal Bargaining," *The Journal of Conflict Resolution*, **VI**, No. 1, March 1962, 52–76.　　　　　　S-Psy

————, "The Effect of Threat Upon Interpersonal Bargaining," *Journal of Abnormal and Social Psychology*, **61**, 1960, 181–189.　　　　　　S-Psy

Dresher, M.: "Games of Strategy: Theory and Applications," the RAND Corporation, 1700 Main Street, Santa Monica, California, May 1961.　　　　　　M & S

Edwards, W.: "Probability Preferences in Gambling," *American Journal of Psychology*, **66**, 1953, 349–364.　　　　　　S-Psy & S

———, "The Theory of Decision-Making," *Psychological Bulletin*, **51**, 1954, 380–417.   S-Psy & S

———, "Utility, Subjective Probability, Their Interaction, and Varian Preferences," *The Journal of Conflict Resolution*, **VI**, No. 1, March 1962, 42–51.   S-Psy & S

Ellsberg, D.: "The Theory and Practice of Blackmail," Lowell Lecture, 1959, and Santa Monica, California: The RAND Corporation, 1959.   S-Pol

Fagen, R. R.: "Some Contributions of Mathematical Reasoning to the Study of Politics," *American Political Science Review*, **LV**, No. 4, December 1961, 888–900.   S-Pol

Faxen, K. O.: "The Theory of Games, Expectation Analysis and Trade Agreements," *Nationalokonomisk Tidsskrift*, November 1949,   S-Ec

Flood, M. M.: "A Stochastic Model for Social Interaction," *Trans. N. Y. Acad. Sci.*, **16**, 1954, 202–205.   S-Psy

———, "Game-Learning Theory and Some Decision-Making Experiments; Environmental Non-Stationarity in a Sequential Decision-Making Experiment," in R. M. Thrall, C. H. Coombs, and R. L. Davis (Eds.), *Decision Processes*, pp. 139–158, 287–299, John Wiley and Sons, 1954.   S-Psy

———, "Some Experimental Games," *Management Science*, **5**, 1958, 5–26.   S-Psy & S

Foster, C. and A. Rapoport: "Parasitism and Symbiosis in an N-Person Non-Constant Sum; Continuous Game," *Bulletin of Math. Biophysics*, **18**, 1956, 219–231.   S-S

Frank, J. D.: "Recent Studies of the Level of Aspiration," *Psychological Bulletin*, **38**, 1941, 218–226.   S-Psy

French, J. R. P., Jr.: "A Formal Theory of Social Power," *Psychology Review*, **63**, 1956, 181–194.   S-Psy

Gamson, W. A.: "A Theory of Coalition Formation," *American Social Review*, **26**, 1961, 373–382.   S-Soc

Glasser, G. J.: "Game Theory and Cumulative Voting for Corporate Directors," *Management Science*, **5**, 1958, 151–156.   S-Ec

Goldhamer, H. and E. Shils: "Types of Power and Status," *The American Journal of Sociology*, **45**, 1939, 171–182.   S-Soc & S

Harsanyi, J. C.: "Approaches to the Bargaining Problem Before and After the Theory of Games: A Critical Discussion of Zeuthen's, Hicks', and Nash's Theories," *Econometrica*, **24**, 1956, 144–157.   S-Ec & Pol

———, "Bargaining in Ignorance of the Opponent's Utility Function," *The Journal of Conflict Resolution*, **VI**, No. 1, March 1962, 29–38.   S-Ec & Pol

——— "Measurement of Social Power in N-Person Reciprocal Power Situations," *Behavioral Science*, **7**, No. 1, January 1962, 81–91.   S-Ec & Pol

———, "Measurement of Social Power, Opportunity Costs, and the Theory of Two-Person Bargaining Games," *Behavioral Science*, **7**, No. 1, January 1962, 67–80.   S-Ec & Pol

———, "On the Rationality Postulates Underlying the Theory of Cooperative Games," *The Journal of Conflict Resolution*, **5**, 1961, 179–196.   S-Ec & Pol

Haywood, O. G., Jr.: "Military Decision and Game Theory," *Journal of the Operations Research Society of America*, **2**, 1954, 365–385.   S-Pol

———, "Military Decision and the Mathematical Theory of Games," *Air University Quarterly Review*, **4**, No. 1, Summer 1950, 17.   S-Pol

Hoggatt, A. C.: "An Experimental Business Game," *Behavioral Science*, **4**, 1959, 192–203.   S-Ec & S

Iklé, F. C. and N. Leites: "Political Negotiation as a Process of Modifying Utilities," *The Journal of Conflict Resolution*, **VI**, No. 1, March 1962, 12–28.   S-Pol

Kalisch, G. K.: "Some Experimental N-Person Games," In R. M. Thrall, C. H. Coombs, and R. L. Davis (Eds.), *Decision Processes*, John Wiley and Sons, 1954.   S & M-S & M

Kaufman, H. and G. M. Becker: "The Empirical Determination of Game-Theoretical Strategies," *Journal of Experimental Psychology*, **61**, 1961, 462–468. S-Psy

Koo, A. Y.: "Recurrent Objections to the Minimax Strategy," *Review of Economics and Statistics*, **XLI**, February 1959, 36–43. S-Ec

Kort, F.: "Predicting Supreme Court Decisions," *APSR*, **LI**, March 1957, 11–12. S-Pol

Kuhn, H. W.: "Extensive Games and the Problem of Information," *Annals of Mathematics Study*, No. 28, Princeton University, Press, 1953, pp. 189–216. M-M

Lerner, D. and H. S. Lasswell (Eds.): "Mathematical Models in the Social Sciences," *The Policy Sciences*, Stanford University Press, 1951, pp. 129–154. S-S

Lieberman, B.: "Human Behavior in a Strictly Determined 3×3 Matrix Game," *Behavioral Science*, **5**, 1960, 317–322. S-Psy

Loomis, J. L.: "Communication, the Development of Trust and Cooperative Behavior," *Human Relations*, **12**, 1959, 305–315. S-Psy

Luce, R. D.: "A Definition of Stability for N-Person Games," *Annals of Mathematics*, **59**, 1954, 357–366. M & S-Psy

————, A Note on the Article "Some Experimental N-Person Games," *Contributions to the Theory of Games*, **4**, 1959, 279–285. M & S-Psy & S

————, "Ψ-Stability: A New Equilibrium Concept for N-Person Game Theory," Mathematical Models of Human Behavior, Proceedings of a Symposium, 1955, Dunlap and Associates, pp. 32–44. M-M & S

————, "K-Stability of Symmetric and Quota Games," *Annals of Mathematics*, **62**, 1955, 517–527. M-M & S

————, and E. W. Adams: "The Determination of Subjective Characteristic Functions in Games

With Misperceived Payoff Functions," *Econometrica*, **24**, 1956, 158–171.   M

Lutzker, D. R.: "Internationalism as a Predictor of Cooperative Behavior," *Journal of Conflict Resolution*, **4**, 1960, 426–430.   S-Pol & Psy

Maccoby, M.: "Social Psychology of Deterrence," *Bulletin of the Atomic Scientists*, **17**, 1961, 278–281.   S

March, J. G.: "An Introduction to the Theory and Measurement of Influence," *American Political Science Review*, **49**, 1955, 431–451.   S-Pol

———, "Measurement Concepts in the Theory of Influence," *Journal of Politics*, **19**, 1957, 202–226.   S-Pol

Marschak, J.: "Rational Behavior, Uncertain Prospects, and Measurable Utility," *Econometrica*, **18**, 1950, 111–141.   M & S-Ec & S

McDonald, J.: "Poker: An American Game," *Fortune*, **37**, No. 3, March 1948, 128.   P

McMurry, R. W.: "War and Peace in Labor Relations," *Harvard Business Review*, November-December, 1955.   S

Minas, J. S., A. Scodel, D. Marlowe, and H. Rawson: "Some Descriptive Aspects of Two-Person Non-Zero-Sum Games, II," *The Journal of Conflict Resolution*, **4**, 1960, 193–197.   S-Psy & S

Morgenstern, O.: "Effective and Secure Deterrence: The Oceanic System," *Royal Canadian Air Force Staff College Journal*, 1960.   S-Pol

———, "The Theory of Games," *Scientific American*, **180**, 1949, 22–25.   S

Nash, J. F.: "Equilibrium Points in N-Person Games," *Proceedings of National Academy of Science, USA*, **36**, 1950, 48–49.   M-M

———, "Non-Cooperative Games," *Annals of Mathematics*, **54**, 1951, 286–295.   M-M

———, "The Bargaining Problem," *Econometrica*, **18**, 1950, 155–162.   M & S-Ec & M

———, "Two Person Cooperative Games," *Econometrica*, **21**, 1953, 128–140.   M & S-Ec & M

Osgood, C. E.: "A Case for Gradual Unilateral Disengagement," *Bulletin of the Atomic Scientists*, **16**, 1960a, 127–131.   S-Pol

Pruitt, D. G.: "An Analysis of Responsiveness Between Nations," *The Journal of Conflict Resolution*, **VI**, No. 1, March 1962, 5–18.   S-Pol & S

· Quandt, R. E.: "On the Use of Game Models in Theories of International Relations," *World Politics*, **14**, 1961, 69–76.   S-Pol

Raiffa, H.: "Arbitration Schemes for Generalized Two-Person Games," *Annals of Mathematics Study*, No. 28, Princeton University Press, 1953.   M & S-M & Ec

Rapoport, A.: "Lewis F. Richardson's Mathematical Theory of War," *Journal of Conflict Resolution*, **1**, 1957, 244–299.   S-Pol & S

———, A Chammah, J. Dwyer, and J. Gyr: "Three-Person Non-Zero-Sum Non-negotiable Games," *Behavioral Science*, **7**, No. 1, January, 1962, 38–58.   S-Psy & S

———, and C. Orwant: "Experimental Games: A Review," *Behavioral Science*, **7**, No. 1, January 1962, 1-37.   S-S

Riker, W. H.: "A Test of the Adequacy of the Power Index," *Behavioral Science*, **4**, No. 2, April, 1959.   S-Pol

———, and D. Niemi: "The Stability of Coalitions on Roll Calls in the House of Representatives," *ASPR*, **LVI**, March 1962, 58–65.   S-Pol

Sakaguchi, M.: "Reports on Experimental Games," *Stat. Applied Research, JUSE*, **7**, 1960, 156–165.   S-S

Schelling, T. C.: "Bargaining, Communication, and Limited War," *The Journal of Conflict Resolution*, **1**, 1957, 19–36.   S-Pol

———, "Experimental Games and Bargaining Theory," *World Politics*, **14**, 1961, 47–68.   S-Pol

Schubert, G. A.: "The Study of Judicial Decision-Making As an Aspect of Political Behavior," *American Political Science Review*, **52**, 1958, 1007–1025. (Ulmer, *op. cit.*, pp. 276–289.)   S-Pol

Seligman, B. B.: "Games Theory and Collective Bargaining," *Labor and Nation*, **8**, 1952, 50–52.   S-Ec & S

Shapley, L. S.: "A Value for N-Person Games," in H. W. Kuhn and A. W. Tucker (Eds.), *Contributions to the Theory of Games* vol. II, Princeton University Press, 1953, pp. 307–317.   M-M

————, "Simple Games: An Outline of the Descriptive Theory," *Behavioral Science*, **7**, No. 1, January 1962, 59–66.   M-S & M

————, and M. Shubik: "A Method for Evaluating the Distribution of Power in a Committee System," *American Political Science Review*, **48**, 1954, 787–792.   S-Pol & S

————, and M. Shubik: "Solution of N-Person Games with Ordinal Utilities," *Econometrica*, **XXI**, No. 2, 1953.   M-Ec & M

Shubik, M.: "A Game Theorist Looks at the Antitrust Laws and the Automobile Industry," *Stanford Law Review*, **8**, July 1956, 594–630.   S

————, "Games, Decisions and Industrial Organization," *Management Science*, **6**, No. 4, July 1960, 455–474.   S-S & M

————, "Information, Risk, Ignorance and Indeterminacy," *Quarterly Journal of Economics*, 1954.   S-Ec

————, "Information, Theories of Competition and the Theory of Games," *Journal of Political Economy*, **LX**, April 1952.   S-Ec

————, "Simulation, Gaming and Theory of the Firm," *Proceedings of the Western Data Processing Center* Dedication, 1959.   S-Ec & S

————, "Some Experimental Non-Zero-Sum Games With Lack of Information About the Rules," *Management Science*, **8**, No. 2, January 1962.   S-S & Psy

————, "The Uses of Game Theory in Management Science," *Management Science*, **2**, October 1955, 40–54.   S-S

————, and G. L. Thompson: "Games of Economic Survival," *Naval Research Logistics Quarterly*, vol. 6, 1959.   M-M & Ec

Singer, J. D.: "Threat-Perception and the Armament-Tension Dilemma," *Journal of Conflict Resolution*, **2**, 1958, 90–105.   S-Pol

Sjoberg, G.: "Strategy and Social Power," *The Journal of Conflict Resolution*, **IV,** June 1960, 163–178. S-Pol

Snyder, G. H.: "Deterence and Power," *The Journal of Conflict Resolution*, **IV,** June 1960, 163–178. S-Pol

Snyder, R. C.: "Game.Theory and the Analysis of Political Behavior," In Stephen K. Bailey et al., "Research Frontiers in Politics and Government," Brookings Institution, 1955, pp. 70–103. (Ulmer, *op. cit.*, pp. 271–276.) S-Pol

Solomon, L.: "The Influence of Some Types of Power Relationships and Game Strategies Upon the Development of Interpersonal Trust," *Journal of Abnormal and Social Psychology*, **61,** No. 2, 1960, 223–230. S-Psy

Stone, J. J.: "An Experiment in Bargaining Games," *Econometrica*, **26,** 1958, 286–296, S-S & Ec

Thomas, C. J. and W. L. Deemer: "The Role of Operational Gaming in Operations Research," *Journal of the Operations Research Society of America*, **5,** No. 1, February 1957, 1–27. S-Pol

Ulmer, S. S.: "The Analysis of Behavior Patterns in the United States Supreme Court," *Journal of Politics*, **22,** November 1960, 629–653. (Ulmer, *op. cit.*, pp. 248–254.) S-Pol

Vanacke, W. E. and A. Arkoff: "An Experimental Study of Coalitions in the Triad," *American Social Review*, **22,** 1957, 406–414. S-Soc & Psy

Willis, R. H. and M. L. Joseph: "Bargaining Behavior, I: 'Prominence' as a Predictor of the Outcome of Games of Agreement," *Journal of Conflict Resolution*, **III,** 1959, 102–113. S-Psy & Pol

Wilson, K. V. and V. E. Bixenstine: "Forms of Social Control in Two-Person, Two-Choice Games," *Behavioral Science*, **7,** No. 1, January 1962, 91–102. S-Psy

Zellner, A.: "War and Peace: A Fantasy in Game Theory?" *The Journal of Conflict Resolution*, **VI,** No. 1, March 1962, 39–41. S-S

Index

Choice, points, 20, 21
  political, 75, 110, 119, 135, 139
  social, 135, 136, 138, 139
Choreography, 273
Cinna, 41
Civil defense, 238
Coalition, 45, 47, 48, 52, 75, 85, 86,
    133, 168, 169, 172, 290
  formation, 56
  minimal winning, 142
  winning, 159, 174
Codes, design of, 35
Colonel Blotto, 226
Collusion, 22, 89, 90, 215
Color, 51
Combinatoric, 94
Command system, 35
Commissar, 51
Committee, 112, 113, 115, 116, 118,
    141, 143, 175, 180
  bicameral, 111
Communicate, 39
Communication, 40, 44, 55, 68, 89,
    299, 307, 324, 326, 336, 345, 355
  internal, 34
Comparison, interpersonal, 52, 53
Competition, 22, 55, 306, 326
  free, 139
Competitive process, 28
Competitor, 18, 22
Complex system, 72
Computer, 12, 28, 29, 63, 73
  digital, 71, 73
  electronic, 7
  establishments, 7
  high speed digital, 65
  programs, 65
  simulation, 71
  techniques, 69
Conciliation, 215
Conditions, information, 11
Conflict, 8, 9, 57, 60, 87, 88, 89, 90,
    199, 306, 323
  interpersonal, 333
  resolution, 336

Conflict, situation, 32
  social, 77
Congress, 144, 146, 166, 167, 168,
    170, 171, 177
Congressmen, 159
Consistency, 138
Constitution, 158
Contingency, 13, 20, 28
  planning, 270
Continuity, 123, 124, 125, 127, 130,
    131
Control, 8, 74, 338
  behavior, 343
  fate, 343
  system, 35
Convexity, 123, 124, 126, 130
Coombs, C. H., 59, 120
Cooperate, 37
Cooperation, 8, 22, 44, 46, 55, 87,
    306, 326
  degree of, 69
Cooperative, 30, 41, 46
  solution, 50
Coordinate, 33, 34, 85
Coordination, 33, 34
  games of, 33
Core, 48
Counterincident, 64, 65
Counterstrike, 64, 68
Counterthreats, 55, 89
Countervailing forces, 45
Country, 12
Cournot, A. A., 5
Credibility, 40
Creed, 51
Crossman, R., 211, 212, 219
Cues, 33
Customs, 33
Cycle, business, 39
Czechoslovakia, 262
Czechoslovakians, 28

Dahl, R. A., 183, 184, 185, 186, 189,
    192, 205
Danger, 13

Thermonuclear war, 59
Thibault, J. W., 76, 336, 339, 343
Thomas, C. J., 261
Thompson, G. L., 6, 68, 275
Thrall, R. M., 59, 120
Threat, 11, 22, 28, 30, 40, 53, 55, 60, 68, 69, 75, 89, 316, 327
Threat, bilateral, 330, 332
Threat, unilateral, 330, 332
Threaten, 21
Ticktacktoe, 84
Timing, 27
Tizard, H. T., 223
Tools, mathematical, 6
Tools, methodological, 4
Topology, 82
Transitive, 58
  relation, 123
Trap door, 31, 32
Truel, 43
Tucker, A. W., 37, 44, 56, 68
Tukey, John W., 75, 227, 226, 229
Tullock, G., 165
Tzu, Sun, 76

Uncertainty, 30, 61, 69, 74, 95, 96
Unilateral power, 196
Unions, labor, 8
United Kingdom, 224
United Nations, 50, 264, 311
  Security Council, 147
United States, 34, 53, 68, 86, 140, 168, 211, 219, 264, 266, 268, 272
  Congress, 141
Utility, 14, 19, 52, 53, 54, 58, 74, 81, 83, 84, 85, 88, 95, 96, 98, 99, 100, 101, 102, 103, 104, 105, 106, 107, 108, 109, 123, 136, 137, 138, 169, 187, 199, 244, 340
  function, 59, 195

Valuation, 14, 53
Value, 18, 25, 27, 28, 31, 32, 33, 37, 45, 46, 48, 50, 51, 54, 56, 58, 59, 61, 64, 68, 74, 75, 84, 89, 99, 292

Value, individual, 58, 135
  social, 58
  systems, 45, 60, 135
Van Wagenen, R., 280
Venturini, K., 219
Vertices, 20, 21, 24
Viable, 60
Vice President, 144
Vickrey, W., 56, 291
Von Manstein, Erich General, 263
von Neumann, John, 6, 17, 18, 19, 44, 45, 46, 47, 48, 60, 68, 74, 81, 82, 83, 86, 90, 96, 121, 214, 216, 219, 226, 229, 286, 290, 291, 304, 305
Vote, 153, 154, 159
  simple majority, 146
Voting, 29, 75, 135, 136
  paradox of, 136, 138
  procedure, 72
  system, 49

Wald, A., 121, 122, 124, 128
Wald criterion, 122, 125, 129
Walras, L., 110
War, 13, 22, 24, 26, 40, 59, 60, 61, 64, 65, 97, 98
  atomic, 40, 62
  cold, 136, 275
  hot, 136
  nuclear, 209, 215
  thermonuclear, 212
Warfare, guerilla, 59
Warfare, nuclear, 9, 23, 26, 211
Waskow, Arthur, 213
Weakland, J., 344
Weapons, 60
  bacteriological, 11
  evaluation, 226
Weather, 9, 11
  conditions, 12
Welfare, 30, 31, 32, 36, 47, 50
  function, social, 138
  weak, 47
White House, 41, 60